STATISTICS
a first course

Walker, McLean & Matthew

Hodder & Stoughton

A MEMBER OF THE HODDER HEADLINE GROUP

ACKNOWLEDGEMENTS

The tables in Appendix 1 first appeared in *Three figure Tables for Maths and Science*, and are reproduced by kind permission of Thomas Nelson.

Orders: please contact Bookpoint Ltd, 39 Milton Park, Abingdon, Oxon OX14 4TD. Telephone: (44) 01235 400414, Fax: (44) 01235 400454. Lines are open from 9.00 - 6.00, Monday to Saturday, with a 24 hour message answering service. Email address: orders@bookpoint.co.uk

British Library Cataloguing in Publication Data
Walker, James A.
   Statistics: First Course. – 3Rev.ed
   I. Title   II. McLean, Margaret M.
   III. Matthew, James W.
   519.5

ISBN 0 340 55246 8

First published 1993
Impression number   17   16   15   14   13   12   11   10   9   8
Year   2004 2003 2002 2001 2000 1999 1998

Copyright © 1993 James A. Walker, Margaret M. McLean
               and James W. Matthew

Published previously as *Ordinary Statistics* ISBN 0 1731 0871 1, first imprint, 1973.
Copyright © 1973, 1983 James A. Walker and Margaret M. McLean
               1992 James A. Walker, Margaret M. McLean and
               James W. Matthew.

Typeset by Keyset Composition, Colchester, Essex.
Printed in Great Britain for Hodder & Stoughton Educational, a division of Hodder Headline Plc, 338 Euston Road, London NW1 3BH by Scotprint Ltd, Musselburgh, Scotland.

To the teacher

Statistics in the form of graphs, figures, opinion polls, and so on are increasingly important. Young people leaving school or college should have some knowledge of how this information is collected, what the various types of graph mean and above all how reliable the information is likely to be. A critical and perhaps even cynical view of the data presented by the popular press, television, advertisements, and so on, should be fostered.

This book introduces the basic ideas of Statistics and Probability in a modern way. It is intended to be a complete course in Statistics from basic principles to examination courses. The subject matter covers the various English Examining Board GCSE level Statistics Syllabuses, the Scottish Examination Board Short Course on Statistics and the descriptors for the modular courses of the Scottish Vocational Education Council. Teachers may omit sections or chapters not required for their own students; this may be done without any loss of continuity.

Even if students are not studying Statistics as an examination subject, a familiarity with statistical methods is a very valuable tool when dealing with other subjects where, nowadays, there is an increasing emphasis on work of an investigative nature.

Unfortunately, in some parts of the work there is bound to be some sheer, arithmetical 'slog'. This is unavoidable by the very nature of the subject. To minimise this, the use of such aids as calculators, mathematical tables and computers should be encouraged.

As much as possible, the students should collect their own data, decide how to present it graphically and how to interpret it.

In Statistics textbooks, there are a number of different notations used for the arithmetic mean, standard deviation, and so on. The notation and formulae used in this book are shown on the next page.

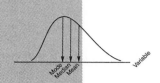

NOTATION AND FORMULAE

N, X, $\bar{X}$, s refer to samples and n, x, μ, σ to populations

ARITHMETIC MEAN

$$\bar{X} = \frac{\Sigma X}{N} \quad \text{or} \quad \frac{\Sigma fX}{\Sigma f}$$

$$\mu = \frac{\Sigma x}{n} \quad \text{or} \quad \frac{\Sigma fx}{\Sigma f}$$

STANDARD DEVIATION

$$s = \sqrt{\frac{\Sigma(X - \bar{X})^2}{N}} \quad \text{or} \quad \sqrt{\frac{\Sigma f(X - \bar{X})^2}{\Sigma f}}$$

$$\sigma = \sqrt{\frac{\Sigma(x - \mu)^2}{n}} \quad \text{or} \quad \sqrt{\frac{\Sigma f(x - \mu)^2}{\Sigma f}}$$

STANDARD VARIABLE

$$z = \frac{X - \bar{X}}{s} \quad \text{or} \quad \frac{x - \mu}{\sigma}$$

BINOMIAL DISTRIBUTION

$$\mu = Np; \quad \sigma = \sqrt{(Npq)}$$

POISSON DISTRIBUTION

$$\mu = \lambda; \quad \sigma = \sqrt{\lambda}$$

COEFFICIENT OF RANK CORRELATION

$$R = 1 - \frac{6\Sigma d^2}{n(n^2 - 1)}$$

SAMPLES OF SIZE N (N LARGE) FROM AN INFINITE POPULATION

$$\mu_{\bar{x}} = \mu; \quad \sigma_{\bar{x}} = \frac{\sigma}{\sqrt{N}}$$

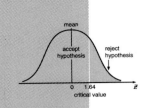

CONTENTS

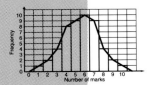

INTRODUCTION

Statistics is the name given to the science of collecting facts and studying or analysing them. The facts or 'data' can cover a tremendous range of subjects. They may be quite simple facts like how many bottles of milk a family buys every week or the goal average of a favourite football player. On the other hand, they may be extremely complex facts of the world of industry or nuclear physics and which can only be analysed by using computers.

If the data available on a subject are incomplete the answers we get to problems will only *probably* be true and are sometimes called predictions. An example of this is found in weather forecasting. Information about temperatures, wind, rain, barometric pressure etc. is collected in weather stations all over the world, on land and sea and even high in the air by means of weather balloons. Also, much information is obtained via satellite pictures showing weather fronts and so on. When the weather forecasters have studied all this data, they have to predict what is *likely* to happen and, of course, they know they are taking the risk of being wrong in their forecast.

Although statistics are becoming more and more widely used these days, their use is not a modern science by any means. For centuries people have collected information of various kinds and then put it to use. The Romans, for instance, conducted accurate censuses to count the number of people in the countries they conquered. It tells us in the Bible that Jesus was born in Bethlehem because Mary and Joseph had to travel there for the Roman Census. The Romans required that, on a certain date, every man (with his family) had to return to his birthplace to be counted. The purpose of the Roman Census was mainly to count the people who should have been paying taxes.

In this country a national census has been conducted every ten years since 1801, except for 1941 when the Second World War was in progress. Also, every birth, death and marriage must be registered. These two sources of statistics give essential data to the Government for the efficient management of the country. (See Chapter 15)

Statistics are all around us today. Whenever we open a newspaper we see facts and figures about something—what the 'average' person spends on drink and tobacco; unemployment figures; road accident figures; business conditions; opinion polls. Often these facts are accompanied by a graph, diagram or chart of some kind. When we turn to the sports pages of the paper, we find them full of statistics about football, hockey, golf, etc.

In science and medicine, statistics are vitally important. Doctors, researching into new medicines and new treatments for diseases, very carefully collect and study the data from their experiments. In this way, they discover how effective the medicine or treatment may be. New drugs must be exhaustively tested for several years before

1

they are released for general use.

Manufacturers spend millions of pounds in building laboratories and employing scientists and mathematicians to conduct research into new types of building materials, car engines, chemicals, new synthetic fibres and materials, and so on. A great deal of this research is concerned with collecting data and drawing appropriate conclusions. If the results are not what is wanted then a new batch of experiments is set up, more data is collected and further conclusions drawn. This process may have to be repeated for months or even years, before the scientists achieve what they are after.

As you see, statistics are part of every aspect of our daily life and in this book we shall be looking at how data can be collected to give as accurate a picture as possible, and seeing how we can interpret this data.

_____

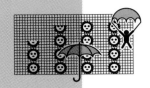

1 THE COLLECTION AND REPRESENTATION OF DATA

COLLECTION OF DATA

Collecting data may, at first glance, appear to present no problems but one of the most difficult tasks of a statistician is collecting accurate data.

Some facts are very easy to collect. For instance, there can be no doubt about the number of goals scored by football teams during a season as they are recorded by the Football League. On the other hand, if you ask a child how many packets of potato crisps or sweets he or she ate in the last month, it is very unlikely that an accurate answer would be obtained.

There are different types of data which we may wish to collect; there are 'measurable' things like height, weight, and so on; and 'countable' things such as the number of children in a family, the number of deaths due to motor accidents.

Some data is much less easy to obtain, for example, the personal opinions, preferences or habits of people. Collecting information of this nature involves questioning people and this is where many difficulties can arise. There are two main methods of obtaining data from people, personal interviews and questionnaires. These methods are extensively used in market research and opinion polls. With both of these methods the list of questions must be formulated very carefully.

Personal interviews

In personal interviews, the investigator asks the questions and notes down the answers. If the interviewee does not understand a question then some additional information may be given. Obviously, the interviewer must not show any bias which could influence the interviewee's answers. This method has a very good response rate as most people are happy to answer a few questions. It is clear, however, that personal interviews are very time-consuming and, if paid interviewers are used, can be very expensive.

There is an increasing trend now to use telephone interviews. The response to these is not so successful since people are not so ready to answer questions from an anonymous voice at the end of a 'phone line. The interviewees have no way of checking the credentials of the caller and they may resent the intrusion into their privacy.

Questionnaires

A questionnaire is a printed list of questions given to a selection of people. They usually have to answer the questions on their own

3

without any help from the investigator. For a small local survey the forms may be delivered by hand or by post for a large-scale survey. There are many advantages to a postal questionnaire, for example, the forms can be distributed quickly and easily over a large area at a low cost, uniformity is maintained, the people receiving the questionnaires have time to give careful thought to their answers and can also refer to their records if necessary. There are also considerable disadvantages to postal questionnaires, in particular the poor response rate. Many people will show no interest in the questions and not bother to answer them, simply tossing the form into the dustbin. Another problem which may arise is that there is no one to explain any questions that are not understood. Also, the returned questionnaires may well show some kind of *bias* in so far as only a particular type of person may go to the bother of answering, for example, people with very strong views on the subject under survey.

Some official data is collected by post, for instance, income tax returns and electoral registration forms. People are legally bound to fill in these forms and return them.

Design of questions and questionnaires

Having considered how to ask the questions, we must think very carefully of *what* questions are to be asked. They must be very carefully worded so that as far as possible there can be no doubt about their meaning. For instance, if we ask: 'How many good meals did you have last week?' the person questioned has to decide exactly what is meant by a good meal. Does it mean a substantial three-course meal or does it mean a well-cooked meal? Also, people's ideas will vary about what constitutes a substantial meal or a well-cooked one.

We must recognise the fact that when questioned, people may be either intentionally or subconsciously dishonest.

Also, in trying to please the interviewer, or to put themselves in a good light, people often give the answer they think is *expected*. The person should be questioned in such a way that he or she has no suspicion what the 'right' answer may be.

A series of questions which builds up the required answer may be formulated. These may be self-checking in some way. For example, the same questions may be put in several ways and any inconsistency in the replies is revealed. If any inconsistency is very marked then that particular questionnaire must be scrapped.

Suppose you wish to conduct a survey of how many people have been seriously ill over the past year. The bald question would be: 'Have you been seriously ill over the past year?'. Various types of response are likely to be forthcoming. Some people would be unwilling to admit, even to themselves, that they had been very ill; some people would not know how ill they had been and some would be inclined to exaggerate a minor illness. You would, of course, get a number of honest replies, but which ones and how many? In a case like this, a series of 'leading questions' can build up a correct picture for the investigator.

1 *Did you attend the doctor last year?*
2 *Were you attending the doctor regularly?*
3 *Were you confined to bed for more than a day or two?*
4 *Did you need to go to hospital?*
5 *How long were you in hospital?*
6 *What kind of treatment did you receive; an operation, medication, and so on?*
7 *How long a convalescence did you have?*

These 'small' questions are more likely to be answered correctly, since the person being interviewed usually does not sense the drift of the questions and so give a 'loaded' answer.

In designing a successful questionnaire, certain rules should be adhered to:

1 *The form should be well designed, attractive, and as short as possible.*
2 *There should be sufficient space for the answers and this space should be clearly*

linked to the question. For instance,
number each question and answer, or
leave a space between each question and
the following one.

3 *The questions must be simply worded and*
straightforward.

4 *They should be of such a nature that the*
answers are 'yes' or 'no', or a precise
answer such as a number or place.

5 *There must be no ambiguity, only one*
interpretation should be possible.

6 *Any questions of a personal nature*
should be very tactful.

7 *Avoid questions involving calculations.*

8 *Avoid leading questions, that is, those of*
the type 'Do you agree that . . .'.

9 *Multiple-choice questions are often*
useful. In this type of question, the
person ticks the appropriate answer from
a list of categories.

For example:

Please indicate your age group

under 18 ☐ 18–29 ☐ 30–44 ☐ 45–59 ☐
60 and over ☐

In *market research*, questions of this type are
often used to 'qualify' a response.

For example:

The value for money of Brand X is

excellent	☐
good	☐
fair	☐
poor	☐

Before embarking on a large scale survey, a
'pilot' survey may prove useful. This trial run
should show up any flaws or faults in the
design of the questionnaire.

So far, we have considered 'primary' data,
that is, information collected by the
investigator. It is also possible to use
'secondary' data, that is information already
collected for some other purpose. Before
using secondary data, it is important to
ensure that it is 'reliable' information. A great
deal of statistical information is collected and
published by government departments and a
good reference library should be able to
provide such publications. The Central
Statistical Office (London) produces many

publications, including:
- *The Annual Abstract of Statistics*
- *The Monthly Digest of Statistics*
- *Economic Trends*
- *Regional Trends*
- *Social Trends.*

The Registrar General for England and
Wales and the Registrar General for Scotland
publish Annual Reports which give
information concerning vital statistics and
censuses.

Having now considered how to ask
questions and what kind of questions to ask,
the remaining problem is whom you ask. This
is a difficult problem to solve.

If some information is wanted about a
particular small group of people, then each
person in the group can be questioned
individually. If, however, you want
information about a large number of people,
say the population of a large city or indeed
the population of Great Britain, then it is
impossible to question every one of them
(except, of course, in a Government Census).
In this situation, and this is the most usual
one, we must question a *sample* of the
population.

How do we choose a sample which is
representative of the whole group? If you pick
out every hundredth name in a telephone
directory, you are not considering people
without a telephone. This would give a *biased*
sample. If you stopped every fiftieth person
in a street near a factory at five o'clock, then
your sample would be biased towards factory
workers. If you stopped every fiftieth person
at ten thirty a.m. near a busy shopping
centre, then your sample could be biased
towards people without daytime jobs.

You may, of course, *want* a sample which is
biased towards a certain group. If a market
research firm is looking at the effect of
advertising on attendance at a theme park,
then the sample should be biased towards
households with children between 5 and 15.

One way of obtaining a reasonably
unbiased sample is to use the electoral roll of
the town and go through it picking out every

fiftieth or hundredth name (depending on how many people are to be in the sample). This, however, does not take into account people under the age of eighteen years, a factor that could be allowed for by making sure that a number of young people were also questioned.

Another kind of sample to take is a *random sample*; this is dealt with in **Chapter 3**. A rather complicated way of obtaining a really *representative* sample of a given population is used by good market research firms, but it involves a great deal of work and is outside the scope of this book.

The purpose of choosing a sample need not be to answer questions, it may be to find out other information such as the weights, or heights of the sample members.

PRACTICAL WORK

Pay close attention to any facts and figures, graphs and charts in newspapers or magazines and cut out the articles. Use these cuttings to compile a scrapbook, either on an individual or class basis. Discuss the data collected. Is it interesting? Is it informative? Is it well 'put over'? Is it pushing a particular point of view? Discussions like this may lead you to conduct a similar survey.

It would be a very good thing at this point in your statistics course to compile a *data base* which could be drawn on subsequently when you have learned more about statistical operations. A data base is a collection of the same observations, or measurements, for a number of separate individuals or things. This *raw data* is tabulated in some way, for instance, on a large sheet of paper or on filing cards in a box or using a computer program.

Design a questionnaire which will give you information about your fellow students. Decide how many questions should be on the form and how many students should be asked to take part in the survey. The more questions and students you have the more comprehensive your data base will be.

Suggestions

1. Male or female. 2. Age last birthday (years). 3. Hair colour. 4. Eye colour. 5. Height (cm). 6. Weight (kg). 7. Shoe size. 8. Ideal occupation (as an adult). 9. Favourite colour/food/drink/hobby/sport/school subject.

There is really no limit to the number or variety of facts you can find out from your survey.

Your survey need not be conducted in school. You could design a questionnaire and distribute it to friends, relations and neighbours.

Once you have collected your answered forms, find a very large sheet of paper and fill in a table of the type shown below.

STORING DATA

Suppose we had gathered the name, sex, age, height, shoe size, maths mark and science mark of each pupil in a small class, we could store this data in a data base in the form of a large table as shown on the opposite page. The columns are called *fields* and the rows are the individual pupil *records*.

The data could then be used to answer such questions as:

1 *Which pupil had a shoe size greater than 7?*

ID number	Male/Female	Age (years)	Hair colour	Eye colour	Height (cm)
001	M	14	red	green	175
002	M	14	fair	blue	162
003	F	15	dark	blue	165
004	F	15	fair	brown	170

2 *Which male pupils scored a mark greater than 50 in each examination?*

3 *Which male pupils, whose age is greater than 180 months, were less than 165 cm tall?*

The data could also have been stored on cards in individual pupil's records or in a computerised data base.

Computerised data bases are widely used, not only for their speed of searching but also for their analysing and displaying facilities.

If you have access to a computerised data base you could enter the data shown in the table and use the computer to answer the questions in Exercise A. If you do not have access to this aid, the questions can still be answered by examining the table directly.

EXERCISE A

1 Which pupils had a shoe size of less than 5?

2 Which pupils scored a mark greater than 59 in the mathematics examination?

3 Which pupils were less than 184 months old?

4 Which pupil whose name begins with the letter S had a height greater than 165 cm?

5 How many pupils who scored a mark greater than 49 in the mathematics examination scored less than 60 in the science examination?

6 Which female pupils had a height greater than 165 cm?

7 Which pupil aged greater than 185 months had a shoe size of less than 6?

8 How many pupils aged greater than 184 months, and with a height greater than 160 cm, scored a mark greater than 59 in the mathematics examination?

9 Which male pupil whose age is greater than 184 months had a height less than 170 cm?

10 Which pupil(s) whose height is less than 170 cm, have a shoe size greater than 5, scored a mark greater than 59 in the mathematics examination and a mark greater than 69 in the science examination?

REPRESENTATION OF DATA

Once we have collected and stored our data, we need to present it in an attractive and eye catching manner. The obvious way of doing this is by some kind of graph or chart.

By now you should have started your collection of graphs and charts and by the time you have finished this chapter you should be able to decide whether these

Data base of Class 3B (10 pupils)							
ID number	Name	Sex	Age (months)	Height (cm)	Shoe size	Maths mark	Science mark
1	Denzil	m	179	152	5	28	36
2	Frank	m	188	180	11	80	84
3	Gino	m	185	173	8	75	75
4	Henry	m	186	168	7	62	80
5	Tom	m	182	159	6	45	51
6	Fatima	f	188	157	3	70	74
7	Norma	f	185	166	5	41	44
8	Pauline	f	182	161	4	50	52
9	Shaheen	f	183	159	8	68	70
10	Susan	f	184	170	6	32	38

graphs and charts are good or misleading representations of the data.

PICTOGRAPHS

One of the most arresting ways of illustrating statistics is by using a graph in the form of pictures. This kind of graph is called a **pictograph** (sometimes **pictogram**). These pictures may be of cars, houses, milk bottles, aeroplanes, people, and so on, reduced in size but drawn to a definite scale for purposes of comparison.

A principal teacher of mathematics wished to make her pupils aware of how the money required to run the mathematics department has been spent.

Figure 1.1 shows one way of illustrating these figures in a pictograph. The widths of the 'money bags' are drawn in proportion to the amounts of money.

Make up a pictograph of your own to illustrate the same figures. Then compare your pictographs.

Figure 1.2 shows the number of cases of tinned peaches sold by four shops in a month. Study the pictograph and see if you think this is an accurate way to represent the data. If you think it is not, give reasons for your answer. This pictograph reveals clearly the weakness of this kind of graph.

Fig. 1.1

For each £ spent

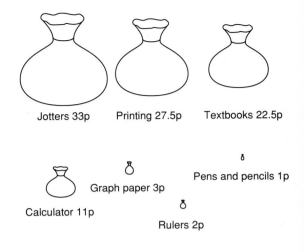

Calculator 11p   Rulers 2p

For each £ spent:		
		Cost (p)
Jotters	cost	33
Printing	,,	27.5
Textbooks	,,	22.5
Calculators	,,	11
Graph paper	,,	3
Rulers	,,	2
Pens and pencils	,,	1

Shop A sold twice as many cases as Shop B and so the cube for Shop A is of side 4 cm while the cube for Shop B is of side 2 cm, that

Fig. 1.2

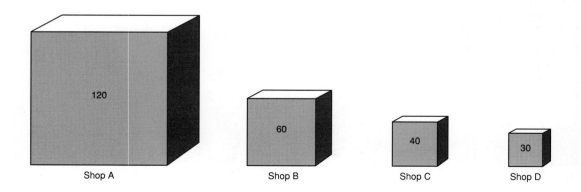

8

is, the dimensions for the first cube are twice what they are for the second *but* the resulting picture produces the impression of volume and Shop A *apparently* has achieved a great deal more than twice Shop B's sales. How much more according to volume?

In drawing pictographs of this kind, even when keeping the linear dimensions in proportion to the data, the resulting pictures can convey quite a different impression.

Figure 1.3 is a much more accurate pictograph of the data. One small case is used to represent every ten cases.

Fig. 1.3

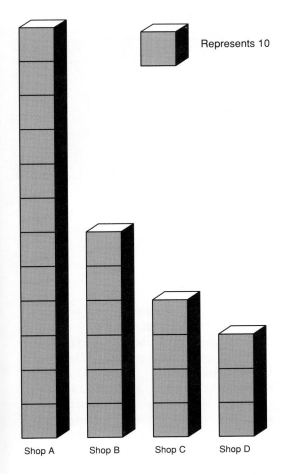

EXERCISE B

1 Study this pictograph and answer the questions below.

Fig. 1.4
The number of hours of bright sunshine in January

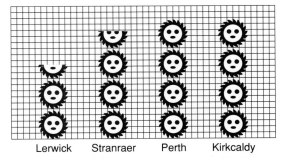

Lerwick   Stranraer   Perth   Kirkcaldy

 Represents 10 hours

a) Why has this been drawn on squared paper?
b) What does one 'sun' represent?
c) How many hours of bright sunshine did each of the four places have?
d) What does half a 'sun' stand for?
e) What would a quarter of a 'sun' stand for?

2 The number of jumps made by members of a parachuting club last year was as follows:

Roberto	10 jumps
Sandra	32 „
Tom	6 „
Raschid	14 „
Graham	8 „

Draw a pictograph to illustrate this using a parachutist, to represent 4 jumps.

Watch these points:
a) Make the parachutists the same size.
b) Space them out evenly.
c) Give the pictograph a title.
d) Show your scale.
e) Put in the parachutists' names.

9

3 The rainfall (in cm) recorded one year for these places was as follows:
Renfrew—90; Kinloss—25; Benbecula—110; Dunoon—210; Helensburgh—125.
Draw a pictograph to illustrate this using an umbrella, to represent 10 cm of rain.

4 The numbers of driving lessons required by 4 pupils to pass their driving tests are shown below.

James	18 lessons
Syeda	12 ,,
Denzil	15 ,,
Margaret	24 ,,

Draw a pictograph to illustrate this information. Choose your own picture and scale.

5 A small poultry farmer with free range hens sold the following numbers of eggs each month. Draw a pictograph to show this, choosing your own scale.

January	5 dozen
February	4 ,,
March	9 ,,
April	14½ ,,
May	12 ,,
June	10½ ,,

Find out some data for yourselves and draw pictographs to show it.

BAR CHARTS

The pictographs you were drawing and looking at in the last section are an attrative way of presenting data but they have two main drawbacks which you have probably found out for yourselves, namely:

1 *They take a long time to draw well.*
2 *They are difficult to read accurately when there are bits of pictures.*

If instead of a column of pictures, we draw a plain column, then we overcome both difficulties.

Figure 1.5 is a **bar chart** or **column graph**.

Fig. 1.5
The number of pupils absent from a small school in four weeks

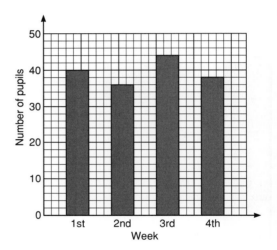

Study the graph and note the following.
1 *The title tells us what the graph is about.*
2 *The columns are all the same thickness and are spread out evenly along the horizontal axis.*
3 *The vertical axis has a scale (like a ruler) which tells us the number of pupils.*
4 *The columns rise to the correct height for each week measured against the vertical scale.*

1 In a school one year, a second-year class decided to investigate how all the pupils travelled to school. Figure 1.6 shows how the first-year pupils travelled to school. Some of the pupils live in country areas well away from normal bus routes and these children are collected by taxis or by small vans used later in the day for transporting meals from the central kitchens to outlying primary schools.
a) What is the most usual method of travelling to school?
b) What is the least usual method of travelling to school?
c) What transport is used by exactly 30 pupils?
d) How do 57 of the pupils travel?
e) How many cycle to and from school?
f) How many pupils are collected by taxis or meals vans?
g) How many first-year pupils were present the day the survey was done?

Fig. 1.6
The means of travelling to school of first-year pupils

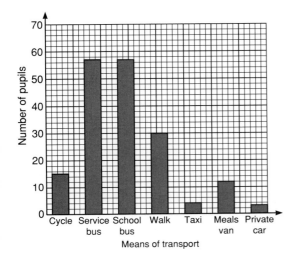

2 Study this graph and answer the questions.

Fig. 1.7
The highest mountain in each continent

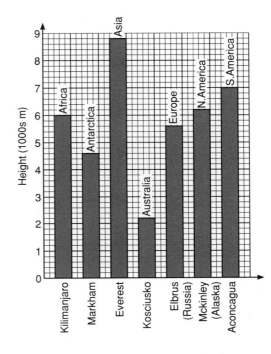

a) Which continent has the highest mountain in the world?
b) Which continent does not have any very high mountains?
c) What is the approximate height of Mount McKinley?
d) Which mountain is approximately 7000 metres high?
e) In which continent is there a mountain about 5900 metres high?
f) Which mountain is slightly more than half the height of Mount Everest?
3 The prices shown in Figure 1.8, on the next page, were for a period of time in 1990.
a) What was the approximate average price of a house in Glasgow?
b) Where was the average house price £24 000?

Fig. !.8
Average house price in each town or city

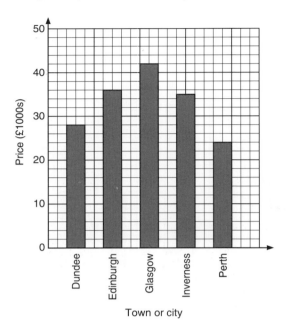

c) Which two towns or cities had nearly the same average house price?

d) Approximately how much greater was the average house price in Edinburgh than in Dundee?

4 Study Figure 1.9 and answer the following questions.

a) Why do you think the columns have been drawn horizontally for this graph?

b) What is the approximate length of the longest river in the world?

c) Which river is about 5400 kilometres long?

d) Which is about 6200 kilometres long?

e) Which two of the rivers shown are most nearly the same length?

5 Draw a bar chart to show the craft and design marks of 4 pupils.

Pupil	Bert	Serjit	James	Mohamad
Mark	74	85	28	53

6 Draw a graph to show the approximate attendances at 4 football matches in 1990.

Match	Raith v Partick	Clyde v Morton	Brechin v Dundee	Airdrie v Falkirk
Attendance	3100	700	2000	4900

Fig. 1.9
Longest rivers in the world

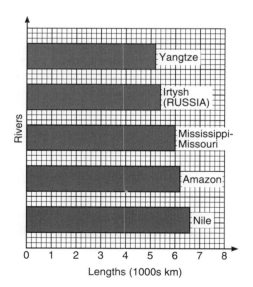

7 The class absences shown in Figure 1.10 were recorded in a school during a 'flu epidemic for two consecutive school weeks in February. (Notice how we can use column graphs for comparison purposes.)

a) Which of the two classes was affected first by the 'flu outbreak?

b) On how many days were there more than 10 pupils absent in class A?

c) On how many days were more than 10 pupils of class B absent?

d) What was the largest number of pupils to be absent on any day in either class?

Fig. 1.10
Class absences over two weeks during a 'flu epidemic

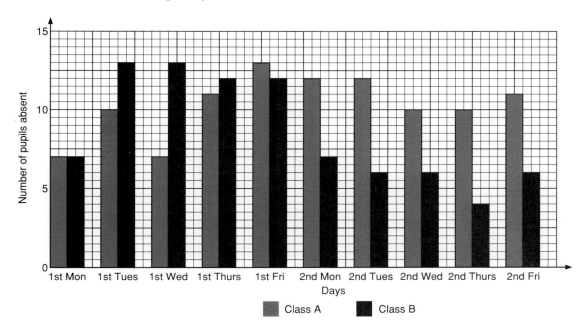

e) Between which two days was there the biggest jump in the absences for:
  i) class A?
  ii) class B?

f) On which days were there more than eight pupils absent in both classes?

8 A pupil conducted a survey in two classes on their favourite flavours in potato crisps. The results are shown below. Draw a graph, similar to the one in question 7, to illustrate this, choosing your own method of shading.

Crisp flavours	Class A	Class B
Smoky Bacon	6	14
Cheese & Onion	8	6
Plain	1	0
Salt & Vinegar	11	8
Spring Onion	4	2

9 Using the information in the table draw a graph to illustrate the pupils'

Pupil	English	Maths	Science
James	60	50	50
Nadeen	63	50	55
Waseem	87	65	57
Maria	54	77	74

examination marks. Group together the subjects for each pupil.

10 Draw a graph to show the level of under-age smoking by pupils at a large school.

Age (years)	Boys	Girls
12	5	3
13	8	8
14	15	20
15	34	45

COMPOSITE BAR CHARTS

This type of bar chart has each bar subdivided into sections which are shaded to illustrate the data and sometimes has the alternative name of **component bar chart**.

Example

The chart in Figure 1.11 shows the land use on three farms.

With this type of graph we can compare each farm to another and also we can compare the land use within each individual farm.

Fig. 1.11
Land use on farms

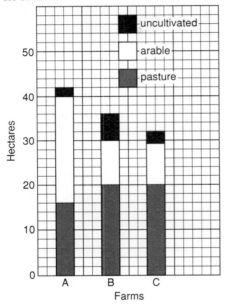

EXERCISE D

1 Study Figure 1.12 and answer the following questions.
a) What was the total staff in 1987?
b) What was the total staff in 1990?
c) By what percentage was the staff reduced between 1987 and 1990?
d) What fraction of the total staff consisted of manual workers in 1988?
e) What fraction of the total staff consisted of clerical workers in 1989?

Fig. 1.12
Staff position of a firm

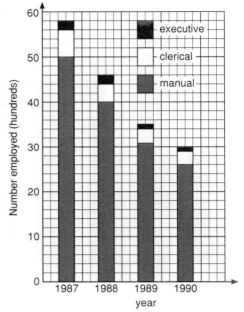

2 Draw a composite bar chart to illustrate the grades obtained by Higher Mathematics candidates in a Scottish school over a number of years.

	Grade		
Year	A	B	C
1987	14	6	12
1988	9	13	18
1989	10	7	20
1990	6	15	24

3 Draw a horizontal column graph to illustrate the following stopping distances for cars. Differentiate between the 'thinking distance' and 'braking distance' by using different shading. These stopping distances are for private cars or small vans with good drivers, perfect brakes, tyres, and so on, in broad daylight with good, dry roads. Larger vehicles under the same conditions may need twice these distances. On wet roads twice the normal distances are required for all vehicles.

Speed (km/h)	Thinking distance (m)	Braking distance (m)	Overall stopping distance (m)
32	6	6	12
48	9	13.5	22.5
64	12	24	36
80	15	37.5	52.5
96	18	54	72

4 Draw a composite bar chart to illustrate the percentage of private medical insurance paid for by employer/individual.

Economic status	Individual pays (%)	Employer pays (%)
Working full-time	48	52
Working part-time	88	12
Not working	90	10

5 The medal positions, of the top four countries, after the Seoul Olympic Games in 1988 are as follows:

Country	Gold	Silver	Bronze
USSR	55	31	46
GDR	37	35	30
USA	36	35	30
Korea	12	10	11

Illustrate this information in the form of a composite bar chart.

LINE GRAPHS

Line graphs show the data by means of drawing a line. This kind of graph is very good for showing upward or downward trends, and is the kind of graph most used and *misused* in newspapers, magazines and advertisements.

Example

Fig. 1.13
Percentage of a city's population aged greater than or equal to four years who listen to the radio during the morning

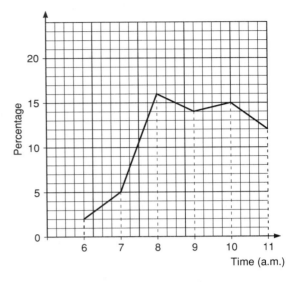

Notice how the points are plotted. A line is taken up from each time to the required percentage. Then the points are joined up with straight lines.

The percentage of the city's listening population increased most between 7 a.m. and 8 a.m. and so the line has the steepest upward slope between those times.

EXERCISE E

1 **a)** Does the graph on the next page (Figure 1.14) show the monthly number of hours of bright sunshine that you would expect?
b) Which two months had less sunshine than you might expect?
c) Between which two months was there the biggest increase in the number of hours of sunshine?
d) Two different periods show an almost identical drop in the number of hours of sunshine. What are they?

15

Fig. 1.14
The number of hours of bright sunshine monthly in a town in the far north of Britain for a year

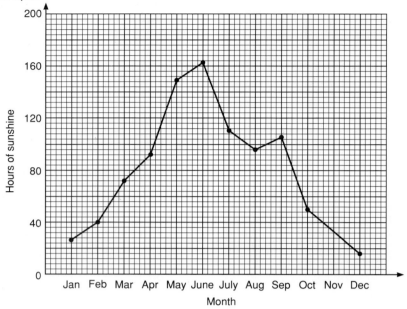

2 In the same year the number of hours of bright sunshine recorded in a town much further south were as follows:
Draw a graph similar to the one in question 1 using these figures (or try to find out the figures for your own town) and compare and contrast the two graphs.

Month	Hours of sunshine
January	57
February	84
March	44
April	136
May	185
June	209
July	188
August	139
September	146
October	75
November	71
December	47

3 The infant mortality rates in the United Kingdom (per 1000 live births) are shown over a period of years.

Draw a line graph to illustrate this information and comment on the graph.

Year	Mortality rate
1981	11.2
1982	11.0
1983	10.1
1984	9.6
1985	9.4
1986	9.5
1987	9.1
1988	9.0

4 The percentage of the population aged 16 years or more who smoke cigarettes is shown below.

Year	Population (%)
1974	45
1976	42
1978	40
1980	39
1982	35
1984	34
1986	33
1988	32

Draw a line graph to illustrate this data and comment on it, giving reasons for the trend it shows.

5 On one diagram draw two line graphs; one to illustrate the monthly high temperature; the other to illustrate the monthly low temperatures which occurred in Moscow one year.

Month	High (°C)	Low (°C)
January	−11	−15
February	−7	−13
March	−3	−9
April	6	−2
May	16	6
June	19	10
July	22	12
August	20	10
September	13	6
October	7	2
November	−2	−6
December	−8	−12

6 Draw a line graph using the figures given below, to show the annual sales of houses owned by local authorities.

Year	Number of houses (1000s)
1976	10
1977	16
1978	30
1979	45
1980	80
1981	100
1982	210
1983	150
1984	100
1985	90
1986	80
1987	110

7 The following figures show the percentage of a large city's population (aged at least four years) who watch television during the afternoon and evening.
Draw a line graph to illustrate this data and comment on the graph.

Time	Percentage watching TV
12.00	9
14.00	16
16.00	14
18.00	22
20.00	33
22.00	41
24.00	5

8 Draw a line graph to show the change in the FT-SE 100 Share Index during a day in July 1990.

Time	FT-SE 100 Index
09.00	2274
10.00	2276
11.00	2293
12.00	2285
13.00	2283
14.00	2281
15.00	2280
16.00	2277
17.00	2275

MISUSE OF LINE GRAPHS

Line graphs often appear in newspapers, magazines and advertisements and can be very uninformative and even misleading.

The 'ten-year growth' of a company is shown in these figures published in a daily newspaper recently.

Year (ended 31st March)	Profit before tax (£ millions)
1981	15.1
1982	17.8
1983	20.5
1984	21.3
1985	22.5
1986	25.0
1987	27.7
1988	29.8
1989	30.9
1990	34.0

Let us look at a few ways in which these figures could be shown graphically.

Fig. 1.15a

Business is doing very nicely

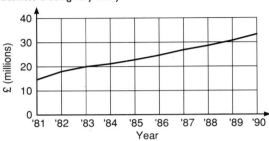

Fig. 1.15b

Business is looking up

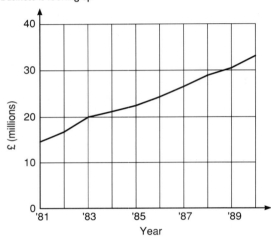

Fig. 1.15c

Business is booming!

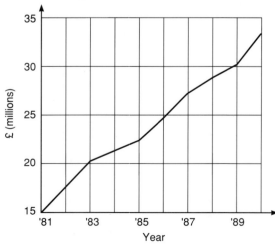

As you can see, it is very easy to alter the 'look' of a line graph by adjusting one or both of the scales.

If you study newspaper graphs you will notice that the vertical scale (often numbers or amounts of money) very rarely starts at zero. The horizontal scale – usually a time scale – can be squeezed closer or spread out to give very different impressions. Indeed, sometimes the time scale is not even regular (for example, Figure 1.16).

As you might imagine, the resulting graph was quite misleading.

Fig. 1.16

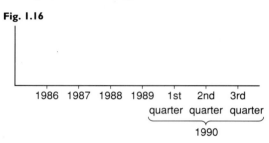

Some graphs, particularly in advertisements, use very vague terms. For instance, some advertisements for headache remedies show graphs of the time it takes the tablets to overcome the 'threshold of pain', making no attempt to define this term. Still, the graph looks impressive!

We must then, when we see graphs in newspapers and so on, take more than just a cursory look (which creates the impression the graphs were intended to create); we must study them carefully, looking at the scales and at the terms used. Only then can we decide what value the graph has.

PIE CHARTS

Another way of illustrating data is a **pie chart**. This is a circle divided up into sections which are usually shaded in various ways.

Figure 1.17 shows a pie chart illustrating the eye colours of a class of 36 pupils.

To read a pie chart you first must measure, for each section, the angle at the centre of the circle.

Fig. 1.17

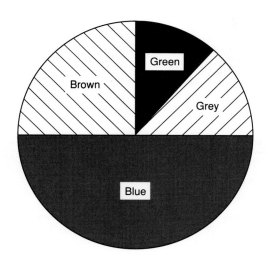

Thus, 'blue   eyes' has an angle of 180°
    'brown   ,,   ,, ,,   ,,   ,,   90°
    'grey   ,,   ,, ,,   ,,   ,,   50°
    'green   ,,   ,, ,,   ,,   ,,   40°

The whole circle represents the whole class, and a fraction of the circle represents the same fraction of the class.

The fraction of the circle representing blue eyes

$$= \frac{180}{360} = \frac{1}{2}$$

Thus, the number of pupils with blue eyes

$$= \frac{1}{2} \text{ of total number of pupils}$$

$$= \frac{1}{2} \times 36$$

$$= 18$$

Similarly, the number of pupils with brown eyes

$$= \frac{90}{360} \times 36$$

$$= 9$$

The number of pupils with grey eyes

$$= \frac{50}{360} \times 36$$

$$= 5$$

The number of pupils with green eyes

$$= \frac{40}{360} \times 36$$

$$= 4$$

Example

Draw a pie chart to illustrate the road deaths in Scotland one year, for boys aged up to and including 19 years.

Pedestrians	=	79
Pedal cyclists	=	5
Drivers or passengers on motor cycles	=	27
Drivers or passengers in motor cars	=	46
Total deaths	=	157

Solution

First, for each type of death, we must change the fraction of the total deaths into the angle to be used in the pie chart.

Pedestrians $= \frac{79}{157}$ of total deaths.

On the pie chart, the angle required

$$= \frac{79}{157} \times 360°$$

$$= 181.2° \text{ (approx.)}$$

Pedal cyclists $= \frac{5}{157}$ of total deaths.

On the pie chart, the angle required

$$= \frac{5}{157} \times 360°$$

$$= 11.5° \text{ (approx.)}$$

19

Drivers or passengers on motor cycles

$$= \frac{27}{157} \text{ of total deaths}$$

On the pie chart, the angle required

$$= \frac{27}{157} \times 360°$$

$$= 61.9° \text{ (approx.)}$$

Drivers or passengers in motor cars

$$= \frac{46}{157} \text{ of total deaths}$$

On the pie chart, the angle required

$$= \frac{46}{157} \times 360°$$

$$= 105.5° \text{ (approx.)}$$

Fig. 1.18
Road deaths for a year in Scotland (boys aged up to and including 19 years)

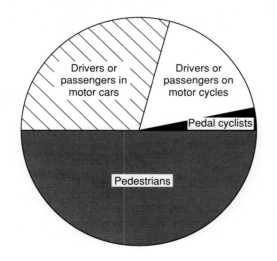

COMPARATIVE PIE CHARTS

Several sets of data can be represented using a series of pie charts. To compare not only the *percentage components* but also the *totals of the components*, the areas of the pie charts must be proportional to the totals of the components.

Example

The breakdown of crops grown on two cereal farms is as follows:

	Area (hectares)	
Crop	Farm A	Farm B
Wheat	60	134
Oats	105	81
Barley	64	118
Others	5	14
	234	347

Solution

Letting R_1, R_2 be the radii of the pie charts to represent farms A and B, we require the ratio:

$$\pi R_1^2 : \pi R_2^2 = 234 : 347$$
$$\text{So } R_1^2 : R_2^2 = 234 : 347$$
$$\text{and } R_1 : R_2 = \sqrt{234} : \sqrt{347}$$

If we draw the pie chart for farm A with the radius $R_1 = 3$ cm then

$$3 : R_2 = \sqrt{234} : \sqrt{347}$$

$$\frac{R_2}{3} = \frac{\sqrt{347}}{\sqrt{234}}$$

$$R_2 = \frac{3\sqrt{347}}{\sqrt{234}}$$

$$R_2 = 3.7 \text{ cm (correct to 1 decimal place)}$$

Fig. 1.19
Crops grown on two cereal farms

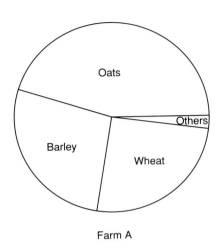

Farm A

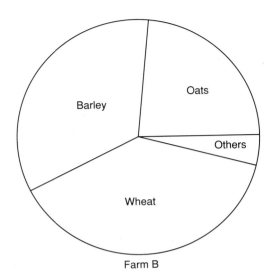

Farm B

and the pie charts would be drawn as shown above.

EXERCISE F ──────────────────

1 Measure the angles of Figure 1.20 and calculate the number of pupils in each category.

Fig. 1.20
Destinations of 180 pupils leaving a school in 1990

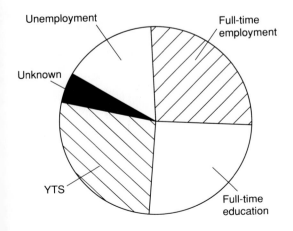

2 Draw a pie chart to illustrate the 40 medals won by the Federal Republic of Germany at the Seoul Olympic Games.

Gold	Silver	Bronze
11	14	15

3 Draw a pie chart to illustrate the composition of the Earth's atmosphere.

Nitrogen	78%
Oxygen	21%
Argon	almost 1%

(very small traces of other gases)

4 This data shows the way in which the world's catch of fish is composed of various types of fish. Draw a pie chart to illustrate this.

33% Herring family (herrings, pilchards, sprats, sardines, shad, white bait and anchovies)

15% Demersal fish (the white fish: cod, haddock, whiting, ling, hake, and the flat fish: halibut, flounder, plaice, sole)

31% Other marine species (including

tuna, barracudas, mullets, perches, sharks, and so on)

11% Freshwater species

2% Salmon

8% Crustaceans and molluscs (crustaceans: lobsters, shrimps, and so on, and molluscs: oysters, mussels, and so on)

5 Draw pie charts to compare the modes of transport usually used by pupils in classes 3X and 3Y to travel to school in the morning. Let the pie chart representing class 3X have a radius of 4 cm.

Mode of transport	Class 3X	Class 3Y
Foot	16	10
Bus	7	6
Car	4	5
Bicycle	3	3

6 The summer sports chosen by pupils in the fourth year were as follows.

Sport	Boys	Girls
Athletics	30	27
Cricket	45	6
Tennis	19	57
Golf	26	18

By drawing pie charts with different radii compare the breakdown of sports selected and the number of boys and girls in the fourth year.

Collect data of your own from your class or another class and draw pie charts to illustrate it.

DISADVANTAGES OF PIE CHARTS

Pie charts have certain disadvantages.

1 *There has to be actual measurement of angles using protractors.*
2 *There is quite a bit of calculation involved.*
3 *The answers in most cases must be approximations.*

However, pie charts have one **advantage**, they show how one whole thing is divided into parts and what size these parts are in relation to each other and to the whole.

COMPUTER PACKAGES

The increasing availability of computer packages capable of representing data allows many more people to draw accurate graphs and charts, for example:

Fig. 1.21
A garage's July car sales by car colour

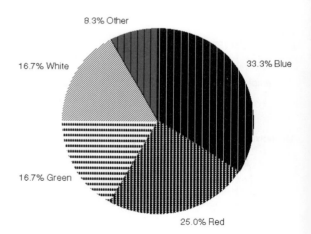

8.3% Other
16.7% White
33.3% Blue
16.7% Green
25.0% Red

Some of the packages even allow you to create your own symbol to use in a pictograph.

If you do have access to a computer package you may wish to use it to answer some of the questions in Exercise G.

Fig. 1.22
Fish caught on a school trip

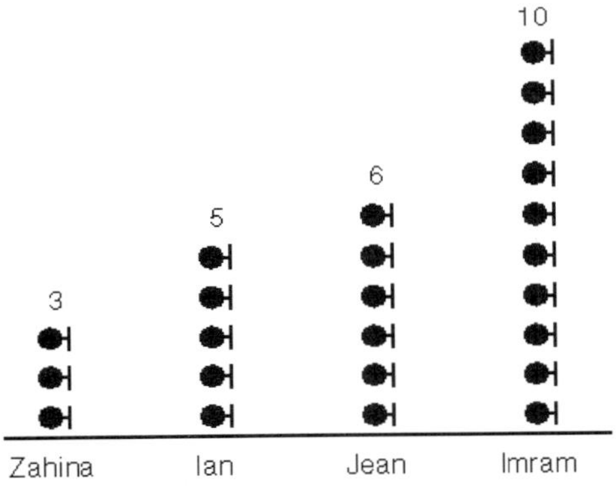

Pupils on fishing trip

Year	Population per passenger car
1981	32.4
1982	27.9
1983	26.0
1984	24.8
1985	24.0

3 Draw a pie chart to show the sector in which employment was first gained by 400 university science graduates in 1989.

	Number of graduates
Public service	28
Education	108
Industry	116
Commerce	48
Other	100

4 Design a symbol and use it to draw a pictograph to show the CD collections of four pupils.

Name	Number of CDs
Denise	10
Imram	20
George	18
Sheila	26

EXERCISE G   Miscellaneous

1 Draw a bar chart to display the average cost of a one-night stay in a luxury hotel in 1985.

Country	Price ($US)
Austria	106
France	189
Italy	116
UK	84
Netherlands	75
Luxembourg	60

2 Draw a line graph to illustrate the figures about passenger cars in the USSR between years 1981 and 1985.

5 Draw a pie chart to show the sources of energy used in the production of electricity in a North American state.

Energy	%
Natural gas	12.3
Water (hydroelectric)	13.7
Oil	15.0
Coal	55.6
Nuclear	3.4

6

	Mark	
Pupil	1st Examination	2nd Examination
Morag	79	82
Henry	52	71
Karen	80	65
Fiona	62	50

This table shows the marks of four pupils in two mathematics examinations. Draw a bar graph to illustrate these results.

a) Which pupil improved their performance most in the second examination?

b) Which pupil had the poorest result over the two examinations?

c) Which pupils improved their mark in the second examination?

7 Draw two line graphs on the same diagram comparing the profits of Company A and Company B over the years 1984–1990.

	Profits (£1000s)	
Year	Company A	Company B
1984	25	25
1985	29	30
1986	34	25
1987	46	23
1988	70	15
1989	82	15
1990	93	10

8 A survey was conducted in two classes in a school asking which European country the pupils would most like to visit.

Country	Class A	Class B
France	7	5
Germany	6	5
Switzerland	7	6
Spain	6	5
Norway	2	4
Greece	1	2
Italy	1	3
	30	30

Illustrate these results:
a) in a compound bar graph
b) in two pie charts.

9

Fig. 1.23
Monthly average temperatures for a holiday resort

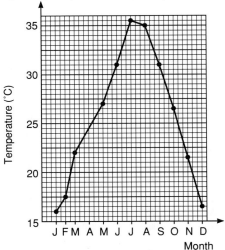

This graph shows the monthly average temperature figures for a holiday resort. Give two reasons why this graph could be deceptive to someone not looking closely at it.

10

Fig. 1.24
Average daily sunshine hours over three weeks

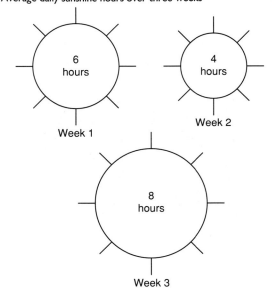

Week 1 — 6 hours
Week 2 — 4 hours
Week 3 — 8 hours

The pictograph in Figure 1.24 illustrates the daily average number of hours of sunshine in a holiday resort over three consecutive weeks. Comment on why this graph might be misleading. Draw a pictograph to illustrate the data in a better way.

11 The graph in Figure 1.25 shows the profits of a company for the years 1983–90. Describe two ways in which this graph is deceptive. Draw a line graph illustrating the same data in what you think is a more accurate manner.

Fig. 1.25
Company profits for 1983–90

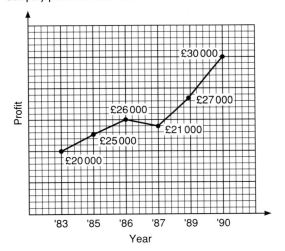

12 The expenditure incurred by two individuals on a seven day skiing holiday was as follows:

Expenses	Cuóng (£)	Mary (£)
Basic holiday	460	260
Lift pass	90	55
Equipment hire	30	25
Meals	80	120
Insurance	15	15
Entertainment	105	80

By drawing pie charts of different radii compare the breakdown and the total costs of each individual's expenditure.

13

Fig. 1.26
(Source of data: International Passenger Survey)

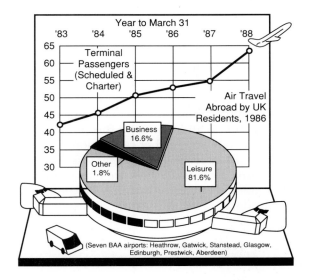

Figure 1.26 shows how information can be presented in an interesting and effective manner, although you must note that the vertical scale does not start at zero and the terminal passenger figures for 1987 and 1988 are only estimates.

Gather some statistics and design a poster to represent them. You may wish to use some of the data from the data base you created.

2 ESTIMATION OF ERROR

Since much of the data that is considered in statistics is obtained by measurement, it is important that we should understand how accurate our information is and, based on this information, how accurate any further calculations will be.

It seems appropriate, then, at this stage in the course to consider how we may estimate the extent of any error that may be contained in our data.

APPROXIMATIONS

Significant figures
58.4819 may be written as:
58.482 correct to 5 significant figures
58.48 correct to 4 significant figures
58.5 correct to 3 significant figures
58 correct to 2 significant figures
60 correct to 1 significant figure.

Decimal places
58.4819 may be written as:
58.482 correct to 3 decimal places
58.48 correct to 2 decimal places
58.5 correct to 1 decimal place
58 correct to the nearest whole number
60 correct to the nearest ten.

EXERCISE A ─────────────

1 Express the following numbers, correct to the number of significant figures shown in the brackets.
   a) 5.632 (3)
   b) 10.08 (3)
   c) 10.03 (2)
   d) 0.00681 (2)
   e) 6.138 (1)
   f) 117.2 (2)
2 Express correct to 1 decimal place.
   a) 11.66
   b) 9.81
   c) 69.008
   d) 0.085
   e) 6.99
   f) 15.849
   g) 15.850
   h) 15.851
3 Express 582 733:
   a) to the nearest 100 000
   b) to the nearest 10 000
   c) to the nearest   1000
   d) to the nearest   100
   e) to the nearest   10

ABSOLUTE ERROR

For certain data the information is found by counting and there can only be one correct answer, for example, the number of pupils on the roll of a particular school, the number of runs scored by a cricket side or the number of goals scored by a hockey eleven during a season. Other information is found by measuring, and this is a very different situation.

In measuring anything whether it be the length of a line, a period of time or the mass of an object we are limited in our accuracy by the equipment available and our own human limitations. We can never find the *exact* measure we are seeking and we must be content with an approximation. The difference between the true measure and that obtained by measurement is called the **error** (though there has been no mistake in the measuring). This error can be reduced, of course, by using more accurate instruments but a measurement can never be exact and so error never can be eliminated completely.

It is important then that we should be aware of what error is implied by our measurements and what the maximum possible error is likely to be.

Let us consider the measurement of a straight line. Using an ordinary ruler the smallest unit of measurement that we can read off, with any accuracy, is a millimetre or 0.1 cm. If our line is measured as 4.9 cm, this means that it measured 4.9 cm *to the nearest* 0.1 cm, that is, the line was *actually* between 4.85 cm and 4.95 cm long. The maximum error then is 0.05 cm above our nominal value and 0.05 below it. This is called the **absolute error**. (Note that the absolute error is half the smallest unit of measurement. In the example above, the smallest unit of measurement was 0.1 cm and the absolute error 0.05 cm.)

Example

For each of the following measurements, find:
a) the smallest unit of measurement.
b) the absolute error.
c) the upper and lower limits of the true measurement.
   i) 5 cm
   ii) 30.6 seconds.

Solution

i) a) The smallest unit of measurement is 1 cm.
   b) The absolute error is half of the smallest unit = 0.5 cm.

c) The upper limit is 5.5 cm
   The lower limit is 4.5 cm.
ii) a) The smallest unit of measurement is 0.1 s.
   b) The absolute error is half of 0.1 s = 0.05 s.
   c) The upper limit is 30.65 s
      The lower limit is 30.55 s.

EXERCISE B

1 For each of the following measurements give:
   a) the smallest unit of measurement.
   b) the absolute error.
   c) the upper and lower limits of the true measurement.

i) 7 cm	v) 12.8 g
ii) 186 m	vi) 2.683 litres
iii) 17 hours	vii) 1.21 miles
iv) 9.2 kg	viii) 16.5 seconds.

RELATIVE ERROR

The absolute error in itself is useful, but it is often more useful to find the **relative error**. This is found by considering the absolute error in relation to the measurement itself.

$$\text{relative error} = \frac{\text{absolute error}}{\text{measurement}}$$

Example

Find the relative error in giving a length as 7.5 cm.

Solution

$$\text{Absolute error} = 0.05 \text{ cm}$$

$$\text{relative error} = \frac{0.05}{7.5}$$

$$= \frac{5}{750}$$

$$= \frac{1}{150}$$

This is often expressed as a percentage:

$$\text{percentage error} = \frac{1}{150} \times 100\%$$

$$= \frac{100}{150}\%$$

$$= \frac{2}{3}\%$$

$$= 0.67\%$$

Notice that whereas the absolute error is a quantity of the same kind as the measurement itself, the relative and percentage errors are numbers only.

In calculating absolute, relative and percentage errors, we always calculate the maximum possible errors and so in practice, the errors are likely to be less than those calculated.

EXERCISE C

1 Calculate for each of the following measurements:
   a) the absolute error
   b) the relative error.
      i) 150 m
      ii) 35 kg
      iii) 1.5 litres
      iv) 2.3 seconds.
   Calculate for each of the following measurements:
   a) the relative error
   b) the percentage error (to 2 significant figures).
      v) 7 cm
      vi) 3.5 kg
      vii) 17 days
      viii) 25.0 g
      ix) 12.50 m
      x) 150.00 litres.

THE SUM AND DIFFERENCE OF MEASUREMENTS

Example 1

What are the upper and lower limits to the sum of 6.4 cm and 1.2 cm (each given to 2 significant figures)?

Solution

6.4 cm lies within the range 6.35 cm and 6.45 cm
and,
1.2 cm lies within the range 1.15 cm and 1.25 cm.
Hence, the maximum sum is:
6.45 + 1.25 = 7.70 cm
and, the minimum sum is:
6.35 + 1.15 = 7.50 cm
Note The apparent sum:
6.4 + 1.2 cm = 7.6 cm
has a (maximum) error of 0.10 cm, this being the sum of the absolute errors of the original measurements, each of which was 0.05 cm.

Example 2

Find the limits within which lies the difference of 6.5 kg and 3.25 kg.

Solution

6.5 kg lies within the range 6.45 kg and 6.55 kg
and,
3.25 kg lies within the range 3.245 kg and 3.255 kg.
The maximum difference is:
6.55 − 3.245 kg = 3.305 kg
The minimum difference is:
6.45 − 3.255 kg = 3.195 kg
Note The apparent difference:
6.5 − 3.25 kg = 3.25 kg
has a (maximum) absolute error of
(3.305 − 3.25) kg or (3.25 − 3.195) kg, both

being equal to 0.055 which is the sum of the absolute errors of the original measurements.

EXERCISE D

1. Find the upper and lower limits of the true sum of the measurements given.
   a) 6.5 cm and 8.2 cm.
   b) 15 g and 17 g.
   c) 17 m and 23 m.
   d) 16 litres and 23 litres.
2. Without actually calculating the sum write out the absolute errors in adding these measurements:
   a) 320 m and 47 m.
   b) 32 kg and 14 kg.
   c) 17.5 g and 5.3 g.
   d) 4.32 cm and 3.18 cm.
3. What are the upper and lower limits of the true differences between the following measurements?
   a) 19 cm and 5 cm.
   b) 13 kg and 8 kg.
   c) 13.5 m and 6.2 m.
   d) 17.6 litres and 14.0 litres.
4. Without working out the differences write down the absolute error in subtracting these measurements:
   a) 35 m and 17 m.
   b) 230 ml and 155 ml.
   c) 17.5 cm and 13 cm.
   d) 45 g and 24.5 g.

THE PRODUCT AND QUOTIENT OF MEASUREMENTS

Example 1

Within what limits does the following product lie, 16 cm × 11 cm?

Solution

16 cm lies within the range 15.5 cm and 16.5 cm and,
11 cm lies within the range 10.5 cm and 11.5 cm.
The maximum product $= 16.5 \times 11.5$ cm^2
$$= 189.75 \text{ cm}^2$$
The minimum product $= 15.5 \times 10.5$ cm^2
$$= 162.75 \text{ cm}^2$$
Thus the true product lies between 189.75 cm^2 and 162.75 cm^2.
The apparent product is:
$$16 \times 11 \text{ cm}^2 = 176 \text{ cm}^2$$
and,
$$(189.75 - 176) \text{ cm}^2 = 13.75 \text{ cm}^2$$
$$(176 - 162.75) \text{ cm}^2 = 13.25 \text{ cm}^2$$
so that the (maximum) absolute error is 13.75 cm^2.

Example 2

Within what limits does the following quotient lie, 195 ÷ 13?

Solution

195 lies within the range 194.5 and 195.5 and,
13 lies within the range 12.5 and 13.5.
The maximum quotient is:
$$\frac{195.5}{12.5} = 15.64$$
and, the minimum quotient is:
$$\frac{194.5}{13.5} = 14.41$$
Thus, the true quotient lies between 15.64 and 14.41.
The apparent quotient is:
$$\frac{195}{13} = 15$$
so, the absolute error is:
$$(15.64 - 15) = 0.64$$
or
$$(15 - 14.41) = 0.59$$
The (maximum) absolute error is 0.64.

EXERCISE E

1 Find the upper limits of the following expressions.

   a) 32×15 **c)** $\dfrac{42 \times 13}{17}$ **e)** $201.5 \div 19.3$

   b) $304 \div 16$ **d)** 14.5×11.3 **f)** $\dfrac{16.3 \times 13.4}{23.7}$

2 Calculate the (maximum) absolute error of these expressions:

   a) 16×13

   b) $210 \div 23$ (figures given correct to 2 significant figures)

   c) $436 \div 19$

   d) $\dfrac{420 \times 32}{120}$ (figures given correct to 2 significant figures).

5 A farmer advertised allotments for rent, measuring 100 m by 50 m (to the nearest metre). Calculate:

   a) the upper and lower limits for the length of boundary fencing required for each plot.

   b) the upper and lower limits for the area of an allotment.

6 A rectangular patio was measured as 4.5 m by 3 m (to the nearest centimetre). Calculate the upper and lower limits of the area of the patio to the nearest square centimetre.

EXERCISE F

1 A bag of cement was measured as weighing 51 kg.
   Calculate:
   a) the absolute error.
   b) the relative error.
   c) the percentage error.

2 In a scientific experiment, the time taken by a rat to find its way through a maze was measured as 63.5 seconds.
   Calculate:
   a) the absolute error.
   b) the relative error.
   c) the percentage error.

3 A joiner cut a piece of wood 18 cm long from a strip 2 m long. If both of these were measured to the nearest centimetre, what are the upper and lower limits for the length of the remaining strip?

4 A churn contained 20 litres of milk (to the nearest 50 ml). Two jugfuls, both of 500 ml (to the nearest 10 millilitre) were drawn off. What are the upper and lower limits of the volume of the remaining milk?

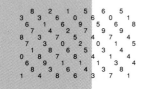

3 SAMPLING

Have you ever sampled a cake or scone from a batch of baking? Presumably you did not eat the whole lot to see what the baking was like. You tasted one cake and assumed that they were all of the same quality. But what if the one you tasted was too near the heat in the oven and was burned? Was this typical of all the cakes or was it an exception? This is the kind of thing we must consider when we take a **sample** of something.

Sampling things is part and parcel of everyday life. A farmer will run his or her hand through a sack of grain and pick out a handful to examine. Samples of cheese may be laid out on the delicatessen counter in a supermarket so that shoppers can taste the cheese and decide whether to buy it. Often manufacturers of breakfast cereals, soap powders, and so on, will distribute small sample boxes of their products to households so that they can try them.

If you stop to think about it, you will find that almost all the facts we know have been discovered by sampling. We know what rivers are like because we have seen a few, not all of them. We know what poetry is like by reading some poems. Hit Parade ratings of popular songs are obtained by questioning a sample of people, or finding out how many records have been sold in selected record shops, not in all record shops.

Sampling is of great importance to manufacturers. They must be constantly on the alert to ensure that their products are of a high standard. In the production of some goods, every article can be tested. For example, every TV set completed in a factory can be switched on to see that it is working. But it would be impractical to test every ball bearing made in a factory to see that it was of standard size.

Many tests are by their nature destructive of the article, for example, testing the length of a light bulb's life or eating a cake to see if it is of good quality. If all such articles were tested in this way, there would be nothing left to sell. So manufacturers take samples of each batch of articles made to check the quality of the product.

In all the situations mentioned above, we assume that the sample gives us information about the whole collection or **population**. We must recognise that whenever we obtain information from a sample and assume that this information holds good for the whole 'population', we run the risk of making a mistake.

The population is the general term given to the aggregate of whatever we are considering. It only means a *human population* when people are being considered.

A numerical characteristic of a population, such as its mean or standard deviation, is called a **parameter**. A quantity calculated from a sample is called a **statistic**.

Since parameters of a given population are based upon *all* its variates, they are fixed for that population. On the other hand, since statistics are based upon only a *part* of the population, they usually vary from sample to sample.

Random sample

This is a sample in which each member of the population has an equal chance of being chosen. For example, a number of even-sized marbles are in a box, some red, some green. The box is given a good shake and five marbles are picked out without looking. A random sample of five marbles has been chosen, each marble in the box having had an equal chance of being picked.

In a card game, the cards are shuffled and dealt so that each player gets a random sample.

It may seem a simple matter to obtain a random sample but in practical situations, particularly where human populations are concerned, it is far from simple.

Even in the card game mentioned above, what if the person shuffling and dealing the cards is a cardsharp? The cards dealt to each player would certainly not be random samples, they would be biased.

How to choose a random sample

If the population we are considering is small, we can allot a numbered card or disc to each member and, by mixing the cards thoroughly, pick out the required sample. Each member whose card is picked is in the sample.

This method, however, is not practical where the population is large. Here we can use tables of **random numbers**.

Random numbers

Sets of random numbers may be obtained from books of tables of random numbers. Or a computer can be used to produce sets of random numbers.

These random numbers may be:
single digits   e.g. 3 2 4 9 8 3 2 5

two-digit numbers   e.g. 13 51 07 88
three-digit numbers   e.g. 139 004 612
and so on.

A set of single-digit random numbers may be used to give two-digit, three-digit numbers, and so on, simply by splitting the row of digits into groups of two, or three, and so on.

For example, 3 2 4 9 8 6 4 0 5 3 9 7 2 3 1
two-digit numbers   32 49 86 40 53 97 23
three-digit numbers   324 986 405 397 231

Use of random numbers to pick a sample

There is a population of 250 scores out of which a sample of 20 is to be chosen using random numbers. So, using a set of random numbers, we require three-digit numbers 250 *or less*, that is, any number above 250 is no use.

Using a set of numbers such as that below:

183 521 906 518 732 190 354 991 035 784 etc.

any number above 250 is discarded and we go through the list until we have the required 20 suitable numbers.

The first suitable numbers from the above list are 183 190 035.

The members of the population which have been given these numbers are those to be used in the sample.

Stratified random sample

This is a sample, made up of random samples from each section or **stratum** of a population, where the size of each of the random samples is proportional to the size of that section of the population.

Quota sample

This is the kind of sample often used in market research surveys. Each interviewer is given definite instructions about the section of the public he or she is to question, but the final choice of actual persons is at his or her own discretion. They might be told, for instance, to question 30 people, including 3 men over 60 years of age; 5 men between 40 and 60; 6 men between 20 and 40; 6 men or boys under 20; 3 young schoolboys; 4 men dressed like business men; 3 men dressed in working clothes – overalls – and so on.

It is up to the interviewer which individuals are questioned. There will probably be a fairly large number of interviewers in various parts of the country conducting their surveys on the same day. Their results are sent to a central office and collated there.

Systematic sample

To obtain a systematic sample, every nth member of the population is taken.

The value of n depends on the size of sample wanted and on the size of the population from which the sample is to be drawn. For example, if there were 2000 names on the electoral roll of a certain town and a sample of size 200 was to be chosen, then every tenth name on the roll would be selected. If, however, a sample of 100 was to be chosen, then every twentieth name would be picked.

Opportunity (or convenience) sample

This is a sample comprising a part of the population which is 'conveniently' close to hand and readily available. Someone might stand in a shopping centre and interview the first 40 people who passed and were willing to answer questions. Obviously, there is a great risk that a sample obtained in this way may be biased and unrepresentative.

Cluster sample

In cluster sampling, the population to be sampled is first broken down into groups or **clusters**. A random sample of these clusters is selected and every member of the chosen clusters is investigated. For example, in a large city the grid lines on a detailed map could be used to provide the boundaries of areas to be investigated. A random sample of these areas would be chosen and used in the survey, perhaps to count the numbers of different types of buildings: factories, shops, houses. Biologists often use a grid system to divide an area into squares for detailed investigation of the flora and fauna. The squares might be as small as $1\,\text{m}^2$.

One obvious disadvantage to this type of sampling is that the clusters may not be representative of the population as a whole. To minimise the chance of this, it is advisable to divide the population into a large number of small clusters rather than a small number of large clusters.

Example

A certain secondary school has a roll of 900, made up as shown below.

Year	1	2	3	4	5	6
Number of pupils	192	183	210	175	92	48

We wish to pick a sample of 90 from the school using a:
a) random sample.
b) stratified random sample.

Solution

a) Random sample
i) Each pupil can be allotted a numbered card or disc. There are shaken in a box and 90 picked out at random. The pupils with these numbers are the ones to be included in the sample.
ii) Random numbers may be used to select the pupils.

b) Stratified random sample

To obtain a stratified random sample of 90 from the school population, the number chosen from each year group must be in proportion to the numbers in each year group relative to the total roll.

Year	Fraction of pupils	Number of pupils
1	$\dfrac{192}{900}$	$\dfrac{192}{900} \times 90 = 19.2 = 19$
2	$\dfrac{183}{900}$	$\dfrac{183}{900} \times 90 = 18.3 = 18$
3	$\dfrac{210}{900}$	$\dfrac{210}{900} \times 90 = 21 = 21$
4	$\dfrac{175}{900}$	$\dfrac{175}{900} \times 90 = 17.5 = 18$
5	$\dfrac{92}{900}$	$\dfrac{92}{900} \times 90 = 9.2 = 9$
6	$\dfrac{48}{900}$	$\dfrac{48}{900} \times 90 =. 4.8 = 5$
		Total = 90

Note Check that the 'rounded off' figures give the correct sample size. If they do not, then a slight adjustment must be made to a suitable figure.

Once the number of pupils from each year group is calculated, then this set of pupils may be selected at random (see (a) above).

EXERCISE A ───────────────────

1 A statistics class want to choose a sample of 100 from a school where the numbers of pupils in each year are shown below.

Year	1	2	3	4	5	6
Number of pupils	290	285	310	175	92	48

a) Explain how this sample could be obtained by picking a random sample.

b) If a stratified random sample is chosen, explain how this could be done and how many pupils from each year group are to be chosen for the sample.

2 In a small village, the population is divided by age groups as shown in the table.

Age (years)	0–4	5–15	16–45	46–65	65+
Number of people	15	41	50	70	14

It is proposed to choose a stratified random sample of 40 from the village. Explain how this should be done and calculate how many people should be picked from each age group.

3 In a primary school, the number of pupils in each class is shown below.

Class	1	2	3	4	5	6	7
Number of pupils	27	29	30	30	33	40	36

The Head wants to pick a stratified random sample of 50 from the pupils. Explain how you would calculate the number of pupils to be chosen from each class and give the numbers. Explain also how you would then pick the actual individual pupils in each class.

4 A factory making children's shoes completes 300 pairs in a day's work. The pairs are numbered from 1 to 300. It is wished to choose a sample of 10 pairs for testing purposes. Use the random numbers given below to show how this sample could be obtained.
2 9 5 2 9 7 9 2 7 9 7 9 7 0 0 2 8 1 2 6 4 1
6 7 2 7 6 2 7 2 0 3 5 9 1 1 6 1 1 1 3 2 7 0
6 1 0 7 3 5 6 3 5 3 5 6 3 1 7 0 8 2 1 4 6 4

5 Another factory, making crash helmets, completes 90 in a day's work. Use the random numbers from the last question to show how a sample of 5 helmets could be picked for testing.

6 A factory has 500 employees, each one having a 'works number'. For the purposes of a survey it is wished to pick a sample of 25 from the workforce.

Explain:

a) how a systematic sample of 25 could be chosen.

b) how a random sample, using the random numbers below, could be chosen.

c) how a random sample could be chosen, without the use of random numbers.

Random numbers

3 5 6 3 6 0 0 8 7 0 0 2 5 9 1 1 5 3 5 6 1
0 8 9 8 1 2 6 6 1 1 1 2 0 5 6 0 2 3 7 0 4
1 6 7 2 9 5 2 9 7 9 2 2 7 6 2 6 1 0 7 9 0
2 5 4 3 1 4 7 2 0 3 7 9 7 9 9 7 9 2 2 7 6
2 5 2 0 9 0 7 3 2 7 6 1 4 3 0 2 7 1 3 3 2
6 2 1 8 2 0 7 0 1 1 5 9 6 5 3 5 7 0 1 6 7
6 1 4 0 6 5 1 6 7 1 9 2 4 1 2 6 2 7 8 3 1

7 Another small factory has 80 employees with numbers from 1 to 80. It is wished to select a sample of 10 employees for a survey.

Explain:

a) how a systematic sample could be obtained.

b) how a random sample could be obtained using random numbers (use the random numbers from the last question).

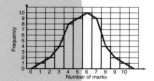

4 FREQUENCY DISTRIBUTIONS

VARIABLES

When we collect information to be used statistically we want to find out about a particular characteristic of a group of people or objects.

For example, we might want to know the heights of the boys in a class, the number of marks scored in an examination by the pupils of a class or the number of tomatoes on each plant in a certain greenhouse. The particular characteristic in which we are interested, is called the **variable**. This variable 'varies' or changes from one member of the group to another.

Variables are of two main types: **qualitative** and **quantitative**. A qualitative variable is one which *describes* a characteristic, for example, the size of a person's feet, small or large. A quantitative variable is one which can be given a numerical value. Quantitative variables are of two distinct types: **discrete** or **continuous**.

A **discrete** variable is one which can only have certain definite values, very often whole numbers, for example, the number of tomatoes on each plant in a greenhouse must be a definite value, in this case a whole number. There might be 2 tomatoes on one plant and 6 on another, but there cannot be 2.683 tomatoes on any plant. Some values of discrete variables are not whole numbers. In shoe sizes there are the 'half' sizes. As a girl's foot grows she may take a size 1, $1\frac{1}{2}$, 2, $2\frac{1}{2}$ but no matter the actual length of her foot, she cannot buy a size 1.75. Shoes can only be bought in certain, distinct sizes.

The various values of a discrete variable can usually be obtained by **counting**. The number of tomatoes per plant can be counted. The number of girls who take a size 2 shoe can be counted.

Let us consider, now, the actual length of a girl's foot as it grows. At the age of 10 it measured 20 cm and at the age of 12 it was 25 cm. There is *no length* between 20 cm and 25 cm that the foot did not measure at some time. At one point in time it measured 21.25 cm, at another time it was 23.6847 cm, and so on. The length of the foot varied continuously; there were no 'gaps' in its length between 20 cm and 25 cm.

A *continuous* variable is one which can take up any value within a certain range. The different values of a continuous variable are usually obtained by some kind of **measurement**. A boy's height or weight varies continuously and may be found by measuring.

EXERCISE A

State whether the following variables are qualitative or quantitative (discrete or continuous).
1 A baby's weight over the first year of its life.
2 The marks of a class in an English examination.
3 The colour of Mary's eyes (blue).

4 The temperature of a person who is ill.
5 The colour of John's hair (red).
6 The batting scores of a cricket team.
7 The speed of an aeroplane during a flight.
8 The length of a boy's left foot from the age of 5 to the age of 10.
9 The shoe sizes of the boy in question 8.
10 The number of goals scored by a football player during a football season.
11 The volume of water used by a town throughout the year.
12 The style of a girl's piano playing (very expressive).
13 Air pressures recorded at a weather station.

STEM AND LEAF CHARTS

Let us consider the data given below which was obtained by counting the number of potatoes in 20 similar bags. It is difficult to form an overall picture of the data without first doing some analysis. One way of doing this to form a stem and leaf chart.

20 14 18 23 9 13 24 31 13 25
21 9 17 10 18 30 19 14 20 15

Each number will be split into a stem and a leaf. We could take the tens as the stems and the units as the leaves. The stems would form a column and the leaves would be written to the right of them as shown opposite. A key is required to allow the reader to interpret the chart.

Stem	Leaf
0	9 9
1	4 8 3 3 7 0 8 9 4 5
2	0 3 4 5 1 0
3	1 0
	0/9 denotes 9

Then the chart is redrawn to show the leaves in increasing order.

Stem	Leaf
0	9 9
1	0 3 3 4 4 5 7 8 8 9
2	0 0 1 3 4 5
3	0 1
	0/9 denotes 9

Back-to-back stem and leaf charts

A back-to-back stem and leaf chart is a useful method of comparing two different but related sets of data.

Example

The following data give the thickness in millimetres of two samples of 25 plastic washers produced by two different machines.

Machine A
3.1 3.4 4.1 3.1 3.0
1.9 4.0 2.5 3.3 1.7
2.8 3.3 4.1 3.1 3.2
3.3 2.9 3.1 3.2 3.3
4.0 2.1 2.3 4.0 3.0

Machine B
1.8 2.8 2.1 2.7 2.9
2.2 2.9 1.9 2.2 3.0
2.8 3.1 2.3 2.8 3.1
2.9 3.3 2.9 3.3 1.9
3.5 4.1 3.4 1.9 4.0

Taking the units as the stems and the tenths as the leaves a back-to-back stem and leaf chart can be drawn, as shown in Figure 4.1 on the next page.
   A comparison can be made by drawing an outline round the leaves (Figure 4.2).
   The data collected suggest that machine A is producing thicker plastic washers than machine B but further samples would have to be taken to verify this conjecture.

Fig 4.1

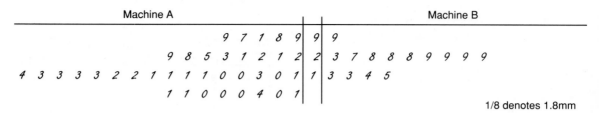

Fig. 4.2

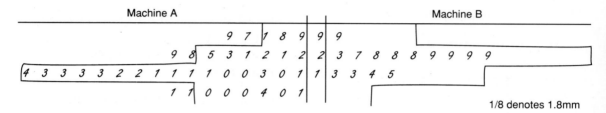

EXERCISE B

1 The weights (to the nearest 0.1 g) of 20 ten pence pieces were recorded as shown below. Draw a stem and leaf chart to display them.

11.4 10.9 11.2 10.8 11.0
11.3 11.2 10.9 11.3 11.1
10.8 11.0 11.1 11.5 10.9
9.9 10.8 11.4 12.1 10.7

2 Draw a stem and leaf chart to show the diameters (to the nearest 0.1 mm) of the following sample of 20 ball bearings.

8.0 5.2 6.0 7.1 8.4 6.1 6.2 9.2 5.1 7.7
7.9 9.1 7.8 7.4 6.6 5.2 6.8 8.1 6.8 6.9

3 Two first-year classes, each consisting of 25 pupils, sat a Craft and Design examination. The results are shown below. Draw a back-to-back stem and leaf chart to compare them.

Class A
30 34 23 41 35
25 47 42 24 19
36 43 36 25 34
33 31 48 40 31
50 37 40 35 39

Class B
13 22 32 44 20
17 19 9 30 43
29 18 31 21 8
15 27 33 28 21
32 28 27 8 17

4 A group of 24 pupils was randomly selected from each of two schools. The pupils were questioned on the distance (to the nearest 0.1 km) which they had to travel between home and school. Draw a back-to-back stem and leaf chart to display the results which are shown below.

School A
2.6 4.1 0.7 1.0 3.1 0.1
1.1 2.4 3.3 4.1 2.9 1.8
1.7 1.3 0.2 2.3 3.0 1.9
0.2 1.3 2.4 1.8 1.9 2.2

School B
3.7 4.2 1.6 2.4 3.5 3.3
4.5 3.1 1.3 2.3 3.4 2.5
3.4 2.8 1.4 0.2 4.0 2.4
4.7 3.6 2.1 1.4 2.1 0.1

FREQUENCY TABLES (UNGROUPED DATA)

The following marks are those scored by 50 students in a short mathematics test, the maximum mark possible being 10.

```
9  7  5  3  7  8  7  8  6  6
3  5  7  5  8  6  5  6  5  9
3  4  1  6  5  2  3  4  7  8
4  2  7  7  4  6  6  4  10 7
6  5  6  4  5  4  4  5  7  6
```

Data presented like this as a collection of single facts (**raw scores**) is not very useful. If you had sat that test and scored a mark of 6, you would like to know how your mark compared with the other marks; whether it was a good mark or a poor one. This data can be tabulated to give us a better idea of the distribution of marks.

One way of doing this is to write down, in order, the possible marks and count up how many pupils scored each mark. The counting is done by means of tally marks. One stroke is marked down for each time the score occurs, every fifth stroke being drawn diagonally across the previous four, making groups of 5. If the score on the list is crossed out as it is tallied, it helps to avoid confusion. The number of times each score occurs is called the frequency of the score.

Scores in a mathematics test		
Score	Tally	Frequency
0		0
1	I	1
2	I I	2
3	I I I I	4
4	ⅡⅡⅡ I I I	8
5	ⅡⅡⅡ I I I I	9
6	ⅡⅡⅡ ⅡⅡⅡ	10
7	ⅡⅡⅡ I I I I	9
8	I I I I	4
9	I I	2
10	I	1
		50

You must always check that the total frequency is the same as the number of scores. If it does not come to the same answer, then you must check the tallying.

This table that we have made is called a **frequency distribution table**, since it shows the frequency with which the various marks occur.

An important thing to take note of here is the **range** of the marks; in this case the marks range from 1 to 10, that is, there is a range of 9 marks.

Now that we have tabulated the data it is much clearer what value a score of 6 has. It is, in fact, the score which occurred most often and this 'fashionable' score is called the **mode**.

Sixteen pupils out of 50 or 32% of the group had a score greater than 6, and 24 pupils out of 50 or 48% of the group had a score lower than 6.

It is often important to know how the frequencies of the various scores compare to one another and to the total frequency.

The **relative frequency** of a score is the frequency of this score compared to the total frequency. For example, in the above table, the relative frequency of the score 6 is 10 out of 50, or 10/50, or 20%, or 0.2.

EXERCISE C

1 These are the heights of 40 second-year girls, measured to the nearest 2 cm. Make a frequency table and then answer the questions below.

```
154  144  152  158  158  154  148  150  160  154
156  152  150  154  158  150  154  156  142  154
152  152  154  152  156  148  150  154  154  152
150  158  156  158  158  154  164  148  152  152
```

a) State whether the variable here is continuous or discrete.
b) What is the range of the heights?
c) What is the modal height?
d) What is the relative frequency of 154 cm?
e) How many girls are 148 cm tall or less?

f) What percentage of the girls are taller than 158 cm?

g) What percentage of the girls are at least 150 cm tall but not more than 156 cm?

2 List the heights of the pupils in your own class and make a frequency table. Find out what the mode and the range of the heights are. Compare your results with those in question 1. Explain any differences or similarities.

3 A pupil collected the following from a third-year class in November 1990. These data are the number of children in the families of the pupils questioned.

```
1  6  3  2  5  9  6  2  3  6
7  3  2  5  4  3  2  6  5  6
4  8 10  5  6  1 10  6  3
```

Make a frequency table.

a) Is the variable continuous or discrete?

b) What is the mode?

c) What kind of family is not taken into account in this table? Why not?

d) How many of the pupils in this class belong to families with more than 6 children?

e) What percentage of the pupils are in families with 3 or less children? (Answer correct to 1 decimal place.)

4 Make a list of the number of children in the families of the pupils in your own class and make a frequency table. Compare your results with those in the last question. Point out any similarities or differences.

5 These are the results of the Scottish football matches (Premier and First Division) one Saturday in the 1990–1991 season.

Premier Division	First Division
1–3	0–3
1–1	1–1
1–3	1–1
1–3	1–1
2–2	3–1
4–1	2–2
0–0	1–3

a) Form a frequency table of the number of goals scored by each team.

b) Is this a continuous or discrete variable?

c) What is the range of goals scored?

d) What is the mode?

e) What is the relative frequency of the mode?

f) What percentage of the teams scored 2 or more goals?

HISTOGRAMS (UNGROUPED DATA)

One of the best ways of representing a frequency distribution graphically is by means of a **histogram**.

This is the frequency table that we made using the marks in the mathematics test earlier in the chapter (p. 39).

Score	0	1	2	3	4	5	6	7	8	9	10
Frequency	0	1	2	4	8	9	10	9	4	2	1

Fig. 4.3
Mathematics test

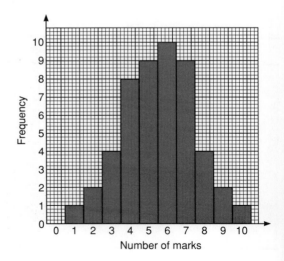

As you see, a histogram is similar to a bar chart but the area of each column must be *proportional* to the frequency of the corresponding class.

The columns can be drawn without leaving space between them because there is a regular scale along the horizontal axis.

The values of the variable are always shown on the horizontal axis and the frequencies on the vertical axis.

EXERCISE D ———————————————

1 The histogram in Figure 4.4 shows the number of points gained by the teams of the Second Division of the English Football League at one stage of a season.
   a) How many clubs are in this league?
   b) What is the range of the points?
   c) What is the mode number of points?
   d) What is the relative frequency of 16 points?
   e) How many clubs gained 22 or more points?

f) How many clubs gained less than 15 points?

2 The histogram in Figure 4.5 illustrates the distribution of the shoe sizes of all boys aged 12–13 years in a school one January.

Fig. 4.5
Shoe sizes of boys aged 12–13 years

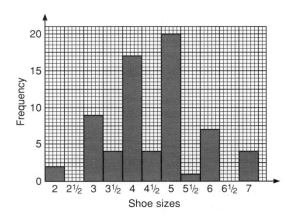

Fig. 4.4
Points scored by teams in the English Second Division

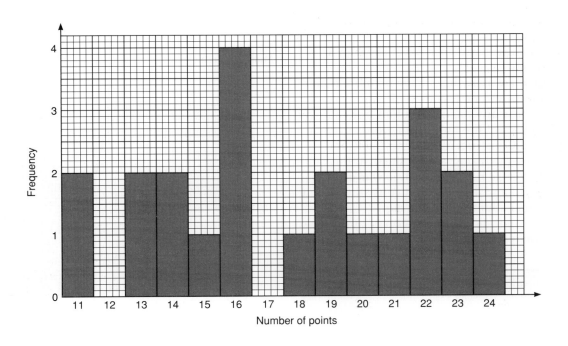

a) Do you notice anything unexpected about the distribution of the frequencies? Can you suggest any reason for this?
b) What is the total frequency of the distribution?
c) What is the modal shoe size?
d) What is the relative frequency of the modal size?
e) What is the relative frequency of size 6?

3 The numbers of words in each line of a page of the book *Redgauntlet* by Sir Walter Scott are shown below. Form a frequency table and draw a histogram of the distribution.

```
11 10  6  8 12  1  9  5
 7  8  8  8  8  9 10  8
 8  8  3  7 13  5 10  9
 7  9  6  8  6  8 11
 9  9  8  9 11  3  6
```

a) How many lines are in the page?
b) What is the modal number of words per line?
c) What is the range of the distribution?
d) What is the relative frequency of 9 words?
e) How many lines have more than 9 words?
f) How many lines have less than 5 words?
g) How many lines have no more than 8 words and no less than 6?

4 Choose any page at random from a novel and count the number of words in each line. Construct a frequency table and draw the histogram for the distribution.

5 A class of new apprentices was given a speed and accuracy test consisting of ten sums; addition, subtraction, multiplication and division of numbers. The results obtained were as follows:

No. of sums correct	0	1	2	3	4	5	6	7	8	9	10
Frequency	0	1	2	6	11	5	2	2	1	2	0

a) Draw a histogram of the distribution.
b) How many pupils took the test?
c) What was the modal number of correct sums?
d) What was the range of the marks?
e) What percentage of the pupils had more than 5 sums correct?

FREQUENCY POLYGONS (UNGROUPED DATA)

Another way of representing a frequency distribution graphically is by means of a line graph called a **frequency polygon**. A frequency polygon is drawn by joining, with straight lines, the mid-points of the tops of the columns of the histogram. Figure 4.6a shows a frequency polygon superimposed on the histogram. Figure 4.6b shows the polygon by itself. To draw the polygon without drawing the histogram first, the points are plotted where the mid-points of the columns would have been.

Fig. 4.6a
Mathematics test

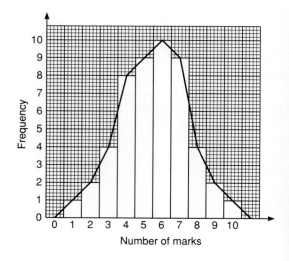

Fig. 4.6b
Mathematics test

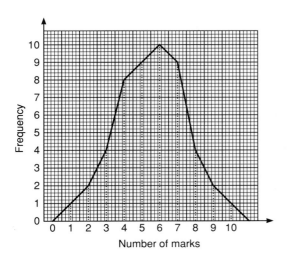

Since the area under the polygon must be equal to the area contained by the columns of the histogram, the polygon ought to be finished off by continuing the line at each end to the horizontal axis to where the next score would have been found.

GRAPHICAL REPRESENTATION OF RELATIVE FREQUENCY DISTRIBUTIONS

Histograms and frequency polygons can be used to represent relative frequency distributions. This is very useful if we want to compare two distributions which have different total frequencies. The two polygons could be drawn on the same graph and a comparison made.

Example

Two classes of students were given a short general knowledge test. The marks were tabulated and the relative frequencies calculated as shown below.

Class A

Score	Tally	Frequency	Relative frequency (%)
0		0	0
1	I	1	2
2	I I	2	4
3	I I I	3	6
4	⊥⊥⊤⊤	5	10
5	⊥⊤⊤ I I	7	14
6	⊥⊤⊤ ⊥⊤⊤ I I	12	24
7	⊥⊤⊤ I I I I	9	18
8	⊥⊤⊤ I I	7	14
9	I I I	3	6
10	I	1	2
		50	

Class B

Score	Tally	Frequency	Relative frequency (%)
0		0	0
1	I	1	2.5
2	⊥⊤⊤ I I	7	17.5
3	⊥⊤⊤ I I I I	9	22.5
4	⊥⊤⊤ ⊥⊤⊤	10	25.0
5	⊥⊤⊤ I	6	15.0
6	I I I	3	7.5
7	I I	2	5.0
8	I	1	2.5
9	I	1	2.5
10		0	0
		40	

The two frequency polygons can then be drawn on the same graph as shown in Figure 4.7 on the next page.

43

Fig. 4.7
Score in a general knowledge test

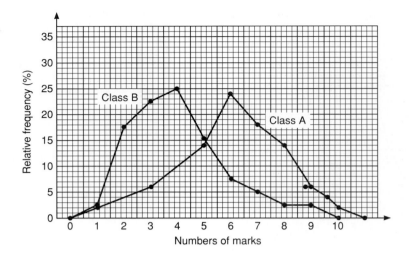

EXERCISE E _____

1 Figure 4.8 shows the number of goals
scored by the teams of the four divisions
of the English Football League one
Saturday.
  a) How many teams scored 1 goal?

b) How many teams scored more than 2
goals?
c) How many teams played that
Saturday?

2 To determine the number of items
purchased on each visit to a small
grocery shop, 50 shoppers were selected
for a survey. The results of the survey
are shown in the table.

Fig. 4.8
Goals scored by the teams in the English Football League one
Saturday

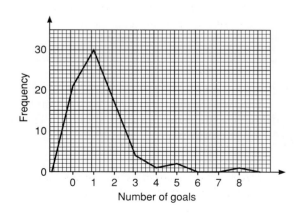

Number of items	Frequency
1	1
2	2
3	6
4	11
5	18
6	7
7	3
8	2

a) Draw a histogram of the frequency
distribution.
b) Draw a frequency polygon on the
histogram.

3 The number of fishing trips made by members of a fishing club last year was recorded as shown below. Without drawing a histogram, draw a frequency polygon for the distribution.

Number of trips	Frequency
0	1
1	3
2	4
3	4
4	5
5	7
6	8
7	9
8	13
9	16
10	18
11	15
12	8
13	6
14	2
15	1

4 Fifty pupils were given two tests in successive weeks. The results were as follows:

Marks	Frequency	
	1st test	2nd test
0	1	0
1	4	0
2	7	0
3	15	3
4	12	4
5	5	7
6	4	20
7	2	8
8	0	5
9	0	2
10	0	1

On the same graph draw frequency polygons for each distribution. (Use a solid line for the first test and a broken line for the second.)

a) What was the modal mark in each test?

b) Comment on the way the marks are distributed. What reason might there be for it?

5 The results of English football matches (Premier and First Division) one Saturday in the 1990–1991 season are shown below.

Premier Division	First Division
1–0	2–3
0–0	5–1
4–3	2–4
2–0	1–2
1–1	1–2
3–3	4–2
1–2	1–1
1–3	2–1
0–1	4–1
0–1	3–2
	1–1
	2–1

a) For each Division form a frequency table of the number of goals scored by each team.
b) Extend each table to include a column showing the percentage relative frequency.
c) On the same graph draw polygons to represent the two relative frequency distributions.
d) Comment on the way the goals are distributed.

6 Measure the heights of all the boys and girls in your class (to the nearest centimetre). Form two percentage relative frequency tables and draw polygons to represent these two distributions on the same graph. Comment on the way the heights are distributed.

FREQUENCY TABLES (GROUPED DATA)

Sometimes the data we are considering has such a large range of scores that it is necessary to collect the scores into groups or classes. The **class interval** is the size of the group chosen. The class interval is decided by looking at the range of the scores and choosing the interval so that there are about 8 to 14 groups.

```
80 93 63 74 51 60 61 53 69 54
50 43 32 70 40 30 55 57 59 55
 4 50 42 47 53 52 67 44 35 48
37 56 39 52 12 44 43 58 49 32
65 64 62 73 21 21 86 67 75 68
```

The figures above are a list of the marks of 50 boys in an examination. First we look through the list and pick out the highest and lowest scores. These are 93 and 4. A good way of grouping these marks is in tens, starting with the group 0–9, then 10–19, 20–29, and so on. This will give us 10 groups. The scores are tallied in exactly the same way as for ungrouped data.

Mark	Tally	Frequency
0–9	I	1
10–19	I	1
20–29	I I	2
30–39	ⅢⅡ I	6
40–49	ⅢⅡ IIII	9
50–59	ⅢⅡ ⅢⅡ IIII	14
60–69	ⅢⅡ ⅢⅡ	10
70–79	IIII	4
80–89	I I	2
90–1	I	1

With grouped data we cannot pick out a single mark as the mode, but we can pick out the **modal class** or **group**. In this frequency distribution, the modal class is the group (50–59) marks.

One point that should be noted here is that a certain amount of accuracy is lost when data is grouped. For instance, from the table, we know that there are 6 scores between 30 and 39. Unless we have the original raw scores we do not know that the actual scores are 30, 32, 32, 35, 37 and 39.

CLASS BOUNDARIES

When selecting a grouping care must be taken to ensure that no gaps are left between the classes and also that the classes are not allowed to overlap. In the above example it would be useless to take classes 0–10, 10–20, 20–30, and so on as here we would not know whether to place a score of 10 in the first or second class. Neither of these difficulties will occur if we have a clear understanding of the nature of our data and of our class boundaries. In the above example the actual marks in the second class are 10–19, but we say that the boundaries enclosing the class are 9.5 and 19.5. If the first few classes are written in a row it helps to make this clearer.

Class	0–9	10–19	20–29	30–39	
Boundaries	9.5	19.5	29.5	39.5	

Thus 9.5 is the boundary separating the first and second classes, that is, 9.5 is the upper boundary of the first class and the lower boundary of the second class. We are in fact taking as our class boundary a measure which is halfway between the largest measure we wish to include in the one class and the smallest we wish to include in the next. With most types of data this is quite straightforward but occasionally, especially when dealing with age, care must be taken, for example, the group of 13-year-old children have ages ranging from 13 years exactly, up to but not including 14 years.

The mid-point of the class is now taken as the average of the upper and lower boundaries of the class. In the above example dealing with marks the mid-point of the second class is 14.5 and for the class of 13-year-old children the mid-point of the class is 13.5 years. The mid-point of the class interval is important, as you will see later, because it is often used to stand for the whole group.

1 Form a frequency table of the test marks of 40 pupils shown below, using class intervals of 5 marks starting at 1–5, 6–10 and so on.

```
20 19 18  6 25 15 16 30 17 25
 2 22  5 22 23  8 15  7  7 12
11 26 21 12 14 28  9 18 13 19
16 31 38 20 33 10 42 16 47 13
```

a) What is the mid-point of the fifth class?
b) What is the upper boundary of the fifth class?
c) What is the lower boundary of the second class?
d) What is the modal class?
e) What is the relative frequency of the third class?
f) What percentage of the pupils scored more than 25 marks?
g) What percentage of the pupils scored more than 10 marks but less than 26?

2 Construct a frequency table for the scores of the 40 pupils who entered a school's putting competition listed below. Use class intervals of 25–29, 30–34, and so on.

```
45 40 39 27 41 32 40 38
39 42 37 42 30 41 32 36
49 44 35 42 42 38 50 36
40 41 31 43 41 48 38 51
44 40 54 49 41 42 48 47
```

3 Listed below are the sales figures for a certain item achieved by the retail outlets of a chain store in one week. Construct a frequency table using suitable class intervals.

```
490 281  47 102 308 100 218
301 190  82 341 121 251 235
 71 472 130  50 183 241 199
369  34 141 240 274  90 153
238 290 315 187 201 283 251
403 375 503 325 381
```

4 The following figures were the number of a rain days (days in which rain fell) recorded at selected stations all over the UK in one year:

```
260 234 209 241 243 268 185
241 253 228 199 158 236 209
173 187 191 207 199 199 172
178 157 188 148 183 160 152
197 171 265 226 235 226 233
180 182 211 202 185 206 209
182 188 164 156 160 250 220
187 195 215 177 191 225 164
209 206 194 205 195 198 177
175 180
```

Construct a frequency table using class intervals of 10 starting at 140–149.
a) What is the mid-point of the fourth class?
b) What is the lower boundary of the sixth class?
c) What is the upper boundary of class 10?
d) What is the modal class?
e) What number of stations recorded less than 200 rain days?
f) What percentage of stations recorded at least 170 rain days and not more than 209?

HISTOGRAMS (GROUPED DATA IN EQUAL CLASS INTERVALS)

To represent graphically frequency distributions with grouped data, we again use histograms. However with grouped data, we must be very careful how we use the horizontal scale.

The frequency distribution of marks that we tallied in the previous section is shown on the next page.

Take particular note of the scale used on the horizontal axis in Figure 4.9. On the actual scale, the class boundaries are used, and the groups are shown above the scale. As you become used to drawing these histograms

Mark	Frequency
0–9	1
10–19	1
20–29	2
30–39	6
40–49	9
50–59	14
60–69	10
70–79	4
80–89	2
90–99	1

Fig. 4.9
Examination marks

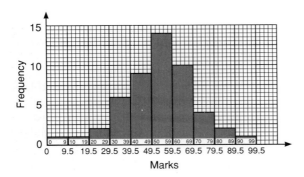

Fig. 4.10
Rainfall recorded in Britain for one year

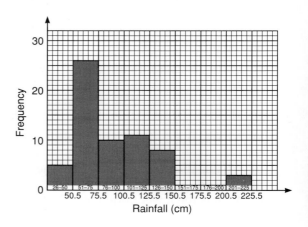

you should start to leave out the groups and simply show the boundaries.

The vertical axis shows the frequency or more precisely the frequency density per class interval. Provided the class intervals are all equal, the heights of the columns on the histogram are the frequencies of the corresponding class intervals. The problem of unequal class intervals is dealt with later in this chapter.

EXERCISE G _____

1 This histogram shows the distribution of the rainfall (in centimetres) recorded at selected stations all over Britain, one year.

a) How many stations were there?
b) What is the upper boundary of the first class?
c) What is the lower boundary of the fifth class?
d) What is the mid-point of the third class?
e) What is the modal class?
f) What is the relative frequency of the modal class?
g) What percentage of the stations recorded a rainfall of more than 125 cm?
h) What percentage of the stations recorded a rainfall of 50 cm or less?

2 The distribution of the weights (in kilograms) of a number of boys is shown in the histogram Figure 4.11.
a) How many boys were weighed?
b) What is the upper boundary for the third class?
c) What is the lower boundary for the third class?
d) What weights are in the third class?
e) What weights are in the fifth class?
f) What is the mid-point of the fourth class?
g) What is the modal class?
h) What is the relative frequency of the modal class?

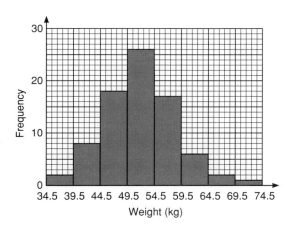

Fig. 4.11
Weights of boys

FREQUENCY POLYGONS (GROUPED DATA IN EQUAL CLASS INTERVALS)

Frequency polygons are used to show frequency distributions with grouped data, as line graphs. To draw a polygon we join up with straight lines the mid-points of the tops of the columns of the histogram.

Example 1

The marks of some pupils in a test are shown below grouped in class intervals of 5.

3 Draw histograms for all the distributions you tabulated in Exercise F (page 47).

4

Age	Frequency
0–4	37
5–9	47
10–14	19
15–19	9
20–24	5
25–29	4
30–34	11
35–39	13
40–44	8
45–49	11
50–54	20
55–59	23
60–64	33
65–69	30
70–74	30
75–79	28
80–84	28
85+	10

Mark	Frequency
0–4	1
5–9	5
10–14	8
15–19	15
20–24	20
25–29	12
30–34	6
35–39	2
40–44	1
45–49	0

The above table shows the number of pedestrians killed in one year, in Scotland, in motor vehicle accidents, according to age in years.

Draw a histogram to illustrate this, without any further grouping.

Comment on the shape of the distribution and give reasons for it.

Figure 4.12a shows the polygon of this distribution drawn on top of the histogram.

Figure 4.12b shows the polygon by itself.

If you study Figure 4.12a you will see that the key points for the polygon are actually above the mid-points of the class intervals, and to draw the polygon on a graph by itself you need only plot the mid-points of the intervals against the corresponding frequencies.

The mid-points of the intervals are shown below the graphs on the next page.

You can draw this like any line graph, plotting the mid-points against the corresponding frequency (see Figure 4.12b).

Fig. 4.12a
Test results

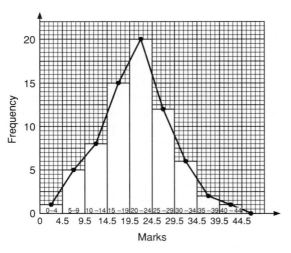

Fig. 4.12b
Test results

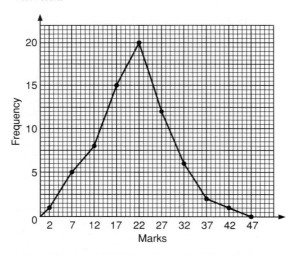

Mid-point of interval	Frequency
2	1
7	5
12	8
17	15
22	20
27	12
32	6
37	2
42	1
47	0

Example 2

Draw the frequency polygon for the following distribution of examination marks.

Mark	Frequency
0–9	1
10–19	1
20–29	2
30–39	6
40–49	9
50–59	14
60–69	10
70–79	4
80–89	2
90–99	1

Solution

First find the mid-points of the class intervals, and then plot the co-ordinates as shown in Figure 4.13, opposite.

Mid-point	Frequency
4.5	1
14.5	1
24.5	2
34.5	6
44.5	9
54.5	14
64.5	10
74.5	4
84.5	2
94.5	1

EXERCISE H

1 Draw frequency polygons superimposed on the histograms you drew for Exercise G.
2 Draw polygons by themselves (adjusting your scale accordingly) for the distributions in Exercise G.
3 The heights of 50 second-year boys were measured to the nearest centimetre in October 1989. In October 1990 the

Fig. 4.13
Examination marks

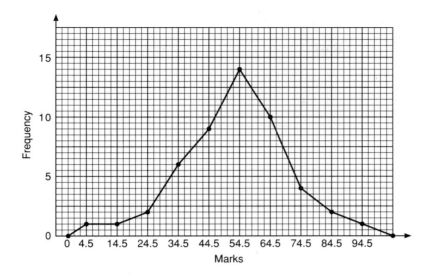

heights of 50 boys in the second year were again measured (to the nearest centimetre). These heights are shown below.

Draw, on the same graph, frequency polygons for each distribution.

Comment on any differences you find.

Height (cm)	Frequency	
	1989	1990
116–120	2	0
121–125	0	0
126–130	0	0
131–135	0	0
136–140	0	1
141–145	5	3
146–150	7	10
151–155	14	20
156–160	11	12
161–165	8	3
166–170	2	1
171–175	1	0

4 The number of words in each of the first hundred sentences of two books were counted. One book was *Moby Dick* by Herman Melville (the story of the giant whale) first published in 1851. The other book was a modern, run-of-the-mill, detective story first published some hundred years later.

The distributions for the number of words are shown below.

Draw polygons for the distributions on the same graph and comment on the way the distributions are dispersed.

What does the graph indicate to you about the 'readability' of the two books.

Moby Dick	
No. of words	Frequency
1–10	30
11–20	23
21–30	22
31–40	15
41–50	4
51–60	0
61–70	3
71–80	1
81–90	1
91–100	0
101–110	0
111–120	1

51

Detective Story	
No. of words	Frequency
1–10	62
11–20	24
21–30	10
31–40	2
41–50	0
51–60	1
61–70	1

5 Choose 2 novels (*not* textbooks) and count the number of words in each of the first 100 sentences and repeat Question 4.

6 Shown below are the number of hours of bright sunshine recorded in 52 selected stations all over Scotland one year, in the months of December and June.

Tabulate the data for each month grouping in suitable class intervals, and draw a frequency polygon for each month on the same graph.

Compare and contrast the two distributions.

Number of hours of bright sunshine
December
16 25 41 20 35 20 16 8 38 23
25 38 38 41 34 39 24 47 45 17
42 44 47 45 51 35 37 51 47 42
42 31 39 55 45 42 33 27 35 40
28 35 39 36 14 14 40 44 43 34
50 43

June
163 153 164 137 177 160 158 148
171 152 169 180 179 152 164 157
181 198 188 163 195 195 209 212
195 204 197 215 206 192 201 149
186 234 192 177 144 120 186 173
176 163 177 175 163 148 161 172
150 136 150 151

Histograms (grouped data in unequal class intervals)

Great care must be taken determining the heights of the histogram's columns when data have been grouped in unequal class intervals. Let us consider an example to illustrate the method of calculating the column heights.

Example

The ages of the 36 employees of a supermarket are as follows:

Age	Frequency	Class interval length (years)
16–24	6	9
25–33	16	9
34–42	9	9
43–60	5	18

As the column heights represent the frequency density per class interval length, a standard class interval length must be selected. The class interval length 9 occurs the most often so its selection will minimise the number of calculations required to obtain the frequency densities per standard class interval length. This is shown below.

Age	Frequency	Class interval length (years)	Frequency density per 9 years
16–24	6	9	6
25–33	16	9	16
34–42	9	9	9
43–60	5	18	2.5

Now a histogram can be drawn for the distribution and is shown in Figure 4.14.

Fig. 4.14
Ages of a supermarket's employees

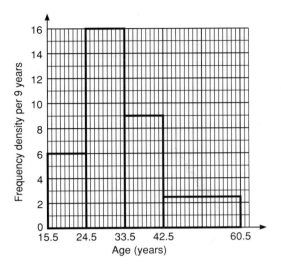

Fig. 4.15
Ages of a supermarket's employees

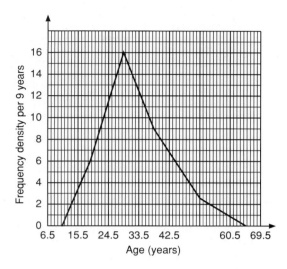

FREQUENCY POLYGONS (GROUPED DATA IN UNEQUAL CLASS INTERVALS)

This table shows the mid-points of the class intervals of the employees' ages in the last example.

Mid-point		20	29	38	51.5
Frequency density per 9 years		6	16	9	2.5

The frequency polygon is obtained in the same way as was illustrated for equal class intervals, and it is shown in Figure 4.15. The polygon is completed by continuing the line at each end to the horizontal axis to the point where the mid-point of the next standard interval would have been found.

EXERCISE I

1 The histogram in Figure 4.16 shows the heights of a school's sixth-year pupils.

Fig. 4.16
Heights of sixth-year pupils

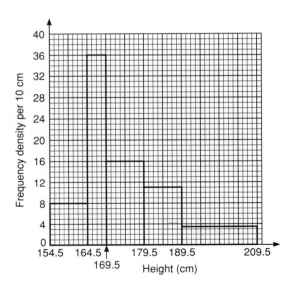

These heights are also shown in a grouped frequency table below.

Height (cm)	Frequency
155–164	8
165–169	18
170–179	16
180–189	11
190–209	7

a) What was the standard interval length used in the histogram?
b) Draw a frequency polygon for the distribution.

2 The mileages of 50 motorists last month were recorded.
a) Draw a histogram for the frequency distribution.
b) Draw a frequency polygon on the histogram.

Mileage	Number of motorists
0–399	4
400–799	12
800–999	26
1000–1199	6
1200–1399	2

3 A class of 30 students were given a Spanish vocabulary test. The results were as follows:

Mark	Number of students
0–19	2
20–39	4
40–49	5
50–59	12
60–99	7

a) Draw a histogram for the distribution.
b) Draw a frequency polygon on the histogram.

4 The weight of each cow in a farmer's herd was recorded and the following grouped frequency table was formed.

Weight (kg)	Number of cows
350–449	3
450–549	6
550–599	12
600–699	7

Without drawing a histogram, draw a frequency polygon for the distribution.

CUMULATIVE FREQUENCY

It is often useful to know how many girls have scored more than a certain mark in an examination or how many boys are less than a particular height. An easy way to answer this type of question is by making a **cumulative frequency** table. A frequency table is converted to a cumulative frequency table by adding each frequency to the total of its predecessors.

Example 1

The marks of 30 pupils in a test are shown below **a)**.

The cumulative frequency table for these marks is shown in **b)**.

a)

Mark	Frequency
0	0
1	2
2	3
3	4
4	6
5	8
6	5
7	1
8	1
9	0
10	0

b)

Mark (up to and including)	Cumulative frequency
0	0
1	(0 + 2) 2
2	(2 + 3) 5
3	(5 + 4) 9
4	(9 + 6) 15
5	(15 + 8) 23
6	(23 + 5) 28
7	(28 + 1) 29
8	(29 + 1) 30
9	(30 + 0) 30
10	(30 + 0) 30

From the cumulative frequency table we can see, for example, that:

23 pupils scored 5 or less marks.

9 pupils scored less than 4 marks.

Example 2

a) is the frequency table we constructed a few pages ago of the marks of 50 boys in an examination.

b) shows the cumulative frequency table for the distribution.

a)

Mark	Frequency
0–9	1
10–19	1
20–29	2
30–39	6
40–49	9
50–59	14
60–69	10
70–79	4
80–89	2
90–99	1
	50

b)

Mark (up to and including)	Cumulative frequency
9	1
19	(1 + 1) 2
29	(2 + 2) 4
39	(4 + 6) 10
49	(10 + 9) 19
59	(19 + 14) 33
69	(33 + 10) 43
79	(43 + 4) 47
89	(47 + 2) 49
99	(49 + 1) 50

Instead of writing

'up to and including   9'

'up to and including 19', etc.,

we can show the mark for the cumulative frequency as:

0– 9

0–19

0–29 etc.

From the above cumulative frequency we can answer these questions readily.

1 How many boys scored less than 50 marks? Answer: 19.

2 How many boys scored more than 59 marks? Answer: 17 $(50 - 33)$.

EXERCISE J

1 This table shows the heights of a class of 30 fourth-year girls measured to the nearest 2 cm.

Height (cm)	Frequency
146	1
148	0
150	1
152	3
154	3
156	4
158	3
160	5
162	6
164	1
166	2
168	1

Construct a cumulative frequency table and answer the following questions.
a) How many of the girls are less than 150 cm tall?
b) What percentage of the girls are at least 158 cm in height?
c) How many girls are over 164 cm?

2 The frequency distribution for the times of some telephone calls was as follows.

Time (s)	Frequency
0–20	0
21–40	2
41–60	4
61–80	7
81–100	11
101–120	28
121–140	20
141–160	16
161–180	10
181–200	6
201–220	3

a) Construct a cumulative frequency table for the distribution.
b) How many calls lasted a minute or less?
c) What percentage of the calls lasted more than 2 minutes?

3 The frequency distribution below shows the weights of fourth-year boys measured to the nearest kilogram.

Weight (kg)	Frequency
35–39	1
40–44	2
45–49	3
50–54	8
55–59	8
60–64	4
65–69	1
70–74	0
75–79	1
80–84	1

Construct a cumulative frequency table.
a) What was the total number of boys weighed?

b) How many boys weighed less than 50 kg?
c) How many boys weighed 60 kg or more?

4 In a major golf tournament, the leading ten players handed in the following scores (4 rounds each).

70 69 68 69 66 68 71 71 71 69
70 69 71 74 75 68 70 74 72 68
69 70 72 68 70 73 69 67 75 73
66 68 67 68 68 70 70 69 65 71

a) Construct a frequency table for the scores.
b) Convert this to a cumulative frequency table.
c) How many rounds of less than 70 were there?
d) How many rounds of more than 71 were there?

CUMULATIVE FREQUENCY CURVES

When we draw the graph of a cumulative frequency distribution we obtain a curve which has a characteristic shape. This curve is called a **cumulative frequency curve** (or **ogive** from a term used in architecture for this shape of curve).

Figure 4.17 shows the cumulative frequency curve for Example 1 of the last section.

Mark	Cumulative frequency
0	0
0–1	2
0–2	5
0–3	9
0–4	15
0–5	23
0–6	28
0–7	29
0–8	30
0–9	30
0–10	30

Fig. 4.17
Test results

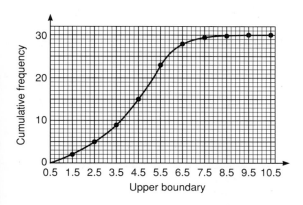

To plot the points of the graph, the cumulative frequency is drawn against the upper boundary of the class, for example:
  2 is plotted against the mark 1.5
  5 against 2.5
  9 against 3.5
15 against 4.5.

Fig. 4.18
Examination results

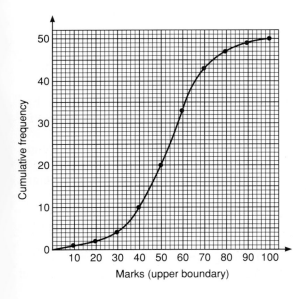

Figure 4.18 shows the cumulative frequency curve of Example 2 of the last section.

Mark	Cumulative frequency
0–9	1
0–19	2
0–29	4
0–39	10
0–49	19
0–59	33
0–69	43
0–79	47
0–89	49
0–99	50

To plot the points of this graph we plot the cumulative frequency against the upper boundary of the class, for example:
  1 is plotted against the mark 9.5
  2 against 19.5
  4 against 29.5
10 against 39.5.

Note: The horizontal scale is marked off in tens but the points are plotted at 9.5, 19.5 etc.

As with any line graph, 2 or more curves may be drawn on the same graph, for purposes of comparison.

EXERCISE K ────────────────

Draw cumulative frequency curves for all the cumulative frequency distributions you tabulated in Exercise J.

EXERCISE L   Miscellaneous ─────────

1 State whether the following variables are qualitative or quantitative (discrete or continuous).
   a) The lengths of the holes on a golf course.
   b) The number of putts taken at the various holes by a player.
   c) The type of weather (sunny).
   d) The length of time taken to play a round of golf.

57

2 The length of each trout in a box was measured, correct to the nearest centimetre, and the results are illustrated in the form of a cumulative frequency curve (Figure 4.19).

Fig. 4.19

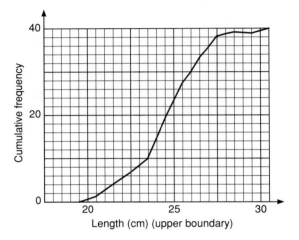

Length (cm) (upper boundary)

a) Use the graph to draw up the cumulative frequency distribution.
b) Use this result to obtain the frequency distribution of the lengths.
c) How many trout were less than 25 cm long?
d) How many trout were 27 cm or more in length?
e) What was the modal length?
f) What was the lower limit of the modal class?

3 At a busy airport the scheduled take-off times of aircraft over a three-hour period were as shown below.

0802 0810 0820 0825 0829 0835
0845 0853 0900 0909 0921 0924
0935 0948 1000 1010 1020 1029
1040 1043 1048 1055 1100

a) List the intervals between the scheduled take-off times.
b) Construct a frequency table for these times.

c) Illustrate the information using a histogram.
d) What is the modal interval between the scheduled take-off times?
e) How many of the intervals were less than the modal interval?

4 The weights of 40 fourth-year pupils were measured to the nearest kilogram and the results are given in the following table.

Weight (kg)	Frequency
35–39	1
40–44	6
45–49	9
50–54	10
55–59	6
60–64	4
65–69	3
70–74	1

The weights of the girls in the group are given in the following frequency polygon.

Fig. 4.20

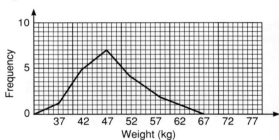

Weight (kg)

a) Use the two sets of data to obtain the frequency distribution of the weights of the boys in the group.
b) What is the modal class for the weight of a boy?
c) What is the modal class for the weight of a girl?
d) What are the limits between which the weights of girls in the modal class must lie?
e) Draw up separate cumulative frequency distributions for the weights of

boys and girls. Draw the two cumulative frequency curves on the same grid and comment on the result.

5 A histogram was drawn to illustrate the distribution of pupils within the various years of the school. The years and the heights of the corresponding columns are given in the table below.

Year	Height (cm)
1	12.5
2	13.5
3	13.0
4	11.5
5	9.5
6	3.0

If the number of pupils in the sixth year was 36 find the number of pupils in each of the other years.

6 The lifetime of 100 electric bulbs was measured and the details are given below.

Lifetime (hours)	Number of bulbs
1000–1199	8
1200–1399	16
1400–1599	28
1600–1799	32
1800–1999	12
2000–2199	4
2200–2399	0

a) What is the modal lifetime?
b) Illustrate the information using a frequency polygon.
c) Construct a cumulative frequency distribution from the above facts.
d) How many of the bulbs had a lifetime which was less than that of the modal class?
e) Construct the cumulative frequency curve.

7 The values of coins in 40 pupils' pockets are shown in this frequency distribution table.

Value of coins (pence)	Number of pupils
0–19	2
20–29	1
30–39	5
40–44	9
45–49	11
50–59	7
60–69	3
70–89	2

a) Draw a histogram of the distribution.
b) Draw a frequency polygon on the histogram.

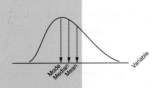

5 MEASURES OF CENTRAL TENDENCY

Data can be more easily understood when tabulated in an orderly fashion in a frequency distribution and then shown graphically. But one single value which characterises the group and which is most easily grasped by the mind, is the **average** of the group.

There are three 'averages' commonly used in statistics:

1 *The **arithmetic mean***
2 *The **median***
3 *The **mode***

A fourth average, the **geometric mean**, whose use is less general, will be considered at the end of the chapter.

THE ARITHMETIC MEAN

This is the 'average' used in arithmetic but in statistics we must be careful always to call it the mean.

To find the mean of a set of scores, we simply add up the scores and divide by the number of scores.

Example

Find the mean of the following numbers.
1, 3, 5, 7, 9, 11, 13, 15.

Solution

$$\text{The mean} = \frac{\text{sum of the scores}}{\text{number of scores}}$$

$$= \frac{1 + 3 + 5 + 7 + 9 + 11 + 13 + 15}{8}$$

$$= \frac{64}{8}$$

$$= 8$$

The formula we use to calculate the mean is,

$$\bar{X} = \frac{\Sigma X}{N}$$

where $\bar{X}$ = mean

Σ means sum of

X represents the single scores

N represents the number of scores.

THE MEDIAN

When a number of scores are arranged in **numerical order**, the median score is the 'middle' score having the same number of scores above it as below. When there is an odd number of scores this is easy as there is a 'middle' score but when there is an even number of scores there is no single 'middle' score and we define the median as halfway between the two 'middle' scores.

Example 1

Find the median of the following golf scores.

72 68 65 70 75 79 73

Solution

First arrange the scores in numerical order.

65 68 70 |72| 73 75 79

median

72 is the median since it has 3 scores above it and 3 below it.

Example 2

Find the median of these boys' heights (measured to the nearest centimetre).

148 161 167 157 162 154

Solution

First arrange in numerical order.

148 154 157 | 161 162 167

median

This time there is an even number of scores and the median is halfway between 157 and 161, that is, the median is:

$$\frac{157 + 161}{2} = 159$$

THE MODE

The mode, as we saw in the last chapter, is the score which occurs most frequently.

EXERCISE A

1 Find the mean, median and mode of the following sets of data.
   a) 15, 11, 6, 3, 2, 14, 13, 7, 10, 11, 9
   b) 24, 21, 20, 25, 21, 27
   c) 5, 2, 2, 1, 3, 3, 3, 4, 4, 3, 3, 4, 2, 3, 2, 4

2 In successive rounds a golfer took the following numbers of strokes:
   90, 69, 70, 70, 73, 71, 80
   Which of the three averages – mean, median or mode – would he prefer to call his 'average' score?
3 The heights (to the nearest centimetre) of some boys are given below.
   162, 159, 162, 167, 165,
   158, 166, 164, 158, 160
   What is:
   a) the median height?
   b) the modal height?
   c) the mean height?
4 Make a list of 5 numbers, 4 of which are smaller than the mean.
5 Make a list of 6 numbers, 5 of which are greater than the mean.
6 If you were handed a box of used pencils of varying lengths, what would be the easiest average – mean, median or mode – to find, and what would be the hardest?
7 In his savings account a boy had the following balances at the ends of 6 successive months. What was his mean balance and his median balance?
   £6.50, £9.75, £4.75, £5.90, £8.40, £5.50

AVERAGES FROM FREQUENCY DISTRIBUTIONS

In the previous exercise, the mean, median and mode were being obtained from raw scores, but we often want to know these averages from data which can be tabulated into, or is already in the form of, a frequency distribution.

The mean from a frequency distribution (ungrouped data)

Example

Calculate the mean of the following test marks of 50 pupils (maximum possible mark 10):

a) without tabulating them.
b) by constructing a frequency table.

```
1  5  5  3  4  6  5  6  4  7
7  6  6  7  4  7  2  3  5  6
8  4  2  6  7  4  7  5  6  4
7  9  7  3  5  8  3  5  4  8
4  6  6  10  7  6  5  9  8  5
```

Solution

a)   The mean $\bar{X} = \dfrac{\Sigma X}{N}$

$$= \frac{277}{50}$$

$$= 5.54$$

b)

Score	Tally	Frequency
0		0
1	I	1
2	I I	2
3	I I I I	4
4	++++ I I I	8
5	++++ I I I I	9
6	++++ ++++	10
7	++++ I I I I	9
8	I I I I	4
9	I I	2
10	I	1
		$\Sigma f = 50$

$$\bar{X} = \frac{(0 \times 0) + (1 \times 1) + (2 \times 2) +}{} $$
$$(4 \times 3) + (8 \times 4) + (9 \times 5) + $$
$$(10 \times 6) + (9 \times 7) + (4 \times 8) + $$
$$(2 \times 9) + (1 \times 10) $$

over 50

$$= \frac{277}{50}$$

$$= 5.54$$

To obtain 277 we multiply the frequency of each score by the score and add the results.

An easier way of doing this is to add another column to the frequency table in which we multiply the frequency (f) by the score (X)

Score (X)	Frequency (f)	f × X	
0	0	(0 × 0)	0
1	1	(1 × 1)	1
2	2	(2 × 2)	4
3	4	(4 × 3)	12
4	8	(8 × 4)	32
5	9	(9 × 5)	45
6	10	(10 × 6)	60
7	9	(9 × 7)	63
8	4	(4 × 8)	32
9	2	(2 × 9)	18
10	1	(1 × 10)	10
	$\Sigma f = 50$	$\Sigma fX = 277$	

$$\bar{X} = \frac{\Sigma fX}{\Sigma f} \quad \begin{array}{l} (\Sigma fX = \text{sum of frequency} \times \text{score} \\ (\Sigma f = \text{sum of frequencies}) \end{array}$$

$$= \frac{277}{50}$$

$$= 5.54$$

EXERCISE B

1 This frequency table shows the number of goals scored by the teams of the

Premier and First Divisions of the English Football League one Saturday.

Number of goals	0	1	2	3	4	5
Frequency		15	16	4	6	2	1

Calculate the mean number of goals scored.

2 Construct a frequency table from the goals scored by the English Premier and First Division teams last Saturday and calculate the mean number of goals.

3 The following table shows the number of children per family in the families of the pupils in a first-year class.

Number of children	1	2	3	4	5	6	7	8	9
Frequency			2	4	10	6	6	3	2	1	0

Calculate the mean number of children per family.

4 Construct a frequency table of the number of children in the families of the pupils in your class and calculate the mean.

5 The following numbers are the number of words in each line of a page chosen from the novel *Westward Ho!* by Charles Kingsley.

```
 7  7  7 10 13  8 10  6  9 12
11  1 12 13  2 11 10 10 13  9
12  1 10  8 12 12 12 12  3  7
10 12  9 10 12 11 12  9  2 11
 8 13
```

Construct a frequency table and then calculate the mean number of words per line.

6 Repeat the last question by choosing any novel and counting the number of words in each line of a page chosen at random.

THE MEAN FROM A FREQUENCY DISTRIBUTION (GROUPED DATA)

Example

Calculate the mean of the following test marks (possible mark 50):
a) without grouping.
b) by grouping in class intervals of 5.

```
 4 23 35 27 32 15 29 19 25 18
36 11 33 12  6 30 20 24 27 25
16 40 21 35 20 17  9 30 14 29
31 26 23 25 21 32 23 18 26 11
28 43 24 43 24 10 37 22 34 23
```

Solution

a)
$$\bar{X} = \frac{\Sigma X}{N}$$
$$= \frac{1206}{50}$$
$$= 24.12$$

b)

Mark	Tally	Frequency
1–5	I	1
6–10	III	3
11–15	IIIII	5
16–20	IIIII II	7
21–25	IIIII IIIII III	13
26–30	IIIII IIII	9
31–35	IIIII II	7
36–40	III	3
41–45	II	2
46–50		0
		$\Sigma f = 50$

When we have a frequency distribution with grouped data, we use the mid-point of the interval to stand for the group, and as before, we add a (frequency × score) column to the table.

Mark	Mid-point of interval (X)	Frequency (f)	fX
1–5	3	1	3
6–10	8	3	24
11–15	13	5	65
16–20	18	7	126
21–25	23	13	299
26–30	28	9	252
31–35	33	7	231
36–40	38	3	114
41–45	43	2	86
46–50	48	0	0
		$\Sigma f = 50$	$\Sigma fX = 1200$

To calculate the mean, we again use the formula:

$$\bar{X} = \frac{\Sigma fX}{\Sigma f}$$

(This time X is the mid-point of the interval.)

$$\bar{X} = \frac{\Sigma fX}{\Sigma f}$$

$$= \frac{1200}{50}$$

$$= 24.0$$

Note When the data is grouped the mean is slightly different from that obtained when we use the raw scores. This is because of the slight loss of accuracy any time data is grouped. The more correct mean is that obtained from the raw scores.

EXERCISE C _____

1 This table shows the marks gained by 50 pupils in a mathematics examination. Calculate the mean mark.

Mark	Frequency
20–29	1
30–39	4
40–49	8
50–59	15
60–69	16
70–79	5
80–89	1

2 The table shows the number of deaths due to railway accidents in Scotland in one year according to the age of the deceased person: Calculate the mean age of death.

Age (years)	Frequency
5–9	1
10–14	1
15–19	3
20–24	2
25–29	1
30–34	1
35–39	1
40–44	1
45–49	1
50–54	1
55–59	5
60–64	2
65–70	1

3 The age distribution of workers in a factory follows. Calculate the mean age.

Age (years)	Frequency
16–20	2
21–25	10
26–30	12
31–35	17
36–40	15
41–45	14
46–50	9
51–55	8
56–60	8
61–65	5

4 These figures show the number of hours of bright sunshine recorded in 52 places in Britain one year for the month of October.

```
50  81  75  90  62  80   92  75  77  74
86  99  75  63  67  73   95  75  71  74
93  94  76  68  79  81  105  83  81  75
71  82  79  76  69  85   75  80  81  47
99  68  71  74  74  85   65  71  74  80
69  68
```

Construct a frequency table using appropriate class intervals and calculate the mean number of hours of bright sunshine.

5 The times taken by rats to pass through a maze are recorded below. Calculate the mean time taken (to 1 decimal place).

Time (seconds)	Frequency
10–14	3
15–19	11
20–24	19
25–29	22
30–34	6
35–39	2

6 A manufacturer of cornflour wanted to check the accuracy of the machines used to fill the packets with cornflour. A sample of 100 packets was selected at random from the conveyor belt and these packets were weighed carefully. The results are shown in the table below. Calculate the mean weight of the packets.

Weight (grams)	Frequency
450–459	1
460–469	7
470–479	40
480–489	44
490–499	6
500–509	2

7 The weekly wages of 80 part-time workers in a company are shown below. Calculate the mean weekly wage.

Weekly wage (£)	Frequency
50–59	2
60–69	10
70–79	16
80–89	24
90–99	16
100–109	11
110–119	1

THE MEDIAN FROM A FREQUENCY DISTRIBUTION

It is very easy to find the median of a set of raw scores by setting the scores out in numerical order and counting along till the middle is found.

The same method is used to find the median of a frequency distribution when the data is ungrouped.

Example 1

Find the median of the following scores.

Score	51	52	53	54	55	56
Frequency	3	4	7	6	3	1

Solution

There is a total frequency of 24, so the median must lie between the twelfth and thirteenth scores. We examine the frequencies to see where the twelfth and thirteenth scores lie. These scores are both 53, so the median must be 53.

When the data we are concerned with is grouped into class intervals, it is only possible from the distribution to say that the median lies in a certain group. To find the median more exactly we draw the cumulative frequency curve for the distribution and then estimate the median from this.

Example 2

Find the median of the marks gained by 50 pupils in an English examination.

Mark	Frequency
21–30	2
31–40	6
41–50	11
51–60	20
61–70	7
71–80	4

Solution

Construct a cumulative frequency table and draw the curve.

Mark	Cumulative frequency
21–30	2
21–40	8
21–50	19
21–60	39
21–70	46
21–80	50

There is a total frequency of 50, so the median lies between the twenty-fifth and twenty-sixth score, that, it is the $25\frac{1}{2}$th score.

We draw a line across the graph at the $25\frac{1}{2}$th score until it cuts the curve and then drop another line to the horizontal axis. Thus from the graph the median is the mark of 54 (see Figure 5.1).

Note If the total frequency is N, then the median is $\frac{1}{2}N + \frac{1}{2}$.

Where N is large the $\frac{1}{2}$ becomes insignificant and the median is taken as $\frac{1}{2}N$.

Fig. 5.1
Cumulative frequency curve of examination marks

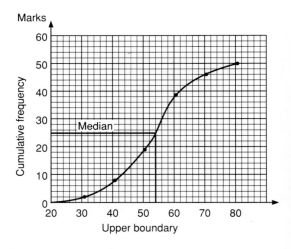

EXERCISE D

1 The frequency curve (Figure 5.2a) shows the marks of 40 pupils in a geography exam.
a) From the curve, estimate the median mark.
b) If 25% of the pupils failed, what was the pass mark?

Fig. 5.2a
Geography examination results

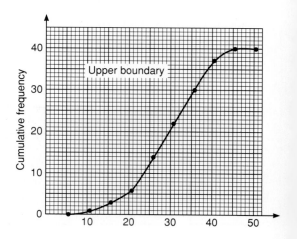

2 The curve in Figure 5.2b, shows the marks of the same class for a history exam.

a) Estimate the median mark from the graph.

b) If the pass mark was 24, what percentage of the class failed?

c) What percentage of the class passed?

Fig. 5.2b
History examination results

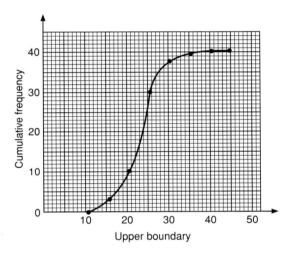

3 Find the cumulative frequency curves you drew for the questions in Exercise J, Chapter 4 (p. 55) and estimate the medians for each distribution.

4 This table shows the number of deaths registered in Wales for each week of a recent year.

Number of deaths	Frequency
450–499	3
500–549	16
550–599	16
600–649	11
650–699	3
700–749	2
750–799	1

Construct a cumulative frequency table, draw the cumulative frequency curve and from it estimate the median number of deaths registered.

COMPARING THE THREE 'AVERAGES'

The mean

Advantages

1 *It can be calculated exactly.*

2 *It makes use of all the data.*

3 *It can be used in further statistical calculations.*

Disadvantages

1 *It can be very misleading if there is an abnormally high or low value, e.g. the ages of 10 pupils in a school are 5, 5, 5, 6, 6, 6, 7, 7, 7, 17 years. The mean age is 7.1 years. In this case 9 of the 10 pupils are below the mean age. The abnormally high value of 17 has unduly affected the mean.*

The median

Advantages

1 *It is simple to understand.*

2 *It is unaffected by abnormally high or low values.*

3 *It is characteristic of the normal group and sometimes represents an actual member of the group, e.g. the pupil of median height in a class can actually be picked out and examined.*

Disadvantages

1 *It cannot be used in further statistical calculations.*

2 *Its value can only be estimated (from a cumulative frequency curve) in grouped distributions.*

3 *In small groups or in groups which have a rather odd pattern of distribution, it may not be characteristic of the group, e.g. in a test there were 6 scores of 5 marks, 2 of 7 marks, 1 of 8 marks and 1 of 9 marks. From these marks the median would be 5 which would not be a good average to use for the group. (In this case, the mean would be a better average to use.)*

The mode

Advantages
    1 *It is simple to understand.*
    2 *It is unaffected by abnormally high or low values.*
    3 *It is the average useful to manufacturers of shoes, clothes, hats, and so on.*

Disadvantages
    1 *It cannot be determined exactly in a distribution where the data is grouped.*
    2 *It cannot be used in arithmetical calculations.*

THE RELATIONSHIP BETWEEN THE MEAN, MEDIAN AND MODE

A frequency distribution which shows a symmetrical curve peaking at the centre is said to be a **normal distribution** and it has the mean, median and mode coinciding at the centre (Figure 5.3).

A distribution which is not symmetrical is said to be *skewed*. In a **negatively skewed distribution** (Figure 5.4) the mean is reduced because of a few very low values of the variable (**outliers**). In a **positively skewed distribution** (Figure 5.5) the mean is *dragged* to the right of centre because of a few very high outliers.

The greater the difference between the mean and the mode, the more skewed the distribution.

Fig. 5.3
Normal distribution

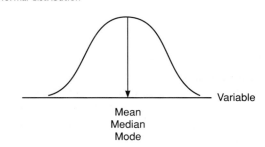

Fig. 5.4
Negatively skewed distribution

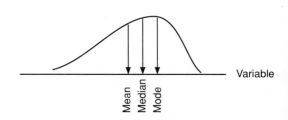

Fig. 5.5
Positively skewed distribution

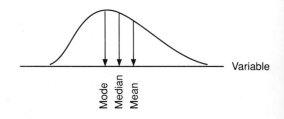

THE GEOMETRIC MEAN

Another average which is sometimes used in statistics is the geometric mean.

The geometric mean of *n* numbers is the *n*th root of their product. For example, the geometric mean of 3, 6 and 9
$$= \sqrt[3]{(3 \times 6 \times 9)}$$
$$= \sqrt[3]{162}$$
$$= 5.5$$

The geometric mean of 3, 6, 9 and 10

$$= \sqrt[4]{(3 \times 6 \times 9 \times 10)}$$
$$= \sqrt[4]{1620}$$
$$= 6.3$$

The calculation of the cube root, fourth root, fifth root, and so on, of numbers may be done quite easily using a scientific calculator.

The geometric mean, however, cannot be calculated if we have negative or zero values of the variable.

Calculation of the geometric mean is one way of reducing the effect of an outlier while still using every value of the variable. For example, the arithmetic mean of 6, 8, 10, 20

$$= \frac{44}{4} = 11$$

The geometric mean of 6, 8, 10, 20

$$= \sqrt[4]{9600} = 9.9$$

From this example, we can see that the geometric mean is less than the arithmetic mean and is a more useful average to employ. In fact, the geometric mean is never greater than the arithmetic mean.

The geometric mean is particularly useful when dealing with a distribution where there is a constant rate of growth or decay. For example, in studying the growth of human populations, or the growth of a sample of bacteria, or the emissions of radioactive particles from a radioactive substance.

Example

£100 was invested at a fixed rate of compound interest. After ten years it had increased to £900. Estimate, using the geometric mean, what the value was five years after the original investment.

Solution

Estimated value $= \sqrt{£100 \times 900}$
$$= \sqrt{£90\,000}$$
$$= £300$$

This is a much more realistic estimate than the arithmetic mean of £500.

1 Calculate the geometric mean of the following sets of numbers (correct to one decimal place).
i) 2, 18   vi) 4, 6, 8, 10
ii) 2, 3   vii) 2, 3, 4, 5, 6
iii) 2, 3, 5   viii) 3, 5, 6, 7, 8
iv) 2, 7, 8   ix) 2, 3, 5, 7, 9, 10
v) 3, 4, 5, 6   x) 1, 2, 3, 5, 7, 9.

2 50 bacteria were counted on a Petri dish in a laboratory. After 30 minutes, the count had gone up to 300. Estimate, using the geometric mean, the number of bacteria 15 minutes after the first count.

3 In another Petri dish, 30 bacteria were counted and after one hour the number had risen to 600. Using the geometric mean, estimate the number of bacteria 30 minutes after the first count.

4 £500 was put away in a safe place and left for six years. By this time, because of inflation, it had a purchasing value of only £150. Estimate, using the geometric mean, and assuming a constant rate of inflation, the purchasing value of the money three years from the time it was stored.

EXERCISE F   Miscellaneous

1 Find the mean, median and mode of the following sets of measures.
a) 3, 3, 5, 5, 5, 7, 7
b) 61, 67, 76, 90, 90, 90
c) 24, 24, 25, 31, 40, 50, 63, 79

2 Find the geometric mean of each of the following sets of measures.
a) 2, 6, 18
b) 5, 10, 15, 20
c) 3, 5, 7, 9, 11

3 A pupil scored the following set of marks in a series of tests:
6, 4, 4, 3, 7, 9, 8, 4, 5, 5, 6
a) Determine the mean, median and mode of these marks.
b) Which of these measures would the pupil prefer to tell her parents was her average?

4 Six hundred items were examined and the number of faults per item was found to be as follows:

No. of faults .	0	1	2	3	4	5	6
Frequency	34	132	185	95	75	64	15

a) State the modal number of faults.
b) Calculate (correct to one decimal place) the mean number of faults per item.
c) Find the percentage of items which were perfect.
d) Find the percentage of items with more than two faults.

5 The length of time, in minutes, spent in the waiting-room of a hospital by 50 patients was as follows:

35 73 46 32 26 49 83 65 29 74
61 36 52 42 32 57 67 47 51 53
27 61 49 36 29 28 55 57 65 61
55 42 54 36 51 32 60 57 47 58
47 61 60 54 61 28 60 42 43 61

a) Group the data in classes, 26–35, 36–45 and so on.
b) Calculate the mean length of time spent in the waiting room.
c) Construct the cumulative frequency distribution, draw the cumulative frequency curve and thus obtain the median time spent in the waiting room.
d) What percentage of the patients spent more than one hour in the waiting room?

6 The weights of 40 lambs were taken and the results are tabulated below.

Weight (kg)	Number of lambs
11–14	0
15–18	8
19–22	16
23–26	11
27–30	4
31–34	1

a) Find the mean weight.
b) Draw the cumulative frequency curve and find the median weight.
c) What is the lower limit of the weights included in the modal class?
d) What percentage of the lambs were less than 25 kg?

7 The first 30 words of a book were taken and the number of letters per word recorded.

No. of letters per word	1	2	3	4	5	6	7	8	9	10	11
No. of words	1	5	8	7	2	3	2	0	0	1	1

a) What is the modal number of letters?
b) Calculate the mean number of letters per word.
c) Find the median number of letters per word.

8 a) Use the cumulative frequency curve drawn in Figure 4.17 (p. 57) to find the median mark for the distribution.
b) Use the cumulative frequency curve drawn in Figure 4.18 to find the median mark for the distribution.
c) Use the cumulative frequency curve drawn in Figure 4.19 to find the median length of a trout.

9 The intervals between the scheduled take-off times of aircraft, over a three-hour period, at a busy airport are shown below. Calculate the mean length of time between take-offs.

Interval (mins)	3	4	5	6	7	8	9	10	11	12	13
Frequency	2	1	3	1	2	2	2	4	2	2	1

10 The weights of some fourth-year pupils, 20 boys and 20 girls measured to the nearest kilogram, are shown opposite. Calculate the mean weight of:
a) the girls,
b) the boys in the sample.

Weights (kg)	Frequency	
	Boys	Girls
35–39	0	1
40–44	1	5
45–49	2	7
50–54	6	4
55–59	4	2
60–64	3	1
65–69	3	0
70–74	1	0

Fig. 5.6b

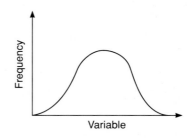

11 The lifetimes of 100 electric bulbs were measured and the results recorded. Find:
a) the mean lifetime,
b) the median lifetime of the bulbs.

Fig. 5.6c

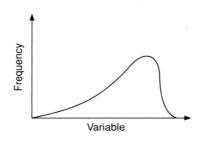

Lifetime (hours)	Number of bulbs
1000–1199	8
1200–1399	16
1400–1599	28
1600–1799	32
1800–1999	12
2000–2199	4

12 For each of the distributions shown in Figure 5.6a–c, which average – mean, median or mode – has the smallest value?

Fig. 5.6a

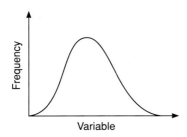

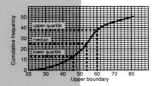

6 MEASURES OF DISPERSION

RANGE

In Chapter 5, we studied measures of central tendency or averages. These averages are very important as they can give us a picture of the group which they represent. However, taken by themselves, they give us a very limited view of the whole picture. As well as the average, we need to know how the rest of the data is grouped around the average, whether it is closely gathered round or scattered more widely. In other words, we have to find some way of measuring how the scores scatter. We need a measure of the spread, scattering or dispersion of the scores.

Examine the data of the weekly wages of ten employees in different factories.

Weekly wage (£)	Employees in factory			
	A	B	C	D
190	2	5	1	0
170	2	0	2	4
150	2	0	4	2
130	2	0	2	4
110	2	5	1	0

In each factory the mean wage is £150. But the way the wages are scattered about the mean is very different in each case. One simple way of measuring the scatter is to consider the **range** of values. The range is defined as the difference between the greatest and the least measures in the distribution. In some situations this is helpful but in this example the range is the same in factories A, B and C. As a measure of dispersion the range is very easily found but is not particularly good. Thus more satisfactory measures are required.

INTERQUARTILE RANGE

In many experimental situations we tend to distrust extreme measures and as a result these measures are often discarded. It is this type of thinking that leads to improved versions of the range called the **interquartile range** and the **semi-interquartile range**.

Just as the median divides a set of scores into two equal parts, the **quartiles** divide a set of scores into four equal parts. There are three quartiles, the lower, the middle and the upper quartiles.

The lower quartile is called Q_1
The middle quartile (usually called the median) is Q_2
The upper quartile is Q_3
Then the interquartile range is $Q_3 - Q_1$
and the semi-interquartile range is
$$\frac{Q_3 - Q_1}{2}$$

Example 1

Find the upper and lower quartiles and the interquartile range for this set of scores:
8, 9, 7, 10, 5, 4, 6

Solution

First write out the scores in numerical order.

Fix the position of the median first, then since there are three scores below the median and three scores above the median the lower quartile is the second score and the upper quartile is the sixth score.

Thus Q_1 (lower quartile) = 5
Q_3 (upper quartile) = 9
and the interquartile range = $9 - 5 = 4$.

Example 2

Find the range and the semi-interquartile range of the following set of scores.
12, 12, 3, 8, 9, 9, 5, 6, 3, 4, 5, 11

Solution

First arrange the scores in numerical order.

3 3 4 | 5 5 6 | 8 9 9 | 11 12 12

$Q_1 = 4.5$ $Q_2 = 7$ $Q_3 = 10$

Then locate the median and since there are six scores below and above the median the lower quartile is the average of the third and fourth scores, and the upper quartile is the average of the ninth and tenth scores.

$$\text{Thus the median} = \frac{6+8}{2} = 7$$

$$\text{The lower quartile} = \frac{4+5}{2} = 4.5$$

$$\text{The upper quartile} = \frac{9+11}{2} = 10$$

$$\text{The semi-interquartile range} = \frac{10-4.5}{2} = 2.75$$

$$\text{The range} = 12 - 3 = 9$$

THE QUARTILES FROM A FREQUENCY DISTRIBUTION

We find the quartiles from a frequency distribution in the same way as we did for the median in Chapter 5, that is, we estimate the quartiles from the cumulative frequency curve of the distribution. When dealing with frequency distributions with a small number of measures we shall again consider the number of measures above and below the median as an aid to the location of the quartiles.

Example

The cumulative frequency table for the marks gained by 50 pupils in an English examination is shown below. Since there are 50 measures there are 25 measures above and below the median and thus the

Mark	Cumulative frequency
21–30	2
21–40	8
21–50	19
21–60	39
21–70	46
21–80	50

lower quartile corresponds to the thirteenth score and the upper quartile corresponds to the thirty-eighth score. Figure 6.1a shows the cumulative frequency curve for the distribution with the median and quartiles shown.

From the graph:
the median = 54
the lower quartile = 46
the upper quartile = 60
and thus the semi-interquartile range

$$= \frac{60 - 46}{2}$$

Fig. 6.1a

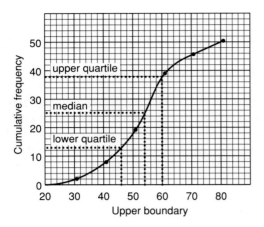

For large values of the total cumulative frequency, N, the fine details covered in the above discussion become rather insignificant and we can say that
the lower quartile corresponds to $\frac{1}{4}N$
the median corresponds to $\frac{1}{2}N$
the upper quartile corresponds to $\frac{3}{4}N$

Fig. 6.1b

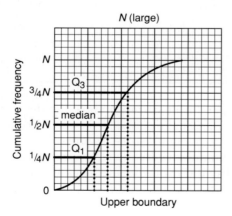

INTERPERCENTILE RANGE

Just as the quartiles divide a distribution into four equal parts, the **percentiles** divide a

distribution into one hundred equal parts. So that:
   the lower quartile is the twenty-fifth percentile,
   the median is the fiftieth percentile, and
   the upper quartile is the seventy-fifth percentile.

Again, as with the quartiles, we estimate the percentiles from a cumulative frequency curve.

Using percentiles we have another measure of the dispersion of a distribution called the **interpercentile range**. This is the range between the tenth percentile and the ninetieth percentile. Again, as with the interquartile range it does not depend on the extreme values, but like the range, the interquartile and semi-interquartile range it does not lend itself to further mathematical treatment.

An easy way to obtain any percentile is to draw another axis to the right of the graph of the cumulative frequency curve and mark the scale from 0 to 100, making 100 level with the total frequency.

If we want to find, say, the tenth and ninetieth percentiles we draw lines across to the curve as shown below and so obtain the values of the variable.

Fig. 6.2

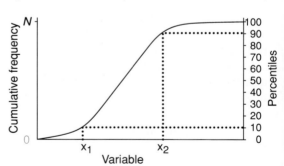

BOX PLOTS

Distributions can be illustrated and compared by using **box plots**. In this form of illustration, adjacent to an appropriate number line, a rectangular box is drawn stretching from the lower to the upper quartile. Across this box a line is drawn to signify the location of the median. From the ends of the box straight lines, usually called whiskers, are drawn parallel to number line as far as the greatest and least measures in the distribution. Thus the range and all three quartiles are illustrated in the diagram. The box plots for the distributions detailed in Examples 1 and 2 (p. 73) are illustrated below.

Fig. 6.3

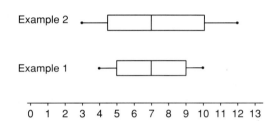

EXERCISE A

1 For each of the following sets of scores find the range, semi-interquartile range and illustrate the distribution using a box plot.
   a) 20, 18, 17, 23, 19, 21.
   b) 11, 12, 13, 15, 7, 6, 5, 10, 14, 8, 9.
   c) 108, 108, 110, 101, 110, 111, 104, 104, 105, 107.
   d) 4, 5, 5, 1, 1, 2, 8, 8, 9, 9, 8, 7, 2.

2 The following cumulative frequency table shows the weight in kilograms of 75 senior boys. Draw the cumulative frequency curve and from it estimate:
   a) The median.
   b) The interquartile range.
   c) The 10–90 percentile range.
   d) How many boys weigh 69.5 kg or less.

Weight (kg) (upper boundary)	Cumulative frequency
66	5
67	8
68	12
69	20
70	35
71	47
72	59
73	68
74	72
75	75

e) How many boys weigh more than 71.5 kg.
f) Illustrate the distribution using a box plot.

3 140 pupils sat two examinations in Spanish. The frequency table shows the distribution of their marks.

Marks	First examination frequency	Second examination frequency
0–10	0	4
11–20	3	6
21–30	10	9
31–40	34	9
41–50	42	12
51–60	32	20
61–70	12	42
71–80	5	22
81–90	2	10
91–100	0	6

Construct cumulative frequency tables and draw the cumulative frequency curves for each examination on the same graph.
a) Estimate the medians.
b) Find the semi-interquartile ranges.
c) If the pass mark for the first examination was 45, how many pupils passed?
d) What percentage of the pupils failed this examination?

e) If 78 pupils failed in the second examination, what was the pass mark?

f) In a few words compare the two distributions and comment on the standard of the test papers.

4 These are the heights (to the nearest centimetre) of some boys and girls of the same age.

Boys' heights
```
159 162 166 158 162 164 158 170
165 165 165 159 162 147 147 160
162 163 164 161 164 162 163 165
163 161 164 161 165 167 162 159
162 167 165 158 166 164 158 160
163 160 161 164 162 162
```

Girls' heights
```
162 157 161 164 162 159 160 164
163 156 165 162 163 161 160 162
164 162 161 162 159 160 162 162
161 160 164 163 164 162 167 161
161 162 159 164 162 165 161 161
158 159 157 165 161 163
```

Form a frequency table for the two distributions using groups starting at 147–148, 149–150 and so on.

Construct a cumulative frequency table and draw the two curves on the same graph.

a) Find the median for each distribution.

b) Find the interquartile ranges.

c) How many girls are 159 cm or less in height?

d) How many boys are 159 cm or less in height?

e) How many girls are taller than 163 cm?

f) How many boys are taller than 163 cm?

g) Compare the two distributions by using two box plots.

5 Sixty pupils sat two examinations, one in French and one in English. The results are summarised in the table.

Mark	Frequency (French)	Frequency (English)
11–20	1	0
21–30	4	1
31–40	10	2
41–50	15	20
51–60	17	32
61–70	9	4
71–80	3	1
81–90	1	0

By drawing cumulative frequency curves estimate the median, quartiles and the semi-interquartile range for each of the distributions.

MEAN DEVIATION

We require a measure of dispersion or variability which takes account of all the measures of the distribution. One such measure is the **mean deviation**. This, as it implies, is the mean of the deviations or differences of the scores from either the mean, median or mode. It is usually most useful to calculate the mean deviation of the scores from the mean since the mean itself depends on all the measures in the distribution.

The mean deviation is calculated as shown in the example below. Since the negative signs must be ignored, any further algebraic development of the concept is made impossible, though the mean deviation would be quite satisfactory for many purposes.

Example

Calculate the mean deviation, from the mean, of the following scores.

10 12 14 16 18 20 22

Solution

The mean, $\bar{X} = \dfrac{\Sigma X}{N} = \dfrac{112}{7} = 16$

Score X	Deviations from mean $\bar{X} = 16$	Deviations taken as positive
10	−6	6
12	−4	4
14	−2	2
16	0	0
18	+2	2
20	+4	4
22	+6	6
		$\Sigma d = 24$

If the deviations were summed as they stand in the second column the answer would be 0, so all the deviations are taken as positive.

The sum of the deviations, $\Sigma d = 24$

$$\text{and the mean of the deviations} = \frac{\Sigma d}{N}$$

$$= \frac{24}{7}$$

$$= 3.43$$

EXERCISE B _____

1 Find the mean deviation, from the mean, of these sets of scores.
   a) 1, 3, 4, 6, 7, 9, 12
   b) 60, 63, 65, 66, 69, 70, 76
   c) 1, 5, 11, 13, 15, 17, 20, 22

VARIANCE AND STANDARD DEVIATION

If we add extra steps to the calculation which was performed to find the mean deviation we obtain other measures of dispersion. In calculating the **variance**, the mean of the distribution is found, the deviations of the scores from the mean are tabulated, these deviations are squared (thus dealing with the negative signs in an acceptable algebraic manner), and the mean of the squares of the deviations is calculated.

$$\text{Thus, } s^2 \text{ (variance)} = \frac{\Sigma(X - \bar{X})^2}{N}$$

where X stands for the various measures, $\bar{X}$ = the mean and N = the number of measures in the distribution.

The square root of this mean is called the **standard deviation**.

$$\text{Thus, } s \text{ (standard deviation)} = \sqrt{\frac{\Sigma(X - \bar{X})^2}{N}}$$

This is the most satisfactory measure of dispersion, since it makes use of all of the scores in the distribution and is also quite acceptable mathematically.

TO CALCULATE THE VARIANCE AND STANDARD DEVIATION

To calculate the variance and standard deviation of the scores, 10, 11, 12, 13, 14, 15, 16, the following method is used.
   1 List the scores in order.
   2 Calculate the mean:

$$\bar{X} = \frac{\Sigma X}{N}$$

$$= \frac{91}{7}$$

$$= 13$$

   3 List the deviations of each score from the mean.

Score X	Deviation of score from mean $X - \bar{X}$	Squares of deviations $(X - \bar{X})^2$
10	10 − 13 = −3	9
11	11 − 13 = −2	4
12	12 − 13 = −1	1
13	13 − 13 = 0	0
14	14 − 13 = +1	1
15	15 − 13 = +2	4
16	16 − 13 = +3	9
		$\Sigma(X - \bar{X})^2 = 28$

4 Square the deviations (this eliminates the negative signs).

5 Sum the squares of the deviations $\Sigma(X - \bar{X})^2 = 28$.

6 Divide this by the number of scores, $N = 7$, which gives the variance.

$$s^2(\text{variance}) = \frac{\Sigma(X - \bar{X})^2}{N}$$

$$= \frac{28}{7}$$

$$= 4$$

7 Take the square root of the answer, which gives the standard deviation.

$$s(\text{standard deviation}) = \sqrt{\frac{\Sigma(X - \bar{X})^2}{N}}$$

$$= \sqrt{\frac{28}{7}}$$

$$= \sqrt{4}$$

$$= 2$$

Example 1

Calculate the mean, variance and standard deviation of the following scores.

22 24 26 28 30 32 34 36

Solution

Score (X)	$X - \bar{X}$	$(X - \bar{X})^2$
22	$22 - 29 = -7$	49
24	$24 - 29 = -5$	25
26	$26 - 29 = -3$	9
28	$28 - 29 = -1$	1
30	$30 - 29 = +1$	1
32	$32 - 29 = +3$	9
34	$34 - 29 = +5$	25
36	$36 - 29 = +7$	49
		$\Sigma(X - \bar{X})^2 = 168$

$$\bar{X} = \frac{\Sigma X}{N}$$

$$= \frac{232}{8}$$

$$= 29$$

$$s^2(\text{variance}) = \frac{\Sigma(X - \bar{X})^2}{N}$$

$$= \frac{168}{8}$$

$$= 21$$

$$s(\text{standard deviation}) = \sqrt{\frac{\Sigma(X - \bar{X})^2}{N}}$$

$$= \sqrt{\frac{168}{8}}$$

$$= \sqrt{21}$$

$$= 4.58$$

Mean $= 29$

Variance $= 21$

Standard deviation $= 4.58$

Example 2

Calculate the mean, standard deviation and variance of this frequency distribution of test marks.

Mark	0	1	2	3	4	5	6	7	8	9	10
Frequency	1	2	3	5	6	7	4	3	2	1	0

Solution

With a frequency distribution we use exactly the same process as shown in Example 1 but to the table we must add a frequency column, an fX column and an $f(X - \bar{X})^2$ column. The formulae used now become

$$s^2(\text{variance}) = \frac{\Sigma f(X - \bar{X})^2}{\Sigma f}$$

and

$$s(\text{standard deviation}) = \sqrt{\frac{\Sigma f(X - \bar{X})^2}{\Sigma f}}$$

$$\bar{X} = \frac{\Sigma fX}{\Sigma f}$$

$$= \frac{152}{34}$$

$$= 4.5 \text{ (correct to 1 d.p.)}$$

$$s^2(\text{variance}) = \frac{\Sigma f(X - \bar{X})^2}{\Sigma f}$$

$$= \frac{150.5}{34}$$

$$= 4.43 \text{ (correct to 2 d.p.)}$$

$$s(\text{standard deviation}) = \sqrt{\frac{\Sigma f(X - \bar{X})^2}{\Sigma f}}$$

$$= \sqrt{\frac{150.5}{34}}$$

$$= \sqrt{4.43}$$

$$= 2.10$$

Mean = 4.5

Variance = 4.43

Standard deviation = 2.10

Note When working with a grouped distribution use the mid-point of the interval to stand for the group and proceed as before.

AN ALTERNATIVE METHOD FOR CALCULATING THE STANDARD DEVIATION

The above method for calculating the standard deviation works fairly well (Example 1) when the mean is a whole number and there is no frequency. However, when the mean is not a whole number and there is a frequency involved and possibly grouped data also, the arithmetical calculation is rather excessive.

From the original formula, the following formula may be derived.

$$\text{standard deviation} = \sqrt{\frac{\Sigma X^2}{N} - \left(\frac{\Sigma X}{N}\right)^2}$$

and with a frequency distribution,

$$\text{standard deviation} = \sqrt{\frac{\Sigma fX^2}{\Sigma f} - \left(\frac{\Sigma fX}{\Sigma f}\right)^2}$$

Mark (X)	f	fX	$(X - \bar{X})$	$(X - \bar{X})^2$	$f(X - \bar{X})^2$
0	1	0	$0 - 4.5 = -4.5$	20.25	20.25
1	2	2	$1 - 4.5 = -3.5$	12.25	24.50
2	3	6	$2 - 4.5 = -2.5$	6.25	18.75
3	5	15	$3 - 4.5 = -1.5$	2.25	11.25
4	6	24	$4 - 4.5 = -0.5$	0.25	1.50
5	7	35	$5 - 4.5 = +0.5$	0.25	1.75
6	4	24	$6 - 4.5 = +1.5$	2.25	9.00
7	3	21	$7 - 4.5 = +2.5$	6.25	18.75
8	2	16	$8 - 4.5 = +3.5$	12.25	24.50
9	1	9	$9 - 4.5 = +4.5$	20.25	20.25
10	0	0	$10 - 4.5 = +5.5$	30.25	0
	$\Sigma f = 34$	$\Sigma fX = 152$			$\Sigma f(X - \bar{X})^2 = 150.50$

This derived formula simplifies the calculation considerably.

Look again at the worked example:

Score X	X²
10	100
11	121
12	144
13	169
14	196
15	225
16	256
ΣX = 91	ΣX² = 1211

$$\text{Mean} = \frac{\Sigma X}{N} = \frac{91}{7} = 13$$

$$s = \sqrt{\frac{\Sigma X^2}{N} - \left(\frac{\Sigma X}{N}\right)^2}$$

$$= \sqrt{\frac{1211}{7} - 13^2}$$

$$= \sqrt{173 - 169}$$

$$= \sqrt{4}$$

$$= 2$$

Look now at Example 2.

Mark X	f	fX	fX²
0	1	0	0
1	2	2	2
2	3	6	12
3	5	15	45
4	6	24	96
5	7	35	175
6	4	24	144
7	3	21	147
8	2	16	128
9	1	9	81
10	0	0	0
	Σf = 34	ΣfX = 152	ΣfX² = 830

$$\bar{X} = \frac{\Sigma fX}{\Sigma f} = \frac{152}{34} = 4.47$$

$$s = \sqrt{\frac{\Sigma fX^2}{\Sigma f} - \left(\frac{\Sigma fX}{\Sigma f}\right)^2}$$

$$= \sqrt{\frac{830}{34} - (4.47)^2}$$

$$= \sqrt{24.41 - 19.98}$$

$$= \sqrt{4.43}$$

$$= 2.10$$

It seems clear that this method is simpler than the basic one for use with a frequency distribution, especially when the mean is not exact.

Note To get the last column in the table '*fX²*', the *fX* column is multiplied by *X* again, that is, $fX \times X = fX^2$.

EXERCISE C

1 Calculate the mean, variance and standard deviation of each of the following sets of scores.
   a) 3, 4, 5, 6, 7, 9, 10, 12
   b) 24, 29, 27, 20, 20, 23, 21
   c) 66, 66, 60, 64, 69, 67, 63
   d) 35, 37, 37, 40, 30, 34, 33, 38
   e) 30, 33, 24, 28, 20, 17, 25, 39, 34, 42
2 In ten successive years in Glasgow the highest temperature (in the shade) for each year was recorded as:
   25, 27, 28, 26, 26, 24, 24, 25, 22, 23 (°C)
   Calculate the mean, variance and standard deviation of the temperatures.
3 In the same ten years, the lowest temperature recorded each year was:
   −11, −4, −9, −7, −11, −10, −7, −12, −10, −12 (°C)
   Calculate the mean, variance and standard deviation of these temperatures.

4 The numbers of days in which rain fell (rain days) each month in a recent year were recorded as follows:

Month	North Scotland	East Scotland	West Scotland
January	25	19	26
February	23	17	21
March	22	18	22
April	22	19	23
May	17	15	18
June	14	12	16
July	12	11	13
August	13	10	13
September	17	15	17
October	22	20	23
November	22	21	22
December	24	22	24

For each region calculate the mean and standard deviation of the number of rain days.

Compare briefly the three distributions explaining any differences or similarities.

5 Below are the heights of 40 fourth-year boys, measured to the nearest 2 centimetres. Calculate the mean height and the standard deviation of the heights.

Height (cm)	Frequency
150	1
152	1
154	2
156	3
158	4
160	4
162	5
164	6
166	4
168	4
170	1
172	2
174	2
176	0
178	0
180	1

6 These are the heights of 30 fourth-year girls measured at the same time as the boys.

Height (cm)	Frequency
146	1
148	2
150	2
152	3
154	3
156	7
158	2
160	5
162	1
164	2
166	1
168	0
170	1

Calculate the mean and standard deviation of the girls' heights and compare them to your answers for Question 5. Give reasons for any differences you find.

7 Measure the heights of a number of boys or girls in your school and calculate the mean and standard deviation.

8 The frequency table below shows the distribution of marks in an examination.

Calculate the mean and standard deviation of the marks.

Mark	Frequency
1–5	0
6–10	2
11–15	4
16–20	11
21–25	20
26–30	10
31–35	5
36–40	3
41–45	2
46–50	1

9 The weights of 40 fourth-year boys measured to the nearest kilogram, are shown below. Calculate the mean and standard deviation of the weights.

Weight (kg)	Frequency
35–39	1
40–44	6
45–49	9
50–54	9
55–59	6
60–64	4
65–69	3
70–74	0
75–79	1
80–84	1

10 Take the weights of 40 fourth-years in your school and calculate the mean and standard deviation. Compare your results with those of Question 9.

11 The table in the next column shows the death rate per 1000 population of a number of countries for the years 1964 and 1989.

Form a frequency table for each of the years by grouping the data starting at 6.0–6.9, 7.0–7.9, and so on. Calculate the mean and standard deviation of the death rates for both years.

12 The times (measured to the nearest second) taken by rats to go through a maze in a laboratory test, are shown below. Construct a frequency distribution and calculate the mean and standard deviation of the times. (Group in threes starting 8–10.)

```
 8 26 12 12 18 15 12 14 16 20 19
14 14 11 17 22  9 21 13 17 24 18
20 17 19 13 18 13 16 20 10 18 24
20 15 26 23 15 19 21 23 18 22 25
25 19 23 16 28 21
```

Country	Death rate per 1000	
	1964	1989
former Eastern Germany	13.5	12.4
Austria	12.3	10.9
Belgium	12.1	10.7
Scotland	11.7	12.7
Eire	11.3	8.8
England and Wales	11.0	11.4
former Western Germany	10.7	11.2
France	10.5	9.0
Northern Ireland	10.2	10.0
Portugal	10.0	9.5
Denmark	10.0	11.6
Norway	10.0	10.6
Sweden	10.0	10.8
Hungary	9.9	13.7
Czechoslovakia	9.6	11.6
Italy	9.6	9.1
USA	9.4	8.8
former Yugoslavia	9.4	9.1
Finland	9.3	9.9
Switzerland	9.2	9.2
Australia	9.0	7.3
New Zealand*	8.8	8.2
Spain	8.7	7.9
Netherlands	7.7	8.4
Canada	7.6	7.3
Poland	7.6	10.1
Japan	6.9	6.4
Israel†	6.0	6.3

*excluding Maoris
†Jewish population only

CALCULATION OF THE MEAN AND STANDARD DEVIATION OF A DISTRIBUTION DERIVED FROM ANOTHER DISTRIBUTION

If we have a distribution with a known mean and standard deviation which is altered by an arithmetical operation, it is possible to deduce the mean and standard deviation of the new distribution without re-calculation.

Suppose we have a distribution ranging from 9 to 23 with a mean of 16 and a standard deviation of 2. If 10 is added to each score, the whole distribution moves up the number line but the *spread* of the scores remains the same (Figure 6.4).

Fig. 6.4

So, the new mean is $16 + 10 = 26$ and the new standard deviation is still 2.

If, however, each score in the original distribution is multiplied by 2, this time the *spread* of the scores is also multiplied by 2 (Figure 6.5).

Fig. 6.5

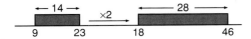

The new mean is $16 \times 2 = 32$ and the new standard deviation is $2 \times 2 = 4$.

EXERCISE D _____

1 A set of marks has a mean of 15 and a standard deviation of 2.
   Write down the new mean and standard deviation if each mark:
   a) is multiplied by 3.
   b) is doubled.
   c) has 10 added to it.
   d) is increased by 5.
   e) is halved.
   f) has 3 subtracted from it.
2 A set of scores has a mean of 100 and a standard deviation of 9.
   Write down the new mean and standard deviation if every score:
   a) is quartered.
   b) is multiplied by 3.
   c) has 10 subtracted from it.
   d) is increased by 20.
   e) is doubled and then increased by 5.
   f) is halved and then decreased by 5.
3 A set of marks has a mean of 23 and a standard deviation of 2.5.
   Write down the new mean and standard deviation if each mark:
   a) is multiplied by 5.
   b) has 1 added to it.
   c) has 3 subtracted from it.
   d) is halved.
   e) is doubled and has 2 added on.
   f) is multiplied by 3 and has 2 subtracted from it.
   g) has 2 added on and is then doubled.
   h) has 1 subtracted from it and is then halved.
4 A set of measures has a mean of 52 and a standard deviation of 7.8.
   Write down the new mean and standard deviation if every measure:
   a) is doubled and has 1 added on.
   b) is halved and has 1 subtracted.
   c) is increased by 5 and then doubled.
   d) has 2 subtracted from it and is then halved.
   e) has 10 added on and is then multiplied by 3.
5 For the following set of figures, calculate:
   2, 5, 7, 7, 8, 9, 11
   a) the mean.
   b) the standard deviation.
   c) the new mean and standard deviation if each figure is doubled and then increased by 5.
6 For the following set of figures, calculate:
   50, 52, 53, 55, 57, 59, 62, 64, 65, 66
   a) the mean.
   b) the standard deviation.
   c) the new mean and standard deviation if every figure is increased by 10 and then halved.
   d) the new mean and standard deviation if every figure is quartered and then has 2 subtracted from it.

STANDARD SCORES

The comparison of measures from different distributions is usually unsatisfactory and the addition of such results frequently produces unexpected results. These difficulties are particularly obvious in the comparison of school examination results and when we add these marks to produce an average performance. The surprising results are usually caused by an unusual mean or dispersion in one or more of the distributions. These difficulties can be overcome if we use what are commonly called **standard** or **standardised scores**. When using standard scores we wish to eliminate the effect of the mean and the dispersion and the first of these is done by subtracting the mean of the distribution from each score. The deviate so obtained is then divided by the standard deviation to remove the effect of the dispersion. The result of this division is called the standard score. Standard scores from different distributions can then be compared or combined without being affected by either bias.

Example 1

A girl scored 50 marks in an English examination where the class mean was 45 and the standard deviation 5. She scored 60 marks in an economics examination where the class mean was 55 and the standard deviation 10. Compare her standing in the two subjects.

Solution

$$\text{Standard score in English} = \frac{50 - 45}{5} = \frac{5}{5} = +1$$

$$\text{Standard score in economics} = \frac{60 - 55}{10} = \frac{5}{10} = +\frac{1}{2}$$

Thus she did better in English than economics compared with the rest of the class.

Example 2

Tom, Gino and Agnes sat examinations in Maths, English and French. Their scores, the class means and standard deviations for each subject are shown in the following table.

	Maths	English	French	Total
Tom	81	50	46	177
Gino	42	57	55	154
Agnes	33	56	65	154
Class mean	48	52	50	
Standard deviation	15	4	10	

Using the given raw scores Tom would be placed first. By using standard scores check the validity of this placing.

Solution

	Maths	English	French	Total
Tom	$\dfrac{81-48}{15}=+2.2$	$\dfrac{50-52}{4}=-0.5$	$\dfrac{46-50}{10}=-0.4$	$+1.3$
Gino	$\dfrac{42-48}{15}=-0.4$	$\dfrac{57-52}{4}=+1.25$	$\dfrac{55-50}{10}=+0.5$	$+1.35$
Agnes	$\dfrac{33-48}{15}=-1.0$	$\dfrac{56-52}{4}=+1.0$	$\dfrac{65-50}{10}=+1.5$	$+1.5$

Standard scores (column header spanning Maths, English, French)

The correct order of merit is Agnes, Gino, Tom.

EXERCISE E

1 Jane scored 66 marks in her geography examination in November where the mean was 60 and the standard deviation 6. In May, when the mean was 40 and the standard deviation 10, she had a mark of 55 for her geography. In which examination did she display more ability?

2 The following table shows the marks of a boy in three successive mathematics examinations.

Examination	Mark	Mean	Standard deviation
First	50	53	3
Second	51	58	7
Third	53	48	5

a) In which examination was his relative standing best?

b) Was his performance better in the second examination than in the first?

3 a) In an English test given to a class, the mean and standard deviation were 64 and 8 respectively. The following table shows the marks of some of the pupils. Complete the table.

Pupil	Mark	Deviate from mean	Standard score
Alan	68	$68-64=4$	$+\frac{1}{2}$
Betty	72	$72-64=8$	$+1$
Eion	56		
Mario	60		
Evelyn	80		
Fay	76		

b) In another English test given to the same class a few weeks later, the mean was 49 and the standard deviation 6. Complete the following table.

Pupil	Mark	Deviate from mean	Standard score
Alan	58		
Betty	52		
Eion	43		
Mario	49		
Evelyn	64		
Fay	55		

c) i) Which of the six pupils improved most?

ii) Which pupil came down most in the second test?

iii) Which pupil was most consistent in the two tests?

4 In the first term John scored 94% in Maths and Mary scored 80% while in the second term John scored 78% and Mary scored 90%. If the mean scores in the first term were 50%, and in the second term, 60%, and the standard deviations in the first term were 20%, and in the second term, 15%, find which pupil had the better average performance.

5 Mary, Rosa and Lois sat examinations in English, French and Latin. The results, the class means and standard deviations are tabulated below. Find the correct order of merit.

	English	French	Latin
Mary	59	73	79
Rosa	58	81	75
Lois	64	74	74
Class mean	52	60	65
Standard deviation	5	10	8

EXERCISE F   Miscellaneous

1 a) Calculate the mean and standard deviation of the following set of measures;
10, 11, 12, 13, 14, 15, 16
b) Without repeating the calculation, state the mean and standard deviation of each of the following sets of measures.
  i) 12, 13, 14, 15, 16, 17, 18
  ii) 20, 22, 24, 26, 28, 30, 32
  iii) 22, 24, 26, 28, 30, 32, 34
c) The measures in **a)** are scaled to give a mean of 50 and a standard deviation of 12. Find the new values of the measures.

2 For the set of measures;
2, 3, 5, 7, 8, 10, 14
calculate:
a) the median.
b) the interquartile range.
c) the semi-interquartile range.
d) the range.
e) the mean.
f) the mean deviate from the mean.

g) the variance.
h) the standard deviation.
If each measure is doubled and then increased by 5, state the new mean and standard deviation.

3 For the set of measures;
9, 10, 12, 15, 18, 20, 22, 23, 24
calculate:
a) the range.
b) the median.
c) the interquartile range.
d) the mean.
e) the mean deviate from the mean.
f) the variance.
g) the standard deviation.
If each measure has 2 subtracted from it and is then halved, state the new mean and standard deviation.

4 For the set of measures;
17, 14, 8, 5, 9, 13, 22, 20
calculate:
a) the range.
b) the median.
c) the interquartile range.
d) the mean.
e) the standard deviation.
If each measure is multiplied by 5 and then has 10 subtracted from it, write down the new mean and standard deviation.

5 For the set of scores;
3, 4, 4, 11, 9, 3, 8, 7, 5
calculate:
a) the mode.
b) the range.
c) the median.
d) the interquartile range.
e) the semi-interquartile range.
f) the mean.
g) the mean deviate from the mean.
h) the variance.
i) the standard deviation.
If each score has 5 added to it and is then divided by 3, write down the new mean and standard deviation.

6 The mean and standard deviation of a set of scores are 50 and 12 respectively. The measures are altered by scaling so that a raw score of 44 becomes a scaled score of 55.
a) If the mean of the scaled scores is 60, find their standard deviation.
b) If the standard deviation of the scaled scores is 20, find their mean.

7 Find the mean deviate from the mean of the following sets of measures:
a) 9, 11, 12, 13, 14, 15, 17.
b) 18, 22, 24, 26, 28, 30, 34.

c)

Measure	0	1	2	3	4	5
Frequency	11	14	10	5	3	1

d)

Measure	Frequency
1–5	1
6–10	3
11–15	5
16–20	7
21–25	13
26–30	9
31–35	7
36–40	3
41–45	2

8 For each of the distributions given in question 7 calculate the variance.

9 For the distribution of measures given in question 7(d) draw a cumulative frequency curve and use it to find:
a) the median.
b) the semi-interquartile range.
c) the interpercentile range.

10 The yield of a group of 80 fruit trees was measured correct to the nearest kilogram. The results of the survey are given in the next column.

Yield (kg)	Number of trees
10–14	3
15–19	18
20–24	27
25–29	22
30–34	6
35–39	4

a) Estimate the median yield.
b) Find the interquartile range of the distribution.
c) Find the mean yield.
d) Find the standard deviation of the distribution.

11 The table given below shows the marks gained by 30 pupils in a test.

Mark	1	2	3	4	5	6	7	8	9	10
Frequency	0	1	0	3	7	6	5	3	4	1

Calculate the mean and standard deviation of these results. What is the modal mark?

12 The age distribution of workers in a factory was as follows:

Age in years	Frequency
16–20	2
21–25	10
26–30	12
31–35	23
36–40	17
41–45	13
46–50	9
51–55	6
56–60	4
61–65	4

a) Calculate the mean and standard deviation of this distribution.
b) Draw the cumulative frequency curve for this distribution and use it to find the median, interquartile and interpercentile ranges.

13 **a)** Find the mean and standard deviation of the following set of measures.

Length (cm)	1	2	3	4	5	6	7
Frequency	1	4	5	7	1	1	1

b) Use the above result to obtain the mean and standard deviation of the following distribution.

Weight (kg)	61	62	63	64	65	66	67
Frequency	5	20	25	35	5	5	5

14 Calculate the mean and standard deviation of the distribution.

Measure	Frequency
50–59	3
60–69	10
70–79	18
80–89	24
90–99	20
100–109	5

15 To calculate the mean and standard deviation of a set of marks, 60 was subtracted from each mark and then the mean and standard deviation of the new scores were found to be 4 and 12 respectively.
a) What was the mean of the original set of marks?
b) What was the standard deviation of the original set of marks?

16 A group of candidates for a post were given three tests. After two tests, candidates X, Y and Z appear to be the best of the group. Their results in these tests and the means and standard deviations are tabulated below.

Test	Mean	Standard deviation	Scores		
			X	Y	Z
1	70	6	79	85	80
2	55	10	70	62	68

At this stage, which candidate has the best total standard score? In the third test where the mean is 40 and the standard deviation is 12, Y has a score of 58. If X beat Y on total standard score by 0.3, what was X's raw score in the third test?

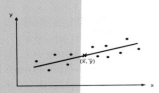

7 REGRESSION AND CORRELATION

THE RELATIONSHIP BETWEEN TWO VARIABLES

So far, we have only considered the values of one variable at a time. We are, however, often interested in examining the relationship between two variables. When changes in one variable are matched with similar changes in the other, there may be a **causal** or **cause and effect** relationship between the two variables. Many people are interested in finding causal relationships, for example, doctors investigating new drugs, agriculturalists working with new weedkillers or fertilisers, or scientists involved in research work. Causal relationships are found not only in the field of scientific work, but also in the world of business, for example, studying the effect on sales figures of an advertising campaign, or the effect of staff training schemes on the efficiency of a company.

A relationship may exist between two variables without it being a causal relationship. For example, if you measure the heights and the reading speeds of a group of children (aged 6 to 16 years) you will find that with increasing height there is an increase in reading speed. Common sense tells us that reading speed is not dependent on height. In fact, both these variables are linked to a third variable, age. The relationship between the heights and the reading speeds is an example of a **spurious**

correlation. The aim of this chapter is: to find a method of illustrating the measures so that their *interdependence*, if it exists, can be seen; to measure the amount of their interdependence; and to use the given data to estimate other results concerning the given situation.

SCATTER DIAGRAMS

The standard method of illustrating this type of situation is by using a **scatter diagram**. This consists of laying out each of the measures along one of the axes of a grid, then considering each item in turn. The two measures for that item act exactly like an ordered pair and thus like the coordinates of a point on the grid. Each item considered is thereby linked to one point on the grid and that point can be plotted in the normal way. It is usually marked on the grid as a dot. The points corresponding to all of the items being measured are similarly located on the grid and plotted, and thus a scatter of dots is built up on the grid.

Example

The reading speeds in words per minute and the intelligence quotients of a group of 12 children were measured and are tabulated on the next page.

Child	Reading speed (words per minute)	Intelligence quotient
A	120	80
B	140	90
C	100	90
D	170	100
E	130	100
F	190	105
G	220	110
H	140	110
I	180	115
J	240	120
K	200	125
L	270	130

The scatter diagram (Figure 7.1) is built up as follows. The axes are set to cover a suitable range of measures of reading speed and intelligence quotient. Each child is then considered in turn and the two measures (for example, for child A, a reading speed of 120 and an intelligence quotient of 80) locate one point on the grid and this point is marked with a dot. Similar dots are entered in turn for the other children and the complete scatter diagram will consist of 12 dots.

From an examination of the pattern of dots obtained it can be accepted that the above results help to support the belief that there is some linkage between reading speed and intelligence quotient, but since there is some scattering of the points plotted, indications are that the two measures are not very closely linked. It must also be accepted that no conclusive results could ever be obtained from such a small sample of the population.

The distribution of points plotted on a scatter diagram can give an indication of the relation which exists between the two characteristics being measured. Three basic forms of scatter diagram are shown in Figure 7.2. In Figure 7.2a the points plotted are scattered at random over the grid and this indicates that the measures are not related. Figure 7.2b shows the other extreme position. The points are scattered along a straight line and this is the typical

Fig. 7.1

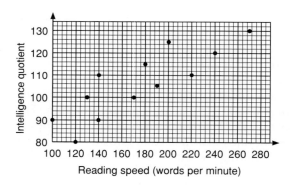

Fig. 7.2a

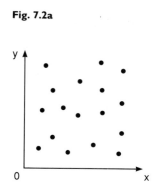

Fig. 7.2b

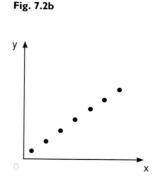

Fig. 7.2c

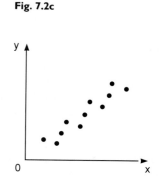

diagram for measures which are directly proportional to each other. In a scatter diagram like Figure 7.2c the closer the points are to being on a straight line, the greater the degree of their possible linkage.

For measures to be related it is not necessary that the scatter diagram approximates to a straight line through the origin or even to any straight line. If the points plotted on the scatter diagram fit some straight line or curve this can be taken as evidence for some relation between the measures and it then becomes necessary to put the relation into algebraic form.

REGRESSION

The results of scientific experiments can often be illustrated by the use of scatter diagrams and if these results indicate that the measures under consideration are related, it is desirable that the results are interpreted in a mathematical form. If the points plotted are almost on a straight line then the line which most nearly fits all of the points must be drawn. This line is called the **best fitting line** or the **regression line**. If the measures are such that the points plotted are almost exactly on a straight line then there are few complications about drawing the line which most nearly fits all of the points, but if the points are more scattered it then becomes possible to draw two regression lines. If the variables are, for convenience, called x and y then one line is called the regression line of x on y and in it the values of y are assumed to be accurate and the points deviate from the straight line because of errors in the measurement of x. These deviations in the values of x will hereafter be called **offsets**. Once drawn, this regression line can be used to estimate the value of x which would correspond to a given value of y. The other regression line, called the regression line of y on x, is drawn in a similar fashion except that the roles of x and y are interchanged.

DRAWING OF REGRESSION LINES (BEST FITTING) LINES

There are available various ways of drawing regression lines. In this study we shall concentrate upon two of the more straightforward approaches and in neither of these do we make provision for either of the variables being accurate. Since neither variable is considered dominant the offsets will be taken to be lines drawn from the points which have been plotted perpendicular to the best fitting line.

By inspection

In this approach we attempt to draw, without any calculation, a line which most nearly fits all of the data. This is not the line which goes through the largest number of the dots but the line which most nearly goes through them all. The test for this situation is that the offsets on the one side of the line should balance those on the other side and the total of all offsets should be a minimum. To be precise we should be considering the squares of the offsets but that refinement is just too difficult and, for most purposes, it is sufficient to work with the offsets as discussed above.

Fig. 7.3

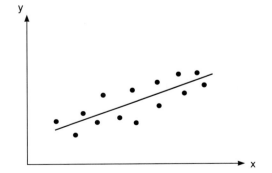

By using the mean values of the variables

In this approach we take as the main point on the regression line the point $(\bar{x}, \bar{y})$, where $\bar{x}$ is the mean value of all the x co-ordinates of the points being considered, and $\bar{y}$ is the mean value of all of the y co-ordinates. Having added this point to the diagram we must now by inspection draw, through this point, the line which most nearly fits all of the points under consideration.

Since personal judgement comes into both of these approaches there is the opportunity for different people to draw different lines, but in most cases these variations should not be very large.

Fig. 7.4

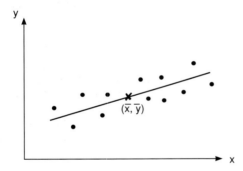

Example

The marks of 8 pupils from tests in maths and science are shown below.

Pupil	1	2	3	4	5	6	7	8
Maths	5	8	10	11	14	15	18	23
Science	5	14	9	16	19	14	18	25

Draw a scatter diagram using the maths marks for the x-axis and the science marks

for the y-axis, and draw in the line of best fit by using the point $(\bar{x}, \bar{y})$. Using this line find the average science mark of pupils whose maths mark is 20, and the average maths mark of pupils whose science mark is 20 (assuming that the group tested is representative of all the pupils).

Solution

Once the eight points have been plotted (Figure 7.5, opposite) the values of $\bar{x}$ and $\bar{y}$ are calculated.

$$\Sigma x = 104.$$

the mean value of x:

$$\bar{x} = \frac{\Sigma x}{N} = \frac{104}{8} = 13$$

$$\Sigma y = 120.$$

The mean value of y:

$$\bar{y} = \frac{\Sigma y}{N} = \frac{120}{8} = 15$$

This gives the point $(\bar{x}, \bar{y}) = (13, 15)$ which is added to the figure and the best fitting line through this point is drawn.

This line can be used to find the average y-value for a given x-value and vice versa. It should be noted that this average refers to the underlying population and not to the sample. Also that these averages apply only to the range of values of the variables covered by the sample. So for a maths mark of 20, the average science mark would be $22\frac{1}{2}$, and for a science mark of 20, the average maths mark would be $17\frac{1}{2}$.

Extrapolation

If we extend the best fitting line beyond the range of values of the variables covered by the sample, we are said to be **extrapolating** the results. In this situation we cannot have the same level of confidence about any results

Fig. 7.5

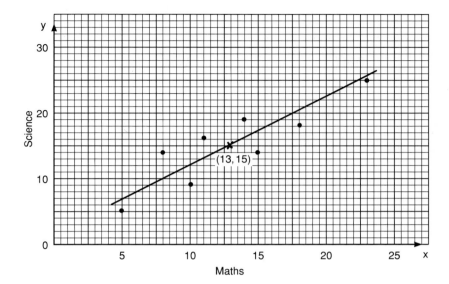

obtained from these extensions. Results obtained in this way are estimates only and they would be valid only if the population behaved in the same way for this wider range as it did in the sample. We have no evidence to back up that assumption.

EXERCISE A ─────────────────

1 The following table shows the results of tests in English and French given to 10 pupils. Draw a scatter diagram to illustrate the marks, taking the English marks for the x-axis and the French marks for the y-axis. Use a scale of 2 cm for 10 marks on both axes.

Pupil	A	B	C	D	E	F	G	H	I	J
English	10	14	20	23	28	35	38	43	47	52
French	8	15	17	12	24	20	29	22	27	36

Use inspection to draw the best fitting line. Use this line to find:
a) the average mark in French for pupils getting a mark in English of
i) 15   ii) 50

b) the average mark in English for pupils getting a mark in French of
i) 15   ii) 30

2 The marks in the table for art and drama are the result of tests given to eight pupils. Draw a scatter diagram to show them, taking the art marks for the x-axis and the drama marks for the y-axis (scale, 10 marks for 2 cm on both axes).
Use inspection to draw the best fitting line. Use this line to find:
a) the average mark in drama for a pupils getting a mark in art of
i) 15   ii) 30
b) the average mark in art for a pupil getting a mark of 20 in drama.

Pupil	1	2	3	4	5	6	7	8
Art	9	14	16	17	22	27	30	33
Drama	12	14	20	16	22	29	28	35

3 A group of pupils were given two tests in economics with a time gap of two

months between the tests. The results for eight of these pupils are shown below. Draw a scatter diagram to illustrate these results, taking test 1 as the x-axis (2 cm for 10 marks) and test 2 as the y-axis (2 cm for 10 marks).

Test 1	25	30	32	40	44	47	55	63
Test 2	27	25	28	34	37	33	37	47

Draw the best fitting line using the point $(\bar{x}, \bar{y})$.
a) From this line find the average mark of pupils in test 2 who scored a mark in test 1 of:
i) 37   ii) 50
b) By extending the line estimate the likely mark in test 2 of a pupil who scored 20 in test 1.

4 The points awarded by two judges to six competitors in an ice-skating competition are shown in the table. Plot the points to obtain a scatter diagram, taking the marks of the first judge for the x-axis (scale for both axes; start at 4.8 and take 1 cm for every 0.1 of a point). Using the point $(\bar{x}, \bar{y})$ draw the line of best fit on the diagram.
What average score (to the nearest 0.1) would be given by the second judge when the first judge awards
a) 5.2?   **b)** 5.5?

Skater	1	2	3	4	5	6
1st judge	5.9	5.0	5.4	4.8	5.3	5.7
2nd judge	5.8	5.1	5.3	5.1	5.5	5.6

5 A group of pupils were given tests in French and German. The results are shown in the table. Draw a scatter diagram to illustrate them (French for x-axis, German for y-axis). Use the point $(\bar{x}, \bar{y})$ to draw in the best fitting line.

Pupil	1	2	3	4	5	6	7	8
French	8	31	37	11	26	18	15	22
German	9	34	35	15	28	20	14	21

Use this line to find:
a) the average German mark for a French mark of:
i) 15   ii) 30
b) the average French mark for a German mark of:
i) 25   ii) 30
By extending the line estimate the possible French mark corresponding to a German mark of 45.

6 Two successive tests in English were given to a group of pupils. The marks of six of the pupils are shown below. Illustrate the marks in a scatter diagram (test 1 x-axis, test 2 y-axis) and draw in the line of best fit using the point $(\bar{x}, \bar{y})$.

Pupil	1	2	3	4	5	6
Test 1	25	42	50	30	61	32
Test 2	19	27	35	16	40	22

a) Estimate the mark gained in the second test by a pupil who scored in the first test a mark of:
i) 25   ii) 55
b) By extending the line in both directions estimate the mark in test 1 corresponding to a mark in test 2 of:
i) 12   ii) 45

7 Some children were tested to find their scores in an IQ test and their marks in a maths test. The results are shown in the table. Use these results to draw a scatter diagram taking the IQ scores for the x-axis.
Using the point $(\bar{x}, \bar{y})$ draw the best fitting line.

IQ score	Maths mark
96	27
98	20
104	50
110	38
117	57
123	69
126	54
128	63
130	78
132	89
135	70
141	93

Use this line to estimate the maths mark for a child with an IQ score of:
a) 113   **b)** 140   **c)** 131

8 Some engineering apprentices were given two tests in maths at an interval of two months.

Test 1	35	80	93	85	61	47	41	74
Test 2	40	75	79	80	54	52	42	66

Draw a scatter diagram, and draw in the line of best fit, using the point $(\overline{x}, \overline{y})$.
a) What mark in the second test would be expected if the marks in the first test were:
i) 50   ii) 70   iii) 90?
b) By extending the line find the mark in the first test corresponding to a mark in the second test of:
i) 30   ii) 85.

9 The same people were given two tests in technical drawing at an interval of one month.

Test 1	10	60	60	20	29	25	53	47
Test 2	11	45	35	23	17	25	32	36

Draw a scatter diagram to show these results, and using the point $(\overline{x}, \overline{y})$ draw in the best fitting line. Estimate the marks

gained in the second test for first test marks of:
a) 20   **b)** 42   **c)** 59.

EQUATION OF THE REGRESSION LINE

Once the regression line has been drawn it is usually necessary that the equation of the line be expressed in mathematical terms. Consider the line PQ shown below.

Fig. 7.6

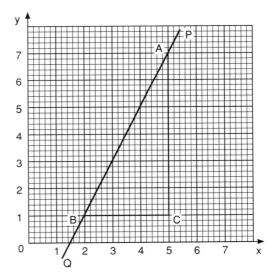

On the line select two points A and B which are well separated, one near each end of the line. From these points, A and B, draw lines AC and BC parallel to the axes to complete the right-angled triangle ABC. The standard form of the equation of a straight line is $y = mx + c$ where m is the gradient of the line and c is a constant. If the coordinates of the points A and B are represented by the symbols $A(x_A, y_A)$ and $B(x_B, y_B)$, then the gradient of AB $= m$ is given by:

$$\frac{CA}{BC} = \frac{y_A - y_B}{x_A - x_B}$$

In the context of regression this fraction is called the **coefficient of regression**. Once the value of m has been established the constant c can be obtained by the substitution of the coordinates of either A or B into the equation $y = mx + c$. A good choice of the points A and B can help to reduce the weight of calculation. The points should be chosen so that the coordinates can be read without the use of too many decimals or fractions and since the calculation involves division by BC it is desirable that the length BC be chosen so as to make for an easy division.

Example

Consider the regression line drawn in Figure 7.5 and find the equations of the regression line. Also, use the equation to estimate the value of y which would correspond to
a) $x = 12$ b) $x = 22$.

Solution

To keep the calculation straightforward we can take $A(18, 20\frac{1}{2})$ and $B(8, 10)$ and let the equation of the line be of the form $y = mx + c$, then:

$$m = \frac{y_A - y_B}{x_A - x_B} = \frac{20\frac{1}{2} - 10}{18 - 8} = \frac{10\frac{1}{2}}{10} = 1.05$$

The value of c can be found using this value of m and the coordinates of B.
    That is:
$10 = 1.05 \times 8 + c$
$\therefore c = 1.6$

So the equation of the regression line is:

$y = 1.05x + 1.6$.

When $x = 12$, $y = 1.05 \times 12 + 1.6 = 14.2$
When $x = 22$, $y = 1.05 \times 22 + 1.6 = 24.7$

EXERCISE B

1 Find the equation of the regression line which passes through:
a) $(7, 8)$ and $(4, 2)$.
b) $(2, 5)$ and $(5, 2)$.
c) $(5, 6)$ and $(21, 14)$.
d) $(2, 3)$ and $(8, 7)$.

Fig. 7.7

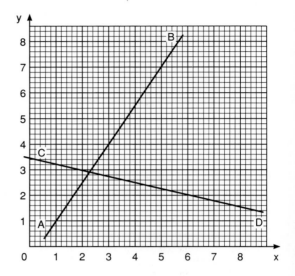

2 Figure 7.7 above shows two regression lines. Find the equation of:
a) AB.   b) CD.
3 Draw the scatter diagram corresponding to the following data.

x	3	7	11	13	20	25	30	37
y	6	9	10	12	14	18	21	22

On the diagram draw by inspection the best fitting line and find its equation. Use the equation to estimate the value of y which corresponds to $x = 34$.

4 Draw the scatter diagram and the best fitting line by using the point $(\bar{x}, \bar{y})$ for the following measures of x and y.

x	2.2	2.8	3.4	4.0	4.2	5.4	6.0
y	7.4	6.4	6.0	4.5	3.8	1.8	1.6

Find the equation of the best fitting line and use that equation to find:
a) the value of y when $x = 3$.
b) the value of y when $x = 5$.

5 The marks obtained by 8 students in a formal examination and in an objective test in mathematics are tabulated below. The marks listed under the symbol x are those for the formal test and under y are the marks in the objective test.

x	5	10	14	15	24	27	32	33
y	10	11	12	14	15	17	20	20

Illustrate these measures on a scatter diagram. Draw the regression line by using the point $(\bar{x}, \bar{y})$ and find its equation.

6 Draw a scatter diagram to illustrate the following measures. On the diagram draw the regression line by using the point $(\bar{x}, \bar{y})$ and find its equation.

x	5	9	10	15	20	23	30	32
y	10	13	15	18	21	22	26	31

7 Draw a scatter diagram to illustrate the distribution below.

On the scatter diagram draw the regression line by using the point $(\bar{x}, \bar{y})$ and find its equation.

x	y
86	120
90	104
93	100
94	80
95	74
96	47
98	96
100	25
100	20
105	50
110	10

8 A body is dropped from a helicopter and its height above ground level is estimated at various times after release. The following table gives the results of these observations, where y measures the height above ground level in metres and t measures the time after release in seconds.

t	2	3	4	5	6	7	8
y	380	360	320	270	220	160	80

Since it is known that the height should be given by a formula of the type $y = mt^2 + c$ draw up a table showing the mapping of y against t^2 and illustrate this mapping on a scatter diagram. Draw the best fitting line for this diagram by inspection and use it to find the values of m and c.

Assuming that the regression line can be extended, estimate:
a) the height from which the body was dropped, that is, the value when $t = 0$.
b) the time taken by the body to reach the ground, that is, the value of t when $y = 0$.

9 The cost of producing lace decreases as the amount of lace produced increases and some measures relating to this fact are illustrated in the following table. x is the length of lace produced in hundreds of metres and y is the cost of the lace in pence per metre.

x	$\frac{1}{4}$	$\frac{1}{3}$	$\frac{1}{2}$	2	3	6
y	29	22	15	7.5	5.5	5

Since it is known that x and y are connected by an equation of the form $y = m/x + c$ draw up a table showing the corresponding values of $1/x$ and y and plot these results on a scatter diagram.

Draw the best fitting line for this diagram by inspection and thus find the values of *m* and *c*.

Assuming that the regression line can be extended, estimate:

a) the cost per metre of lace if 1000 metres are produced.

b) the number of metres of lace that must be produced so that the cost per metre is 4.5 pence.

CORRELATION

While regression measures the line which best fits a certain set of measures, it takes no account of how closely these measures approximate to that line. In the study of correlation the interest is in measuring the degree by which two distributions match each other. The type of measure that is used for this purpose is called the **coefficient of correlation** and it is assessed on a scale which runs from +1 through zero to −1. A coefficient of correlation of +1 means that the two distributions match each other perfectly and this would correspond to a scatter diagram like that shown in Figure 7.8 where all of the points plotted lie along the leading diagonal of the grid.

A coefficient of correlation of −1 would correspond to a pair of distributions where the measures are in completely opposite order, that is, the first of the one distribution is last in the other, the second in the first

distribution is second last in the other distribution and so on. This type of situation would correspond to a scatter diagram like that shown in Figure 7.9 where all of the points plotted lie along the other diagonal of the grid.

A zero coefficient of correlation would correspond to a pair of distributions which were completely unconnected and would have a scatter diagram like Figure 7.10, where the entries are scattered at random over the grid. Intermediate values of the coefficient of correlation correspond to distributions whose scatter diagrams are intermediate between these extreme cases.

There are fundamentally two methods of assessing a coefficient of correlation, one depends on the actual measures in the two separate distributions being considered and is called the **product-moment coefficient of correlation**. The other which is called the **coefficient of rank correlation** depends only on the order of merit of the measures in the distributions. The first of these methods involves a considerable amount of heavy calculation and so in this study only the second of these methods of arriving at a measure of correlation will be used.

COEFFICIENT OF RANK CORRELATION

The theory behind this measure is beyond the scope of the present study and thus only the

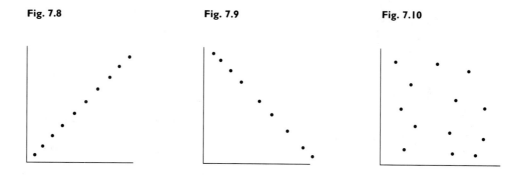

Fig. 7.8   **Fig. 7.9**   **Fig. 7.10**

procedure will be discussed now. Each distribution must first be put into an order of merit and traditionally this is taken in a descending order. Each item being considered has two ranks allocated to it and the difference between these two ranks can be found. If the symbol d is used to represent this difference then the coefficient of rank correlation can be written as:

$$R = 1 - \frac{6\Sigma d^2}{n(n^2 - 1)}$$

where n is the number of items in the distributions.

If two or more measures in one distribution are equal it is convenient, though not mathematically justifiable, to allocate to them a rank which is the average of the ranks which they would have occupied if they had been different. For example, if the third and fourth measures in a distribution are equal they would both be allocated the rank $3\frac{1}{2}$ or if the fifth, sixth and seventh are equal they would all be allocated the rank 6.

Even measures which cannot be measured numerically or exactly can be used in this context. All that is required is that the items can be put into an order of merit in respect of the quality being measured, such as depth of colour, or age of trees or rocks.

Example 1

Consider the distributions of reading speeds and intelligence quotients quoted on page 90. The calculation of the coefficient of rank correlation can be tabulated as below.

Coefficient of rank correlation:

$$R = 1 - \frac{6\Sigma d^2}{n(n^2 - 1)}$$

$$= 1 - \frac{6 \times 40}{12 \times 143}$$

$$= 1 - 0.14$$

$$= 0.86$$

A high coefficient of correlation, as in the above case, does not prove that there is a **causal** or **cause and effect** relationship between the two variables. In certain cases the relationship may be causal and it often is in practical or scientific situations. But in general we can say that if the coefficient of correlation is high then the two variables seem to change together. Remember that no general conclusion can ever be drawn from a single study of a small sample.

Child	Reading speed	Intelligence quotient	Rank in reading speed	Rank in intelligence quotient	d	d²
A	120	80	11	12	−1	1
B	140	90	$8\frac{1}{2}$	$10\frac{1}{2}$	−2	4
C	100	90	12	$10\frac{1}{2}$	$+1\frac{1}{2}$	$2\frac{1}{4}$
D	170	100	7	$8\frac{1}{2}$	$-1\frac{1}{2}$	$2\frac{1}{4}$
E	130	100	10	$8\frac{1}{2}$	$+1\frac{1}{2}$	$2\frac{1}{4}$
F	190	105	5	7	−2	4
G	220	110	3	$5\frac{1}{2}$	$-2\frac{1}{2}$	$6\frac{1}{4}$
H	140	110	$8\frac{1}{2}$	$5\frac{1}{2}$	+3	9
I	180	115	6	4	+2	4
J	240	120	2	3	−1	1
K	200	125	4	2	+2	4
L	270	130	1	1	0	0
					$\Sigma d^2 = 40$	

Example 2

In Chapter 1 we quoted the following distribution of maths marks and heights.

Maths mark	80	75	62	45	28
Height (cm)	180	173	168	159	152

In these distributions the ranks are identical so all the measures of d will be zero and thus the coefficient of correlation will be 1. Since there is obviously no real linkage between height and marks in maths this is an example of a **spurious correlation**.

EXERCISE C

1 Calculate the coefficient of rank correlation for the following distributions of x and y (see p. 95).

x	10	15	23	30	35	45
y	11	19	18	27	29	33

2 Calculate the coefficient of rank correlation of the distributions listed in Question 3 of Exercise B of this chapter.
3 Calculate the coefficient of rank correlation of the distributions listed in Question 4 of Exercise B of this chapter.
4 Calculate the coefficient of rank correlation of the distributions listed in Question 5 of Exercise B of this chapter.
5 Calculate the coefficient of rank correlation of the distributions listed in Question 6 of Exercise B of this chapter.
6 Calculate the coefficient of rank correlation of the distributions listed in Question 7 of Exercise B of this chapter.
7 Six candidates sat a written examination and were also interviewed for the award of a bursary. The written examination

was marked out of 100 and the interview was graded A, B, C, D, or E in descending order of merit. The results were as follows:

Candidate	1	2	3	4	5	6
Written examination	80	78	60	55	53	48
Interview	C	A	B	B	D	C

Find the coefficient of rank correlation for the two sets of measures.
8 Calculate the coefficient of rank correlation for the following distribution of heights and maths marks for a small group of pupils and comment upon the result.

Height (cm)	157	166	161	159	170
Maths mark	70	41	50	68	32

9 Calculate the coefficient of rank correlation for the following distribution of height and shoe size for a group of 5 students. Comment upon your result.

Height (cm)	152	180	173	168	159
Shoe size	5	11	8	7	6

10 The marks in maths and science for a group of students are listed below. Calculate the coefficient of rank correlation for these measures and comment upon the result.

Maths	28	80	75	62	45	70	41	50	68	32
Science	36	84	75	80	51	74	44	52	70	38

11 The marks in mathematics and French for a group of 10 children are listed below. Calculate the coefficient of rank correlation for these measures.

Pupil	Mathematics	French
A	18	40
B	32	68
C	44	53
D	47	35
E	56	84
F	71	75
G	76	58
H	84	26
I	86	48
J	93	77

12 The heights, weights and shoe sizes of a group of 15 senior boys and 15 senior girls, in a school, are shown in the following tables.

Calculate the coefficient of rank correlation for:
a) height against weight of girls.
b) height against weight of boys.
c) height against shoe size of girls.
d) height against shoe size of boys.

Boys height (cm)	Weight (kg)	Shoe size
181	71	$9\frac{1}{2}$
173	70	8
184	69	$8\frac{1}{2}$
183	57	7
163	57	7
184	79	9
170	62	$8\frac{1}{2}$
180	73	9
165	54	$7\frac{1}{2}$
178	70	11
168	54	7
178	60	8
180	68	9
180	65	8
173	70	$9\frac{1}{2}$

13 Find the order of merit of the teams in the Premier Division of the English Football League at the end of each of the last two years. (Ignore the teams which were relegated and promoted at the end of the first of these two years.) Find the coefficient of rank correlation for these two orders of merit. Repeat this exercise using a division of the Scottish League.

Girls height (cm)	Weight (kg)	Shoe size
154	66	$5\frac{1}{2}$
170	57	$6\frac{1}{2}$
173	80	8
163	54	$4\frac{1}{2}$
160	53	5
164	54	5
163	53	6
160	62	$4\frac{1}{2}$
160	45	$4\frac{1}{2}$
163	53	5
168	60	7
162	55	$3\frac{1}{2}$
169	60	7
165	57	4
163	57	6

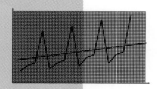

8 APPLICATIONS OF THE MEAN

TIME SERIES AND MOVING AVERAGES

If we investigate some measure, such as the daily takings of a shop, the quarterly profits of a company, the annual number of deaths from some disease, and record the data at regular intervals over a period of time, we obtain what is known as a **time series**. Often this type of series will contain a **cyclic** or **seasonal** variation. If we consider the likely pattern of the daily takings of a shop we would expect a low reading for each Monday and high readings for the days at the end of each week. The table shown below contains

Time		Sales (£1000s)
1987	1st quarter	147
	2nd quarter	196
	3rd quarter	315
	4th quarter	42
1988	1st quarter	161
	2nd quarter	220
	3rd quarter	415
	4th quarter	64
1989	1st quarter	212
	2nd quarter	286
	3rd quarter	487
	4th quarter	74
1990	1st quarter	215
	2nd quarter	324
	3rd quarter	464
	4th quarter	75

details of the total value of the new cars sold by a garage each quarter for a period of four years. This is a time series.

Over the years the sales in each quarter exhibit the same pattern. The high sales figures for the third quarter are caused by the new registration plates being available on 1st August, and the last three months of the year being a particularly bare time for new car sales.

When a time series is illustrated graphically the horizontal axis should always show the time, and the measure should be shown on the vertical axis. Figure 8.1 illustrates the information given in the table.

The irregularity of this type of graph disguises the general **trend** of the data. It is useful to add to the graph a further set of points, and the line joining them in order to bring out the overall trend of the data. This further set of points is known as the **moving average**. When we are dealing with quarterly figures, as in this case, a four-point moving average would be appropriate. The first of these averages is the average of the figures for the four quarters of 1987. The second average is the average of the second, third and fourth quarters of 1987 and the first quarter of 1988. The third average is the average of the third and fourth quarters of 1987 and the first and second quarters of 1988. Further averages are obtained in succession by omitting the oldest measure and taking into account one new measure each time. We continue in this manner until we have reached the last four

Fig. 8.1

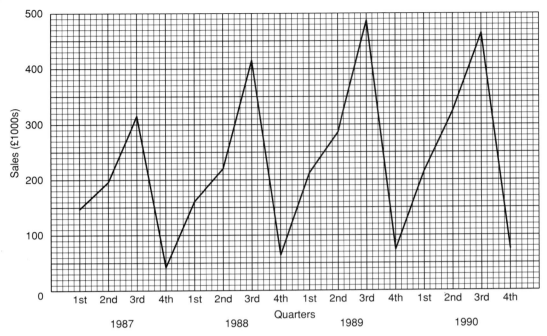

measures. The necessary calculations for the moving averages can be tabulated as shown.

Note particularly that the moving totals and the moving averages are listed opposite the middle point of the time interval concerned. In the table, the first moving total of 700 and the average of 175 are set against the midway point between the second and third quarters. Similarly, when these averages are added to the graph, the points are plotted midway between the quarters. When the average points are joined the resultant graph shows the trend of the data with the seasonal variations removed. The graph of the value of car sales is repeated in Figure 8.2 with the moving averages plotted and joined up. The graph of the moving averages clearly shows the steady increase in sales over 1988 and the first half of 1989 and then the flattening off of the graph thereafter.

Note The moving averages have been shown by open dots and the line joining these points has been shown as a broken line. This is done

Time	Sales (£1000s)	Moving annual total	Moving average
1987			
1st quarter	147		
2nd quarter	196		
		700	175
3rd quarter	315	714	179
4th quarter	42	738	185
1988			
1st quarter	161	838	210
2nd quarter	220	860	215
3rd quarter	415	911	228
4th quarter	64	977	244
1989			
1st quarter	212	1049	262
2nd quarter	286	1059	265
3rd quarter	487	1062	266
4th quarter	74	1100	275
1990			
1st quarter	215	1077	269
2nd quarter	324	1078	270
3rd quarter	464		
4th quarter	75		

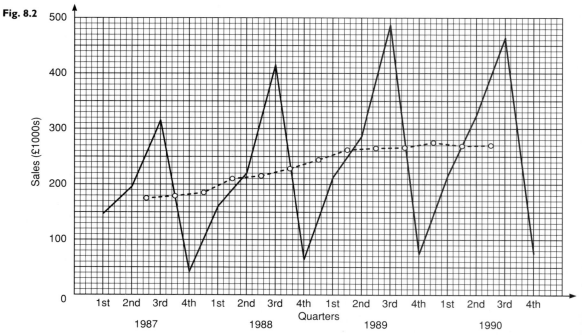

Fig. 8.2

Sales (£1000s) — vertical axis with markings at 100, 200, 300, 400, 500

Quarters: 1st 2nd 3rd 4th (1987) | 1st 2nd 3rd 4th (1988) | 1st 2nd 3rd 4th (1989) | 1st 2nd 3rd 4th (1990)

to distinguish clearly the two sets of points and the two lines.

In this example as four measures were averaged it is a four-point moving average. If the data had been given in terms of monthly figures then it would have been appropriate to average successive sets of 12 measures and this would have been called a twelve-point moving average. When seasonal variations are to be smoothed out then it is essential that sets of measures for complete seasons be taken for the calculation of the moving averages.

Moving averages can be used to smooth out a graph when the irregularities are the result of variations other than seasonal variations. The only change is that as there is no complete season available as the obvious size of group for the calculation of the averages, an arbitrary choice must be made in the matter.

Example

The number of deaths from 'flu in England and Wales over a period of 17 years is shown in the following table.

Year	Number of deaths
1972	3008
1973	3164
1974	1235
1975	1442
1976	6699
1977	1267
1978	1340
1979	838
1980	514
1981	626
1982	716
1983	796
1984	346
1985	626
1986	587
1987	190
1988	285

Here the choice of the size of the moving average is quite arbitrary but it is useful to look at the distribution of particular high and low readings. There were locally high readings in 1976 and 1983 and there were locally low results in 1974, 1980, and 1987. Since two of these gaps were 7 years and the other one 6 years, we should consider a

104

seven-point moving average as the most appropriate. The calculation for the seven-point moving averages is shown below and Figure 8.3 shows the raw results and the moving averages.

Year	Number of deaths	Seven-year moving total	Seven-point moving average
1972	3008		
1973	3164		
1974	1235		
1975	1442	18 155	2594
1976	6699	15 985	2284
1977	1267	13 335	1905
1978	1340	12 726	1818
1979	838	12 000	1714
1980	514	6097	871
1981	626	5176	739
1982	716	4462	637
1983	796	4211	602
1984	346	3887	555
1985	626	3546	507
1986	587		
1987	190		
1988	285		

EXERCISE A

1 Calculate the three-point moving averages of the following measures:
20, 15, 5, 10, 12, 8, 15, 25, 10, 15
2 Calculate the five-point moving averages of the measures quoted in question 1.
3 In a school in Scotland the number of passes in Higher French for each of the last 12 years was as follows:

Year	Number of passes
1979	41
1980	39
1981	45
1982	42
1983	39
1984	37
1985	35
1986	32
1987	36
1988	37
1989	39
1990	40

Fig. 8.3

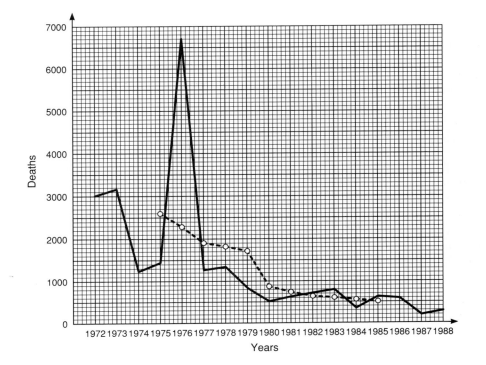

105

Calculate the four-point moving averages for these measures and illustrate the actual number of passes and the moving averages on the same grid. Comment upon the trend of these results.

4 The numbers of reported robberies (in thousands) in England and Wales were as tabulated below:

Year	1st	2nd	3rd	4th
		Quarter		
1986	7.6	7.1	7.2	8.1
1987	8.1	7.7	8.2	8.6
1988	7.9	7.5	8.0	8.1
1989	8.2	7.8	8.0	9.1
1990	8.4	8.4	8.9	

Calculate the four-point moving averages for these measures and plot the actual measures and the moving averages on the same grid.

Identify the quarters where the number of robberies was generally:
a) low.
b) high.

Comment on the trend in the number of robberies.

5 The table lists the number of deaths from 'flu in Scotland over a period of 17 years.

Year	Number of deaths
1972	422
1973	306
1974	145
1975	220
1976	828
1977	164
1978	230
1979	59
1980	117
1981	54
1982	235
1983	178
1984	59
1985	54
1986	121
1987	36
1988	25

Calculate the five-point moving averages for these measures and illustrate the actual measures and the moving averages on the same grid.

6 The daily takings of a gift shop for the five weeks prior to Christmas are shown in the table. Calculate the six-point moving averages for the takings and plot the takings and the moving averages on the same grid. (The takings are given correct to the nearest £10.) Note that two days each week have relatively low takings and suggest possible reasons for this. Comment on the trend of the takings.

	Week 1	Week 2	Week 3	Week 4	Week 5
	Daily takings (£)				
Monday	360	400	460	450	450
Tuesday	530	590	680	750	710
Wednesday	460	390	350	500	390
Thursday	620	750	920	1040	870
Friday	850	940	1380	1520	1210
Saturday	1200	1320	1750	2150	1650

7 The sales by the gas supply system (in millions of therms) over a period of four years are listed below. Calculate the four-point moving averages and plot the raw data and the moving averages on the same grid.

Year	1st	2nd	3rd	4th
		Quarter		
1984		3500	2300	5000
1985	6900	3800	2500	5300
1986	7200	3700	2400	5100
1987	7600	3600	2400	5700
1988	7900			

8 The numbers of notifiable offences recorded in England and Wales, in the category of violence against the person (in thousands) are listed below. Calculate

the four-point moving averages and plot the given data and the moving averages on the same grid.

Year	Quarter			
	1st	2nd	3rd	4th
1986	28.0	32.6	32.1	32.8
1987	29.7	34.7	38.6	38.0
1988	35.5	39.1	40.9	42.7
1989	39.3	45.2	48.3	44.2
1990	41.0	47.0	49.5	

FORECASTING THE FUTURE

Estimations of future results can sometimes be obtained from the graph of the moving averages. If the measures have exhibited a seasonal or some other form of regular pattern of cyclic variations, and if the graph of the moving averages approximates roughly to a straight line, we can make progress. Instead of joining up the moving averages, we can draw the best fitting straight line through these points. This line is usually called the **trend line**. If the points are fairly close to a straight line it is usually possible to draw that line by inspection. Once the trend line has been drawn there are then two basic methods of estimating future measures. Both of these can be illustrated best by using an example. If we return to the example on page 103 dealing with car sales, we can draw the best fitting straight line through the points obtained from the moving averages. The graph with the trend line added is shown in Figure 8.4.

Method 1

If we extend the trend line beyond the last moving average we can see that the line would place the next moving average at 291. This average is the one which would be obtained by averaging the sales for the last

Fig. 8.4

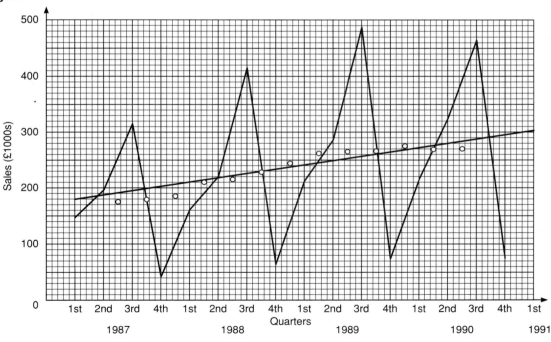

107

three quarters of 1990 with the first quarter of 1991. Thus we can do the following calculation:

$$(324 + 464 + 75 + \text{1st quarter of 1991})/4 = 291$$

that is,

$$324 + 464 + 75 + \text{1st quarter of 1991} = 4 \times 291$$

that is,

$$
\begin{aligned}
\text{1st quarter of 1991} &= 4 \times 291 - (324 + 464 + 75) \\
&= 1164 - 863 \\
&= 301
\end{aligned}
$$

The estimate of sales for the first quarter of 1991 is £301 000.

This method can be extended step-by-step. If we extend the line to the position of the next moving average it would be the average of the last two quarters of 1990 and the first two quarters of 1991, and thus the estimate for the second quarter of 1991 would be obtained.

This is a step-by-step extension and it is very heavily dependent on the last set of readings. In this example the estimate seems rather high and this was caused by the rather poor sales figures for all of 1990.

Method 2

As in the first method the best fitting line is extended again but this time it is extended to the position above the quarter we wish to consider on the horizontal time scale. If we again take the first quarter of 1991 as our point of interest, we see that the line goes through the value 302 at this time. We now go back and note the amount by which each previous first quarter differed from the value given by the best fitting line at that time. In 1987 the line gives a reading of 180 but the actual figure was 147, a difference of −33, and similarly in 1988 the difference was −50, in 1989 it was −29 and in 1990 it was −57. These differences are averaged, which gives an average difference of −42 (correct to the nearest whole number) and this difference is applied now to the value previously obtained

from the trend line to give an estimate for the first quarter of 1990 of 302 − 42 = £260 000.

Whereas method 1 depended heavily on the last three sales figures this method bases its estimate upon the results for similar periods in all previous cycles. Also, this method does not have to work out the estimates in chronological order. It is possible to evaluate the estimate for the last quarter of 1991 in the same way without considering any of the intervening quarters.

EXERCISE B

1 The table shows consumer spending on alcoholic drinks, excluding beer (in hundreds of millions of pounds).

Year	Quarter			
	1st	2nd	3rd	4th
1986	14	16	17	28
1987	15	17	18	30
1988	16	19	20	32
1989	17	20	21	34

These measures, the four-point moving averages and the trend line are shown in Figure 8.5. Use the graph to:
a) estimate by method 1 the spending for the first quarter of 1990.
b) estimate the differences between the actual measures and the values given by the trend line for the second quarter of 1986, 1987, 1988 and 1989 and thus estimate by method 2 the spending for the second quarter of 1990.

2 The quarterly sales of gas to domestic customers (in millions of therms) over a period of four years are listed below.

Year	Quarter			
	1st	2nd	3rd	4th
1984		1700	900	2700
1985	4100	1800	1000	2900
1986	4400	2000	1000	2800
1987	4600	1900	1000	3200
1988	4400			

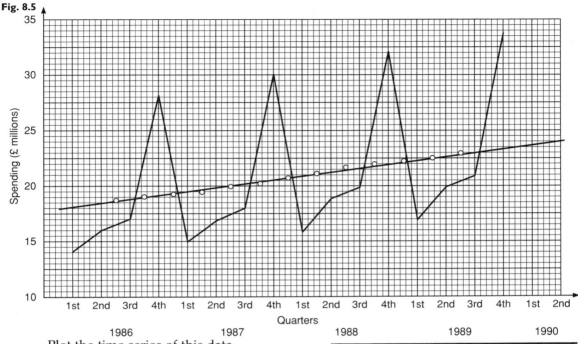

Fig. 8.5

Plot the time series of this data. Calculate the four-point moving averages and add them to the graph. Draw the trend line and use it to estimate the sales in the second and third quarters of 1988 by method 1.

3 Use the data and the work previously done for Question 4 of Exercise A to estimate by method 2 the number of robberies in the fourth quarter of 1990.

4 Use the data and the work previously done for Question 7 of Exercise A to estimate by method 1 the sales in the second and third quarters of 1988, and by method 2 the sales in the third quarter of 1988.

5 Use the data and the work previously done for Question 8 of Exercise A to estimate the number of notifiable offences recorded in the fourth quarter of 1990 by method 1 and the numbers recorded in the first quarter of 1991 by method 2.

6 The table lists the capital expenditure on new building work (in millions of pounds).

Year	Quarter			
	1st	2nd	3rd	4th
1986	248	223	264	343
1987	231	277	324	383
1988	330	368	403	423
1989	312	383	400	492
1990	414	413		

Calculate the four-point moving averages and plot the raw data and the moving averages on the same grid. Draw the trend line and use it to estimate by method 1 the capital expenditure in the third quarter of 1990 and by method 2 the expenditure in the fourth quarter of 1990.

WEIGHTED MEAN

In some situations it is unsatisfactory to calculate the ordinary mean of a set of measures. The situation may be such that greater emphasis must be given to particular

109

measures. This is done by using a weighted mean. The technique is best illustrated by example.

Example 1

To estimate the likely performance of a class in a national examination the pupils sat two separate tests which were both marked out of 100. The teacher considered that the second test was twice as valuable as the first. If a pupil scored 40% in the first test and 55% in the second then on this basis the weighted mean is obtained by averaging the first result with twice the second result.

Weighted mean $= \bar{x}_w$

$$= \frac{40 + 2 \times 55}{1 + 2}$$

$$= \frac{150}{3} = 50$$

Example 2

If in the above example the decision had been to weight the results in the ratio 2:3 then the

weighted mean $= \bar{x}_w$

$$= \frac{2 \times 40 + 3 \times 55}{2 + 3}$$

$$= \frac{245}{5} = 49$$

Example 3

A manufacturer makes three models, A, B and C, on which she reckons to make a profit of £50, £40, £30 respectively. Her results show that for every 2 models of type A which she sells she is able to sell 3 models of type B and 5 of type C. Find the mean profit per article sold.

Weighted mean $= \bar{x}_w$

$$= \frac{2 \times £50 + 3 \times £40 + 5 \times £30}{2 + 3 + 5}$$

$$= \frac{£370}{10}$$

$$= £37$$

In general if the measures $x_1, x_2, x_3, \ldots x_n$ are given weights $w_1, w_2, w_3, \ldots w_n$ then their weighted mean $= \bar{x}_w$

$$= \frac{w_1 x_1 + w_2 x_2 + w_3 x_3 + \ldots + w_n x_n}{w_1 + w_2 + w_3 + \ldots + w_n}$$

EXERCISE C

1 Find the weighted mean of the two measures 5 and 10 if they are given weights of 2 and 3 respectively.

2 Find the weighted mean of the measures 10, 14, 15, 18, 20 if they are given weights of 1, 2, 3, 4, 5 respectively.

3 In the three sections of an examination a candidate scored 40%, 45% and 60%. Find the weighted mean if the three sections are given weights 1, 2 and 2 respectively.

4 An alloy is made by mixing three parts by volume of material A with five parts by volume of material B. If the density of material A is 5 gm per cm³ and that of material B is 9 gm per cm³, find the density of the alloy.

5 The two isotopes of chlorine have atomic masses of 35 and 37. If the two isotopes are normally found in a mixture in the ratio of three of the first to one of the second, find the average atomic mass of the mixture.

6 The two isotopes of copper have atomic masses of 63 and 65. If these isotopes are normally found in a mixture in the proportion of 7 of the first to 3 of the second, find the average atomic mass of the mixture.

INDEX NUMBERS

Two measures can be compared in a variety of ways.

1 *The two measures can be stated.*
2 *The difference between the measures can be given.*
3 *The one measure can be given as a fraction of the other.*
4 *The percentage change can be given.*
5 *The one measure can be given as a percentage of the other.*

The last of these methods of comparison is the concept underlying an **index number**. The only fundamental difference is that in an index number the percentage sign is omitted. Index numbers are at present normally used to express changes in prices and the figure upon which the percentage is calculated is called the **base**.

Example 1

An article which cost £5 in 1988 now costs £7. Find the index number corresponding to the present price if the 1988 price is taken as base.

$$\text{Index number} = \frac{7}{5} \times 100 = 140$$

Example 2

In 1989 the index number corresponding to the cost of an article, on the 1987 cost as base, was 120. The present index number taken on the 1989 cost as base is 105. Find the index number for the present cost taken on the 1987 cost as base.

$$\text{Index number} = 105\% \text{ of } 120$$

$$= \frac{105}{100} \times 120 = 126$$

Example 3

If the index number for an article in 1987 was 120 and at present is 150, both index numbers being taken on the 1985 cost as base, find the index number for the present cost taken on the 1987 cost as base.

$$\text{Index number} = \frac{150}{120} \times 100 = 125$$

EXERCISE D

1 Calculate the index numbers corresponding to the second cost of each of the following commodities taking the first cost as base in each case.

Commodity	1st cost £	2nd cost £
A	2.00	2.10
B	5.50	6.60
C	2.50	2.00
D	34.50	53.20*
E	245	452*

2 For each of the following calculate the present cost if the given index number is the present one and is calculated on the first cost as base.

Commodity	1st cost £	Index number
A	10	105
B	7.80	120
C	0.84	125
D	345	97†
E	345	103†

3 In each of the following examples the 1989 and 1990 index numbers are calculated on the 1988 cost as base. Express the 1990 cost as an index number calculated on the 1989 cost as base.

Commodity	1989 Index number	1990 Index number
A	110	132
B	120	144
C	120	108
D	90	72
E	123	134*

*Correct to the nearest integer
†Correct to the nearest £

111

4 The index number for an item in 1988 was 105, calculated on the 1987 cost as base. In 1990 the index number for the same item calculated on the 1988 cost as base was 140. Calculate the index number for the 1990 cost on the 1987 figure as base.

5 The index number of an article in 1990 was 90, calculated on the 1989 cost as base. The index number of the same article in 1991 was 110, calculated on the 1990 cost as base. Find the index number in 1991 for that article calculated on the 1989 cost as base.

INDEX OF RETAIL PRICES

This measure is frequently quoted in the Press and changes in this measure are frequently used as grounds for wage increase claims. Fundamentally, this index is a combination of the ideas behind weighted means and index numbers. A large representative sample of the population kept a very careful note of all forms of spending incurred by the family over a period of time. From the analysis of all of this information details of the spending of the average family have been obtained. Decisions were then taken as to the classification of all of the items of spending and weights allocated to these classes of spending in proportion to the results obtained from the survey. The total of the weights allocated is normally 1000. The pattern of family spending changes as national habits change and thus the allocation of these weights is kept continually under review.

A particular date is chosen as a base and each class of goods is allocated the index number 100 for that date. Changes in the cost of items within each class can be kept under review and appropriate index numbers can be obtained, at any time, for the various classes of expenditure. The weighted mean of these various index numbers can be calculated and this measure is called the **index of retail**

prices. The full list of details of the weights is too long to be quoted here but a summary of the facts as given recently is as follows:

	Weight
Food	163
Catering	50
Alcoholic drink	78
Tobacco	36
Housing	160
Fuel and light	55
Household goods	74
Household services	41
Clothing	72
Personal goods and services	37
Motoring expenses	132
Fares and other travel	23
Leisure goods and services	79

Example 1

The cost of producing an article is weighted as follows: labour 55, materials 25, plant maintenance and depreciation 20. On the 1988 costs as base the index numbers for these sections of the cost are 160, 135 and 110 respectively. Find the index number corresponding to the present cost of production on the basis of the 1988 costs.

Solution

	Weight	Index number
Labour	55	160
Materials	25	135
Plant	20	110
Total	100	

Present index number

$$= \frac{55 \times 160 + 25 \times 135 + 20 \times 110}{55 + 25 + 20}$$

$$= \frac{14\,375}{100}$$

$$= 144$$

Example 2

If the 1989 index of retail prices had the following weights and indices as based on the 1986 prices, find the 1989 index of retail prices.

Solution

	Weight	Index number
Food	304	124
Tobacco and alcohol	129	126
Housing and durable goods	331	127
Transport	120	119
Misc. goods and services	116	128
Total	1000	

Index of retail prices

$$= \frac{\begin{array}{c}304 \times 124 + 129 \times 126 + 331 \times 127 \\ + 120 \times 119 + 116 \times 128\end{array}}{304 + 129 + 331 + 120 + 116}$$

$$= \frac{125\,115}{1000}$$

$$= 125$$

EXERCISE E

1 A shopkeeper estimates his expenditure using the undernoted headings and allocates the accompanying weights and index numbers to the items taking his 1988 costs as base. Find the weighted index number corresponding to these details.

	Weight	Index number
Wages	140	170
Cost of goods	765	155
Rent and rates	35	210
Maintenance of premises	60	110

2 As part of the evidence for a claim for increased pocket money the boys of a boarding school produced the following details about the weighting of their spending and the changes in costs over the last year.

	Weight	Index number
Sweets	25	125
Comics	10	130
Pictures	35	110
Toys and so on	20	120
Savings and presents	10	120

Find the weighted index number corresponding to these measures and state the percentage increase in pocket money that they would be justified in claiming on this evidence.

3 A householder studied his outlay on food and so on, and allocated weights to the various classes of expenditure as below. From a comparison of prices of the item involved he estimates the attached index numbers, using the 1990 prices as base. Calculate the weighted index number for the range of expenditure.

	Weight	Index number
Groceries	42	105
Meat and fish	20	115
Fruit and vegetables	8	150
Milk and eggs	12	106
Bread and cakes	10	110
Cleaning materials	8	105

4 Calculate the weighted index number corresponding to the following items and

their attached weights and index numbers.

	Weight	Index number
Food	316	121
Tobacco and drink	125	110
Housing	160	115
Clothing	83	109
Durable goods	80	105
Transport	120	112
Services	60	115
Misc. goods	56	110

5 Calculate the index number for all the groups listed below by using the given data.

	Weight	Index number
Food	395	118
Tobacco and drink	115	102
Housing	75	115
Fuel and light	62	114
Clothing	83	98
Durable goods	55	96
Transport	105	112
Misc. goods and services	110	100

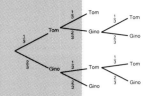

9 PROBABILITY

What does probability mean to you? The name rather suggests a vague likelihood of something happening. There is nothing vague, however, about probability. Mathematically, probability is as precise as any other subject. We can calculate very exactly the probability or chance of a certain event happening when we know the circumstances surrounding it.

If we toss a **fair** (or honest) coin it will land head or tail upwards. There is a '50–50' chance of either. In other words, there is a probability of $\frac{1}{2}$ that a head shows and the same for a tail.

If we are interested in obtaining a head, then we say a head is a **favourable** outcome. The total number of possible outcomes is 2 (a head or a tail). The probability of obtaining a head is 1 out of 2 or $\frac{1}{2}$.

Let us consider rolling a die. The die could show a 1, 2, 3, 4, 5, or 6, that is, there are 6 possible outcomes when a die is thrown. If we are interested in obtaining a 3, then there is a chance of 1 in 6 or $\frac{1}{6}$ of getting a 3; there is also a chance of $\frac{1}{6}$ of getting a 1 or 2 or 4 or 5 or 6.

The probability of a 3 showing:

$$= \frac{\text{number of favourable outcomes}}{\text{number of possible outcomes}}$$

$$= \tfrac{1}{6}$$

What if we wanted to know the probability of a number divisible by 2 showing when a die is rolled? Again the total possible number of outcomes is 6. Now we must calculate the number of favourable outcomes, that is, how many of the numbers are divisible by 2. The number divisible by 2 are 2, 4 and 6. Thus the probability of a numbers divisible by 2 showing:

$$= \frac{\text{number of favourable outcomes}}{\text{number of possible outcomes}}$$

$$= \tfrac{3}{6}$$

$$= \tfrac{1}{2}$$

So far, the probabilities we have considered have been purely theoretical probabilities. Let us now look at some actual results obtained experimentally.

EXPERIMENT 1   Tossing a coin ——————

You all should have a coin to toss and a book and pencil to record your results.

Part 1

Copy this table into your book.
Number of tosses = 50

	Tally	Total
Heads		
Tails		

You must make sure before you begin that you are tossing the coin *properly*. It must spin round in the air before it falls. Now toss the coin 50 times and record the number of heads and tails obtained.

Tally your score as you did for frequency distributions. Finally total up your scores.

Let us compare the experimental results with what could be expected theoretically.

The probability of a head in one toss:

$$= \tfrac{1}{2}$$

The expected number of heads in 50 tosses:

$$= \tfrac{1}{2} \text{ of } 50$$

$$= 25$$

Similarly, the expected number of tails in 50 tosses is 25. Now, compare your experimental results with the theoretical results in this table.

Number of tosses = 50

	Experimental	Theoretical
Heads		25
Tails		25

Part 2

Repeat your experiment, tossing the coin 100 times. Again use a table to record the results. Calculate the theoretical results and compare them with the experimental results as in Part 1.

Part 3

Let us now collect together the number of heads and tails for the whole class from Part 2.

Copy this table into your book. Each member of the class should read out his or her results in turn and everyone should record all the results. As before, calculate the theoretical results and compare them in the table.

Total number of tosses =

	Experimental		Theoretical	
	Heads	Tails	Heads	Tails
Total				

It should have become obvious that the greater the number of tosses of a fair coin we consider, the nearer the experimental results come to the theoretical.

EXPERIMENT 2   Throwing a die ————

A similar experiment may be done using a die. Each member of the class should have a fair (honest) die and a shaker.

Part 1

Copy this table into your book.

Number of throws = 60

	Tally	Total
1		
2		
3		
4		
5		
6		

Roll the die 60 times and record, as before, the number of times 1, 2, 3, 4, 5, 6 turn up.

Now, compare the experimental and theoretical results in a table.

The probability of a 1 in 1 throw:

$$= \frac{\text{favourable}}{\text{possible}}$$

$$= \tfrac{1}{6}$$

The expected number of 1s in 60 throws:

$$= \tfrac{1}{6} \text{ of } 60$$

$$= 10$$

Similarly, the expected number of 2s, 3s, and so on:

$$= 10$$

Number of throws = 60

	Experimental	Theoretical
1		10
2		10
3		10
4		10
5		10
6		10

Part 2

Repeat the experiment, rolling the die 120 times and recording your scores in a table as before. Calculate the theoretical results and compare them, in a table, with the experimental results.

Part 3

As in Experiment 1, collect together the total numbers of 1s, 2s, 3s, and so on, that the whole class had for Part 2. Again calculate the expected theoretical values. Complete this table.

Total number of throws =

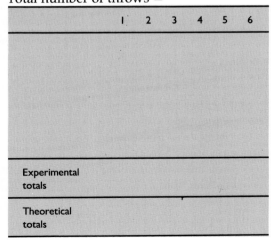

	1	2	3	4	5	6
Experimental totals						
Theoretical totals						

It should be clear, again, that the experimental results come closer to the theoretical results as we use a larger number of throws of the die.

Further experiments are quite easily devised for comparing experimental and theoretical results.

Suggestions

1. A solid regular triangular pyramid (tetrahedron) with the numbers 1, 2, 3, 4 painted on its faces may be rolled in a similar way to a die.
2. A spinner, as shown, can be made easily (but care must be taken). The disc may be marked off into any number of equal segments and either coloured or numbered as wished. The arrow should be able to spin round freely.

Fig. 9.1

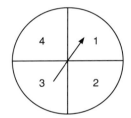

With a spinner of this type, a great many different experiments may be devised.

3. Various experiments may be conducted using books, such as opening a book at random and counting the number of times the tens digit is odd (or even) or a multiple of 2 or 3 etc.
4. On the market is a small roulette wheel that people can use at home. If a member of the class could borrow one of these, many interesting probability experiments could be tried.

BIAS

You may have noticed that in the experiments with the coin and the die, the word 'honest' or 'fair' was used.

117

An honest coin is one which is equally likely to show a head or a tail.

An honest die is one in which each number has a equal chance of turning up.

A coin or die which is not honest is said to be **biased** and it will give biased results.

A two-headed coin would obviously be biased since there is no chance at all of getting a tail.

Dice that are used for gambling can be 'loaded' or weighted so that they tend to land a certain way up.

In a later chapter you will learn how you can test the honesty of a coin or a die, if there are any doubts about it.

In the suggested experiments, you must be wary of introducing any bias. The spinner, for example, would have to be made very carefully. The material of the platform must be of uniform thickness and the circle perfectly round. The segments also must be exactly equal. Another place where great care is required, is in the spinning arrow. It must be able to spin round quite freely.

In the experiment with the book, the book you choose to use, should not be one that has been habitually opened at certain pages or you will find that it opens at these pages more or less automatically. So, examine the book first to ensure that this is not likely to happen.

CALCULATING

PROBABILITIES

One of the difficulties in calculating probabilities is in working out the number of favourable outcomes and the number of possible outcomes. Each example must be considered carefully. Once we know these two quantities, we can very easily calculate the probability using the formula:

probability of an event happening

$$= \frac{\text{number of favourable outcomes}}{\text{number of possible outcomes}}$$

If an event is certain to occur then the number of favourable outcomes is equal to the number of possible outcomes. Thus, the probability of an event which is certain to occur $= 1$.

If an event is certain not to happen then the number of favourable outcomes is 0. Thus the probability of an event which is certain not to occur $= 0$.

If the probability that an event occurs is p and the probability that the event does not occur is q then:

$$p + q = 1 \quad \text{or} \quad q = 1 - p$$

Example 1

A bag contains 50 marbles, 40 black ones and 10 red.
a) What is the probability of drawing a red marble?
b) What is the probability of drawing a black marble?
c) If two black marbles are removed from the bag what is the chance now of drawing a black one?
d) What is the chance of drawing a white marble?
e) What is the probability of drawing either a red marble or a black one?

Solution

a) Number of favourable outcomes $= 10$
Number of possible outcomes $= 50$
Probability of drawing a red marble $= \dfrac{\text{favourable}}{\text{possible}}$

$$p\ (\text{red}) = \tfrac{10}{50}$$
$$= \tfrac{1}{5}$$

b) Number of favourable outcomes $= 40$
Number of possible outcomes $= 50$
Probability of drawing a black marble $= \dfrac{\text{favourable}}{\text{possible}}$

$$p\ (\text{black}) = \tfrac{40}{50}$$
$$= \tfrac{4}{5}$$

c) Number of favourable outcomes $= 38$

Number of possible outcomes $= 48$

Probability of drawing a black marble $= \dfrac{\text{favourable}}{\text{possible}}$

$$p \text{ (black)} = \tfrac{38}{48}$$
$$= \tfrac{19}{24}$$

d) Number of favourable outcomes $= 0$

Number of possible outcomes $= 50$

Probability of drawing a white marble $= \dfrac{\text{favourable}}{\text{possible}}$

$$p \text{ (white)} = \tfrac{0}{50}$$
$$= 0$$

(That is, there is no possible chance of drawing a white marble.)

e) Number of favourable outcomes $= 50$

Number of possible outcomes $= 50$

Probability of drawing a red or black marble $= \dfrac{\text{favourable}}{\text{possible}}$

$$p \text{ (red or black)} = \tfrac{50}{50}$$
$$= 1$$

(That is, it is a certainty that either a red or a black marble is drawn.)

Example 2

Two dice are thrown at the same time. What is the probability that the sum of the two numbers shown is six?

Solution

In this example, the difficulty lies in working out all the possible outcomes. The simplest way to do this is to write down, in order, all the pairs of numbers which could possibly show on the dice. The first number refers to the first die and the second to the other die.

1, 1	2, 1	3, 1	4, 1	<u>5, 1</u>	6, 1
1, 2	2, 2	3, 2	<u>4, 2</u>	5, 2	6, 2
1, 3	2, 3	<u>3, 3</u>	4, 3	5, 3	6, 3
1, 4	<u>2, 4</u>	3, 4	4, 4	5, 4	6, 4
<u>1, 5</u>	2, 5	3, 5	4, 5	5, 5	6, 5
1, 6	2, 6	3, 6	4, 6	5, 6	6, 6

Thus we see that there are 36 possible outcomes, and 5 favourable outcomes.

Probability that the sum of the numbers is 6 $= \dfrac{\text{favourable}}{\text{possible}}$

$$= \tfrac{5}{36}$$

EXERCISE A

1 A bag contains 30 marbles, 25 green ones and 5 red. What is the chance of picking out a green marble?

2 If a letter is taken at random from the word CHRYSANTHEMUM, what is the probability that:
   a) it is a vowel?
   b) it is 'M'?

3 On throwing a die, what is the probability of turning up:
   a) a 6?
   b) a number less than 3?
   c) a number more than 6?
   d) an odd number?

4 If we take a standard pack of 52 playing cards, what is the chance of drawing:
   a) an ace?
   b) the ace of clubs?
   c) a heart?
   d) a king, queen or jack?
   e) a joker?

5 A black card is removed from a pack of cards. What is the probability of drawing:
   a) a black card?
   b) a red queen?
   c) a king?

6 If a number is chosen at random from the numbers 1 to 30 inclusive, what is the chance that a prime number is picked?

7 A box of 2 dozen pencils contains 6 with broken points. What is the probability of picking out one which has not got a broken point?

8 In a car park, there are 100 vehicles, 85 of them are cars, 10 are lorries and 5 are buses. If they are all equally likely to leave, what is the probability of:
a) a bus leaving first?
b) a car leaving second? (If a bus left first.)

9 A box contains 50 coloured pencils, 20 red, 15 blue and the rest green. What is the chance of drawing:
a) a red pencil?
b) a blue or green pencil?
c) a yellow pencil?
d) a red, blue or green pencil?

10 Two dice are thrown. What are the probabilities that the total score is:
a) 5?
b) 1?
c) 10?
d) 14?
e) less than 13?

11 Two pennies are tossed together. What is the probability of two heads showing?

12 If three pennies are tossed together, what is the chance of:
a) three heads showing?
b) less than 2 tails showing?
c) more than 2 tails showing?

13 A coin and a die are thrown together. What is the probability of:
a) a head and a 3 showing?
b) a tail and a 4 showing?
c) a tail and a 7 showing?

14 A solid regular triangular pyramid (tetrahedron) has the numbers 1, 2, 3 and 4 marked on its 4 faces. If it is thrown like a die, what is the probability that:
a) the 1 face lands downwards?
b) the sum of the three faces showing is an odd number?

15 If 2 tetrahedrons like the one in the last question are thrown together, what is the chance that:
a) the sum of the numbers face down is odd?

b) the sum of the numbers face down is a prime number?

16 If a tetrahedron and a coin are thrown together, what is the probability of getting:
a) an odd number and a head showing?
b) a multiple of 2 and a tail?

17 A die and 2 coins are tossed together. What is the chance of obtaining:
a) 2 heads and an even number?
b) 1 head, 1 tail and a number divisible by 3?
c) 2 tails and a number less than 3?
d) 1 head, 1 tail and a number greater than 3?

18 A pair of dice and a penny are thrown together. Find the probability of:
a) a head and a total score of 7 showing.
b) a tail and a total score greater than 10 showing.
c) a tail and a total score less than 13 showing.

19 Four coins are tossed together. What is the probability of obtaining 4 heads?

20 Considering Question 12 and Question 19 could you calculate the probability of getting 5 heads when 5 coins are tossed together, without making an array of the results?

BETTING ODDS

Betting odds are not based on probabilities and are quite different from the examples studied in the previous section which would be classed as examples of **true odds**. Betting odds are only the measure of the amount that the gambler will win, ignoring betting tax, if he or she has made the correct prediction.

Whereas in true odds we usually start from the premise that events are equally likely to occur, we certainly cannot assume that in a horse race each horse is equally likely to win and we cannot consider experimental probability because no two races are ever run under exactly the same conditions.

Bookmakers can offer any odds they like but fundamentally they study the amount of money which has been bet on each horse and select odds such that the gambler will be attracted to place a bet but will result in a profit no matter which horse wins the race.

For example, if the odds quoted on a particular horse are 10 to 1 it means that if a punter backs that horse and it wins then he or she will win ten pounds for every pound staked. It is normal to quote the odds against a horse winning but it sometimes happens that a horse is believed to be very likely to win and then the odds might be quoted as, say, 3 to 1 **on**. This means that the gambler would win one pound for every three gambled on the horse winning.

Betting odds are not always quoted with the second figure as 1. We can have odds of, say, 5 to 2 which means that the punter could win five pounds for every two pounds staked.

Example 1

Ignoring betting tax, find how much better off a man is after two races if in the first race he placed a bet of £5 on a horse which won at 7 to 2, and in the second race he put £10 on a horse which came in last.

Solution

Profit on first race $= \frac{7}{2} \times £5 = £17.50$.
Loss on second race $= £10$.
Profit on the two races $= £7.50$.

Example 2

Bets amounting to a total of £500 have been placed with the bookmaker Honest Joe for the various horses in a race. Of these bets a total of £50 has been bet on a horse called Slowcoach. If Joe plans a profit of £50 on the race find the odds which he should offer for Slowcoach.

Solution

Amount available for payout
$= £500 - £50$ (profit) $- £50$
(winners' stakes returned)
$= £400$
Odds available $= 400 \div 50$ to 1
$= 8$ to 1

EXERCISE B

1 Find the profit made by a woman who places a bet of £5 on a horse which wins at 5 to 1 in the first race and another bet of £5 on a horse which wins the second race at 2 to 1 on. (Ignore betting tax.)

2 Find the total amount received by a punter who places a bet of £5 on a horse which wins the first race at 6 to 1 and then places the original stake and the winnings on a horse which wins the second race at 3 to 2. (Ignore betting tax.)

3 If the gambler in question 2 had, in the third race, placed all of the money got back from the previous two races, including the stake money, on a horse which was offered at 4 to 1 but did not win, find the gambler's total gain or loss on the three races.

4 Mario staked £5 on Thunder in one race at 4 to 1 and £10 on Lightning in another race at 5 to 2 on. List all of the possible outcomes of the two races and for each calculate the total profit or loss on the two bets.

5 A bookmaker is carrying bets amounting to £400 on a race. If horse A is quoted at 5 to 1 and horse B is at 7 to 2, and of the £400, £60 is bet on horse A and £100 on horse B find her profit or loss on the race if:
a) horse A wins.
b) horse B wins.

Mutually exclusive events

In some situations two events cannot occur at the same time. These events are **mutually exclusive**. For example, we could consider the probability of getting a 5 or a multiple of 3 when we roll a die. The probability of getting a five is $\frac{1}{6}$ and the probability of getting a multiple of three is $\frac{2}{6}$, while the probability of getting either a five or a multiple of three is $\frac{3}{6} = \frac{1}{6} + \frac{2}{6}$.

Generalising this position: if we have two mutually exclusive events A and B, then the probability that A or B will occur is equal to the probability that A will occur plus the probability that B will occur.

$$p(\textbf{A or B}) = p(\textbf{A}) + p(\textbf{B})$$

This law is known as the **addition law of probability** and it can be extended to cover three or more mutually exclusive events. If A, B and C are mutually exclusive events then:

$$p(\text{A or B or C}) = p(\text{A}) + p(\text{B}) + p(\text{C})$$

General addition law

The addition law can be extended to cover events which are not mutually exclusive. We could take as an example of this the probability of getting either a multiple of two or a multiple of three when we roll a die.

Probability of getting a multiple of $2 = \frac{3}{6}$

Probability of getting a multiple of $3 = \frac{2}{6}$

Probability of getting either a multiple of 2 or of $3 = \frac{4}{6}$

$$= \frac{3}{6} + \frac{2}{6} - \frac{1}{6}$$

where the $\frac{1}{6}$ is the probability of getting a 6 which came into both of the previous fractions. The **general addition law** can be stated as:

$$p(\textbf{A or B}) = p(\textbf{A}) + p(\textbf{B}) - p(\textbf{A and B})$$

Exhaustive events

If a situation has only a limited number of possible outcomes then these outcomes are said to form a set of **exhaustive outcomes**. If we refer to the tossing of a coin then there are only the two possible outcomes – a head or a tail – and we know that:

$$p(\text{head}) + p(\text{tail}) = 1$$

In general if an experiment has only three possible mutually exclusive outcomes A, B and C then:

$$p(\text{A}) + p(\text{B}) + p(\text{C}) = 1$$

It is useful to remember that the above equation can be varied by transposing one or more terms to give results such as:

$$p(\text{A}) = 1 - p(\text{B}) - p(\text{C})$$

or

$$p(\text{A or B}) = 1 - p(\text{C})$$

Independent events

When the probabilities of certain events occurring are quite unconnected to one another, these events are said to be **independent events**. For example, if a coin and a die are tossed at the same time, the probabilities of getting a head with the coin and a 6 with the die are quite independent of each other.

The probability of a head and a 6 at the same time $= p(\text{H}) \times p(6)$, that is:

$$p(\text{H}) \times p(6) = \frac{1}{2} \times \frac{1}{6} = \frac{1}{12}$$

This can be checked by listing an array of the possible results:

H,1 H,2 H,3 H,4 H,5 H,6
T,1 T,2 T,3 T,4 T,5 T,6

$$p(\text{H and 6}) = \frac{1}{12}$$

In general, if A and B are independent events, then:

$$p(\text{A and B}) = p(\text{A}) \times p(\text{B})$$

This result is known as the **multiplication law of probability** and can be extended so that if A, B and C are independent events, then:

$$p(A \text{ and } B \text{ and } C) = p(A) \times p(B) \times p(C)$$

DEPENDENT EVENTS

If two events A and B are not independent then the probability that the second event occurs depends upon whether or not the first event occurred.

In this situation the multiplication law is amended to give:

$$p(A \text{ and } B) = p(A) \times p(B \text{ given } A)$$

As an example of **dependent events** we can consider a box of 10 pencils, four with broken points. If we select two pencils in order, then the probability that they will both have broken points is:

$$p(\text{both broken}) = \tfrac{4}{10} \times \tfrac{3}{9} = \tfrac{2}{15}$$

Example 1

A tetrahedron with its sides numbered 1, 2, 3, 4 and a die are rolled together. What is the probability of getting:
a) a 4 on the tetrahedron and a 4 on the die?
b) an odd number on the tetrahedron and an even number on the die?

Solution

(These are independent events.)
a) $p(4 \text{ on tetrahedron and 4 on die})$

$$= p(4 \text{ on tetrahedron}) \times p(4 \text{ on die})$$
$$= \tfrac{1}{4} \times \tfrac{1}{6} = \tfrac{1}{24}$$

b) $p(\text{odd number on tetrahedron and even number on die})$

$$= p(\text{odd number on tetrahedron}) \times p(\text{even number on die})$$
$$= \tfrac{1}{2} \times \tfrac{1}{2} = \tfrac{1}{4}$$

Example 2

C and D are two mutually exclusive events with probabilities $\tfrac{1}{5}$ and $\tfrac{1}{10}$ (there are obviously *more* than two possible outcomes).
Calculate:
a) the probability of either C or D occurring.
b) the probability of neither C nor D occurring.

Solution

a) $p(C \text{ or } D) = p(C) + p(D) = \tfrac{1}{5} + \tfrac{1}{10} = \tfrac{3}{10}$

b) $p(\text{not C or D}) = 1 - \tfrac{3}{10} = \tfrac{7}{10}$

Example 3

In an experiment there are three possible outcomes, A, B or C. If $p(A) = \tfrac{1}{5}$ and $p(B) = \tfrac{1}{4}$, calculate:
a) $p(C)$.
b) the probability that either A or C occurs.

Solution

a) $p(C) = 1 - [p(A) + p(B)]$

$$= 1 - (\tfrac{1}{5} + \tfrac{1}{4}) = 1 - \tfrac{9}{20} = \tfrac{11}{20}$$

b) $p(A \text{ or } C) = p(A) + p(C)$
$$= \tfrac{1}{5} + \tfrac{11}{20} = \tfrac{15}{20} = \tfrac{3}{4}$$

Example 4

A spinner with 12 sides, numbered 1 to 12, is spun once. What is the probability of getting:
a) a multiple of 3?
b) a multiple of 4?
c) a multiple of 3 or 4?

Solution

a) $p(\text{a multiple of 3}) = \tfrac{4}{12}$
$$= \tfrac{1}{3}$$

b) $p(\text{a multiple of 4}) = \tfrac{3}{12}$
$$= \tfrac{1}{4}$$

123

c) p(a multiple of 3 or 4) $= p$(a multiple of 3) $+ p$(a multiple of 4) $- p$(a multiple of 3 and 4)

$$= \tfrac{4}{12} + \tfrac{3}{12} - \tfrac{1}{12}$$
$$= \tfrac{1}{2}$$

Example 5

A class consists of 20 boys and 10 girls. Two pupils are selected at random. What is the probability that both are boys?

Solution

p(both boys) $= p$(1st choice is a boy) $\times p$(2nd choice is a boy given that a boy has already been chosen)

$$= \tfrac{20}{30} \times \tfrac{19}{29}$$
$$= \tfrac{38}{87}$$

EXERCISE C

1 If a coin and a die are tossed together, calculate:
  a) the probability of getting a tail with the coin and an even number with the die.
  b) the probability of a head with the coin and a number less than three on the die.
  c) the probability of a head with the coin and a multiple of 3 on the die.

2 The sides of a die are marked with the numbers 2, 2, 4, 4, 6, 6. If the die is rolled twice what is the probability of getting:
  a) a 4 each time?
  b) either a 2 or a 6 each time?
  If the die is rolled three times, what is the probability of getting
  c) a 2 each time?
  d) either a 4 or a 6 each time?

3 There are two spinners, one marked into equal sections numbered 1, 2, 3, 4, 5 and the second one marked into equal sections A, B, C. Calculate the probability of getting:
  a) a 2 and a B.
  b) a 5 and an A.
  c) an even number and an A.
  d) an odd number and either B or C.

4 In an experiment there are three possible outcomes, A, B and C. If $p(A) = \tfrac{1}{3}$ and $p(B) = \tfrac{1}{4}$, calculate:
  a) $p(C)$.
  b) the probability that either A or C occurs.

5 P, Q, R and S are four mutually exclusive events with:

$p(P) = \tfrac{1}{10}, p(Q) = \tfrac{1}{5}, p(R) = \tfrac{1}{4}, p(S) = \tfrac{1}{3}$

Calculate the probability of:
  a) either P or Q occurring.
  b) either Q or S occurring.
  c) neither R nor S occurring.
  d) neither P nor S occurring.

6 A, B, C and D are the four possible outcomes of an experiment.

$p(A) = \tfrac{1}{7}, p(C) = \tfrac{1}{3}, p(D) = \tfrac{1}{2}$

Calculate:
  a) $p(B)$.
  b) the probability of either A or D occurring.
  c) the probability that neither B nor C occurs.
  d) the probability that C or D occurs.
  e) the probability that neither A nor C occurs.

7 A bag contains ten balls numbered 1 to 10. A ball is selected at random from the bag. What is the probability of getting:
  a) a multiple of 2?
  b) a multiple of 5?
  c) a multiple of 2 or 5?

8 What is the probability of throwing 6 tails in 6 tosses of a coin?

9 A box contains 10 black pens and 12 blue pens. Two pens are selected at random from the box. What is the probability that both pens are black?

10 What is the probability of obtaining a total of two with two throws of a die?

11 There are three spinners, the first marked into four equal sections numbered 1, 2, 3 and 4, the second is marked into three equal sections coloured red, blue and yellow, and the third has five equal sections A, B, C, D and E. Calculating the probability of getting:

a) a 3, blue and D.
b) an even number, red and A.
c) a 1, red and E.
d) an odd number, yellow and a vowel.
e) a prime number, either red or blue and a B.

TREE DIAGRAMS

A **tree diagram** is a good way of breaking down a **compound event** into an ordered set of **simple events**. Each branch of the tree should illustrate one possible outcome of the compound event and the tree is a very good way to illustrate the event to ensure that every possible outcome has been included.

Example 1

Consider a box of 10 pens, 6 of them black and 4 red. If two of the pens are selected from the box, in turn, without replacement we can illustrate all of the possible outcomes in a tree diagram. If we position the probability of each happening on the appropriate part of the branch we can use the tree diagram to evaluate the probability of each of the possible outcomes (Figure 9.2).

$p(\text{2 black pens}) = \frac{6}{10} \times \frac{5}{9} = \frac{1}{3}$

$p(\text{2 red pens}) = \frac{4}{10} \times \frac{3}{9} = \frac{2}{15}$

$p(\text{one of each colour}) = (\frac{6}{10} \times \frac{4}{9}) + (\frac{4}{10} \times \frac{6}{9})$

$= \frac{24}{90} + \frac{24}{90}$

$= \frac{48}{90}$

$= \frac{8}{15}$

Example 2

Tom and Gino play a tennis match which is the best of three sets. If the probability of Tom winning any one set is $\frac{1}{3}$ and the probability of Gino winning any one set is $\frac{2}{3}$, find the probability that Tom wins the match.

There are three ways in which Tom can win the match (Figure 9.3). If he wins sets 1 and 2 the match finishes at that point, or he can win sets 1 and 3, or sets 2 and 3. So the probability that Tom wins the match

$= (\frac{1}{3} \times \frac{1}{3}) + (\frac{1}{3} \times \frac{2}{3} \times \frac{1}{3}) + (\frac{2}{3} \times \frac{1}{3} \times \frac{1}{3})$

$= \frac{1}{9} + \frac{2}{27} + \frac{2}{27}$

$= \frac{7}{27}$

Fig. 9.2

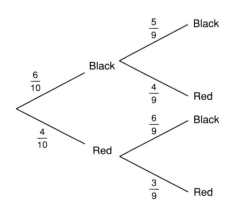

Fig. 9.3

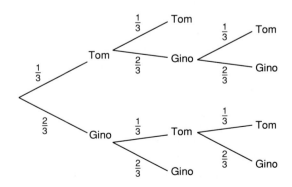

125

1 A box contains 12 cards, five of which are plain and seven are patterned. Two cards are selected in turn without replacement. Illustrate the outcomes in a tree diagram and find the probability that:
   a) both cards are plain.
   b) both cards are patterned.
   c) one card of each type has been chosen.

2 A box contains ten cards of which two are red and eight black. Three cards are chosen in turn without replacement. Illustrate the possible outcomes in a tree diagram and find the probability that:
   a) all three cards are black.
   b) one black and two red cards were selected.

3 In a snooker match which was the best of three frames between Hans and Serge the probability of Hans winning either of the first two frames was $\frac{2}{5}$ but if the match goes to a third frame the probability of each winning that final frame is $\frac{1}{2}$. Find the probability that Hans wins the match and illustrate the solution in a tree diagram.

4 A box contains 10 pencils of which 5 are black, 4 red and 1 blue. Three pencils are drawn in succession without replacement. Illustrate the outcomes in a tree diagram and find the probability that:
   a) all the pencils are red.
   b) one pencil of each colour has been selected.
   c) the blue pencil has not been selected.

CALCULATING EXPECTED FREQUENCIES

The idea of calculating expected frequencies was introduced earlier in the chapter, in the experimental work.

If the probability of a head turning up when a coin is tossed is $\frac{1}{2}$, then when a coin is tossed 10 times you could expect 5 heads to show.

If the probability of obtaining a 6 when a die is thrown is $\frac{1}{6}$, then in 60 throws of a die you could expect $\frac{1}{6}$ of 60 or 10 sixes to show.

The expected frequency = probability of the event happening × number of trials.

Example

A die is thrown 50 times. What is the expected frequency of an even number turning up?

$$\text{Probability of an even number} = \frac{\text{favourable}}{\text{possible}}$$

$$p(\text{even}) = \frac{3}{6}$$
$$= \frac{1}{2}$$

The expected frequency of even numbers $= \frac{1}{2}$ of 50
$$= 25$$

1 If a coin is tossed 100 times, how many tails might you expect to turn up?

2 When a die is thrown 60 times, what is the expected frequency of:
   a) a number less than 4 showing?
   b) a number less than 7 showing?
   c) a factor of 6 showing?

3 If a tetrahedron, with its faces marked 1 to 4, is thrown 80 times, how many times would you expect:
   a) the two-face to be down?
   b) the sum of the faces showing to be more than 7?

4 Two tetrahedrons are thrown 160 times. How many times would you expect the sum of the 2 faces that land downward to be an odd number?

5 What is the expected frequency of two heads showing, if 2 coins are tossed together 80 times?

6 A pack of cards is shuffled and then a card is drawn. This card is replaced and the experiment is repeated another 149 times. Approximately how many times would you expect to pick:
a) a face card?
b) a black card?

7 A town has 1250 children under the age of 10 years who have never had chickenpox. If it is known, from experience, that the probability of a child under 10 catching chickenpox is 0.16, how many of these children would you expect to take chickenpox?

8 In a certain town, 10% of the car drivers have some kind of accident, however slight, in a year's driving. If there are 3672 drivers in the town, what is the expected number of accidents in the coming year?

9 If the probability of school children having defective hearing is 0.08, how many pupils in a school of 1000 could be expected to have defective hearing?

10 Imagine the chance of a footballer breaking a leg during a football season is 0.15. If 60 players sign on with a club at the start of the season, how many of them are likely to break a leg during the season?

11 If the probability that a child has taken measles by the age of 12 is 0.6, how many of the 300 children aged 12 in a school could be expected not to have had measles?

EXERCISE F   Miscellaneous ——————

1 A firm produced the following breakdown of their employees and the occurrence of accidents during the past year (no employee had more than one accident during the year).
a) Calculate the total number of employees.
b) If a member of staff is chosen at random find the probability that he/she is
   i) in production staff and had a minor accident

	Number of staff with:		
	no accident	a minor accident	a serious accident
Production staff	356	43	3
Maintenance staff	24	5	1
Office staff	66	2	0

   ii) in office staff and had a serious accident
   iii) in production or maintenance staff and had an accident of some nature.

2 When a certain coin is tossed the probability of getting a head is 0.6. For this coin find
a) the probability of getting a tail.
b) the probability of getting 2 heads if the coin is tossed twice.
c) the probability of getting at least one head if the coin is tossed twice.
d) the expected number of heads if the coin is tossed 60 times.

3 Explain why the following statements cannot all be true. (P, Q and R are three mutually exclusive results of an experiment.)
The probability of P happening = 0.3
The probability of Q happening = 0.4
The probability of R happening = 0.5

4 Of the 24 pupils in a class, 8 of them use public transport to come to school.
a) What is the probability that:
   i) If a sample of 2 pupils is taken both of them use public transport to come to school?
   ii) If a sample of 2 pupils is taken at most one of them uses public transport to come to school?
   iii) If a sample of 3 pupils is taken none of them uses public transport to come to school?
b) On a particular day only 75% of the class are present. If a pupil is chosen at random find the probability that he/she

127

was present that day and came to school by public transport.

5 It is estimated that three in ten people in Britain go abroad for their holiday.
  a) Calculate the probability that:
    i) If three people are interviewed at random none of them went abroad on holiday last year
    ii) If three people are interviewed at random at least one of them went abroad on holiday last year.
  b) If 100 samples each of three people were taken, how often would we expect to find that all three of the people in the sample had gone abroad on holiday last year?

6 Two fair six-sided dice are thrown at the same time.
  a) Find the probability that the sum of the scores is:
    i) 2   iv) 5
    ii) 3   v) 6.
    iii) 4
  b) If the two dice are thrown 100 times, calculate how often we would expect to get a total score of:
    i) 2   vii) 8
    ii) 3   viii) 9
    iii) 4   ix) 10
    iv) 5   x) 11
    v) 6   xi) 12.
    vi) 7

```
          1  1
        1  2  1
      1  3  3  1
    1  4  6  4  1
  1  5  10  10  5  1
1  6  15  20  15  6  1
1  7  21  35  35  21  7  1
```

10 THE BINOMIAL DISTRIBUTION

The word binomial contains the prefix *bi* meaning two. In the binomial distribution we are concerned with *two* possible events occurring. If a coin is tossed, it will come down either heads or tails. If you go out in the street, the next person you meet will be either male or female. Next Tuesday will either be your birthday or not. In each case there are two possibilities.

If we decide which of the two possibilities is desirable, then there is a probability of its happening and a probability of its not happening. In statistics, we normally say that the probability of a certain event happening is *p* and of its not happening is *q*.

Suppose we have a bag containing 100 balls, some red and some white. If there are 50 of each colour, we have an equal chance of drawing a white one or a red one. Thus the probability of obtaining a red ball is 50% or $\frac{1}{2}$ or 0.5, and the probability of obtaining a white one is the same. The two probabilities add up to 1.

Let us now suppose that in the bag there are 90 red balls and 10 white ones. The probability of drawing a red one is now $\frac{90}{100}$ or $\frac{9}{10}$ or 0.9, and the probability of failing to draw a red one is $\frac{10}{100}$ or $\frac{1}{10}$ or 0.1. Again the two probabilities add up to 1.

If *p* is the probability of drawing a red ball and *q* is the probability of not drawing a red ball, then in each of the above cases, we can say:

$$p + q = 1$$

Consider another example. A school caretaker was clearing out old text books and put a large number of English books and geography books into the same sack, 30% of the books were English books and the rest geography books.

Let *p* = probability of picking out an English book.

Let *q* = probability of picking out a geography book.

In this case,

$$p = \frac{30}{100} \text{ or } \frac{3}{10} \text{ or } 0.3$$

and

$$q = \frac{70}{100} \text{ or } \frac{7}{10} \text{ or } 0.7$$

Again $p + q = 1$ if we select one book. Suppose we want to pick out two books. This time there are four possible outcomes: 2 English books, 1 English book followed by 1 geography book, 1 geography book followed by 1 English book or 2 geography books. The probabilities of the various possible outcomes are thus given by the formulae $p \times p$, $p \times q$, $q \times p$, $q \times q$ and we can note that these terms can be further grouped as p^2, $2pq$, q^2 where p^2 is the probability of getting two English books, $2pq$ is the probability of getting one of each kind and q^2 is the probability of getting two geography books. Since these are the only possible outcomes of our experiment their total must be 1 and thus we note that the terms of the formula
$$(p + q)^2 = p^2 + 2pq + q^2 = 1$$
give the probabilities of the various outcomes of carrying out the experiment twice.

If we extend the above to the selection, in turn, of three books we have the position whereby each of the above results can be followed by the selection of an English or a geography book. Thus the probability of selecting three English books is $p \times p \times p = p^3$. Secondly, there are three ways in which we can select two English and one geography book: the geography one can be selected either first, second or third, and the probabilities of these various outcomes are $q \times p \times p$, $p \times q \times p$, $p \times p \times q$ and the total of these three terms, namely $3p^2 q$ gives the probability of selecting two English and one geography book. Similarly we can show that the probability of selecting one English and two geography books is $3pq^2$ and of selecting three geography books is q^3. The probabilities of the various possible outcomes of three trials are given by the expansion:

$$(p + q)^3 = p^3 + 3p^2 q + 3pq^2 + q^3 = 1.$$

This concept can be extended and thus the probabilities of the various outcomes of n trials of an experiment are given by the terms of the expansion of $(p + q)^n$.

EXPANSION OF $(p + q)^n$

When dealing with low values of n it is reasonable to do the actual multiplications from first principles but for higher values it is essential that we look for a better technique.

If we consider the first few of the expansions of $(p + q)^n$ we obtain the following expansions:

$(p + q)^1 = p + q$
$(p + q)^2 = p^2 + 2pq + q^2$
$(p + q)^3 = p^3 + 3p^2 q + 3pq^2 + q^3$
$(p + q)^4 = p^4 + 4p^3 q + 6p^2 q^2 + 4pq^3 + q^4$

A study of permutations and combinations may lead us to see that the coefficients of the terms in these expansions can be written in terms of the ^nC_r symbols, for example:

$$(p + q)^4 = p^4 + {}^4C_1 p^3 q + {}^4C_2 p^2 q^2 + {}^4C_3 pq^3 + {}^4C_4 q^4$$

and this can lead us to the assumption that the general expansion is:

$$(p + q)^n = p^n + {}^nC_1 p^{n-1} q + {}^nC_2 p^{n-2} q^2 + \ldots + {}^nC_r p^{n-r} q^r + \ldots {}^nC_n q^n$$

We shall now proceed to prove the truth of this expansion by means of induction. Let us assume that the formula is true for some value of n, say $n = m$, that is, we assume that:

$$(p + q)^m = p^m + {}^mC_1 p^{m-1} q + {}^mC_2 p^{m-2} q^2 + \ldots + {}^mC_r p^{m-r} q^r + \ldots {}^mC_m q^m.$$

then,

$$(p + q)^{m+1} = (p + q)^m (p + q)$$
$$= (p^m + {}^mC_1 p^{m-1} q + {}^mC_2 p^{m-2} q^2 + \ldots + {}^mC_{r-1} p^{m-r+1} q^{r-1} + {}^mC_r p^{m-r} q^r + \ldots + {}^mC_m q^m)(p + q)$$

It is impossible for us to carry out this multiplication for the general case but we can consider individual terms of the product. Let us take as our general term the one which involves q^r. We shall obtain two terms in the product which involve q^r and these will be obtained from the product of ${}^mC_{r-1} p^{m-r+1} q^{r-1}$ and q and the product of ${}^mC_r p^{m-r} q^r$ and p. Thus the general term in the product is:

$${}^mC_{r-1} p^{m-r+1} q^r + {}^mC_r p^{m-r+1} q^r$$
$$= ({}^mC_{r-1} + {}^mC_r) p^{m-r+1} q^r$$
$$= {}^{m+1}C_r p^{m+1-r} q^r$$

(Note that it can be proved that

$${}^mC_{r-1} + {}^mC_r = {}^{m+1}C_r)$$

Applying this result to all of the terms of our products we obtain:

$$(p + q)^{m+1} = p^{m+1} + {}^{m+1}C_1 p^m q + {}^{m+1}C_2 p^{m-1} q^2 + \ldots + {}^{m+1}C_r p^{m+1-r} q^r + \ldots + {}^{m+1}C_{m+1} q^{m+1}.$$

That is, if the expansion is true for $n = m$ then it is also true for $n = m + 1$, but the expansion was true for $n = 1$ and by the above it must thus be true for $n = 1 + 1 = 2$. Since it is true for $n = 2$ by the above it must also be true for $n = 2 + 1 = 3$ and by continuing this argument we can obviously prove the rule true for all positive integer values of n.

Thus for all positive integer values of n we have that:

$$(p + q)^n = p^n + {}^nC_1 p^{n-1} q + {}^nC_2 p^{n-2} q^2$$
$$+ \ldots + {}^nC_r p^{n-r} q^r + \ldots + {}^nC_n q^n.$$

and in this expansion the term ${}^nC_r p^{n-r} q^r$ gives the probability of getting $n - r$ successes and r failures in n trials of an experiment.

PASCAL'S TRIANGLE

As some students may find the algebra of the previous section to be beyond the level of their interest we can now look at the number pattern known as Pascal's triangle and use it to obtain the coefficients of $(p + q)^n$. This pattern of numbers is built up and can be proved a valid method of obtaining the coefficients by the same methods as we used in the last section.

It will be seen that each term in the triangle is found by adding together the two terms in the line above which lie on either side of it.

It may already have become obvious that the number of different combinations is always 1 greater than the number of trials of the experiment. For example, if we wish to pick out 6 books together, there are 7 possible different combinations of English and geography books. (Work out the combinations and check for yourself.)

Pascal's triangle, as stated, gives the coefficients of the terms in the expansion of $(p + q)^n$:

$$(p + q)^1 = 1p + 1q$$
$$(p + q)^2 = 1p^2 + 2pq + 1q^2$$
$$(p + q)^3 = 1p^3 + 3p^2 q + 3pq^2 + 1q^3$$
$$(p + q)^4 = 1p^4 + 4p^3 q + 6p^2 q^2 + 4pq^3 + 1q^4$$
etc.   etc.

The way in which Pascal's triangle is used is shown in the following examples.

Example 1

In a certain collection of bulbs 80% are daffodils and the rest are narcissi. Calculate the probability of obtaining 0, 1, 2, 3, and 4 narcissi in a group of 4 bulbs.

Solution

$p = \frac{4}{5} =$ daffodils

$q = \frac{1}{5} =$ narcissi

With 4 bulbs, the expansion is $(p + q)^4 = 1$. The coefficients from Pascal's triangle are 1, 4, 6, 4, 1.

Thus,
$$(p + q)^4 = p^4 + 4p^3 q + 6p^2 q^2 + 4pq^3 + q^4$$

By substituting $p = \frac{4}{5}$ and $q = \frac{1}{5}$, we get
a) $p(0 \text{ narcissus}) = p^4 \quad = \frac{4}{5} \times \frac{4}{5} \times \frac{4}{5} \times \frac{4}{5} = \frac{256}{625}$

	Pascal's Triangle	
Number of trials (n)	Coefficients in the expansion of $(p + q)^n$	Number of different combinations
1	1 1	2
2	1 2 1	3
3	1 3 3 1	4
4	1 4 6 4 1	5
5	1 5 10 10 5 1	6
6	1 6 15 20 15 6 1	7
7	1 7 21 35 35 21 7 1	8
8		9
etc.	etc.	etc.

b) $p(1 \text{ narcissus}) = 4p^3q$
$$= \tfrac{4}{1} \times \tfrac{4}{5} \times \tfrac{4}{5} \times \tfrac{4}{5} \times \tfrac{1}{5} = \tfrac{256}{625}$$

c) $p(2 \text{ narcissi}) = 6p^2q^2$
$$= \tfrac{6}{1} \times \tfrac{4}{5} \times \tfrac{4}{5} \times \tfrac{1}{5} \times \tfrac{1}{5} = \tfrac{96}{625}$$

d) $p(3 \text{ narcissi}) = 4pq^3$
$$= \tfrac{4}{1} \times \tfrac{4}{5} \times \tfrac{1}{5} \times \tfrac{1}{5} \times \tfrac{1}{5} = \tfrac{16}{625}$$

e) $p(4 \text{ narcissi}) = q^4 \quad = \tfrac{1}{5} \times \tfrac{1}{5} \times \tfrac{1}{5} \times \tfrac{1}{5} = \tfrac{1}{625}$

Check: $(p + q)^4$ must equal 1:

$$\tfrac{256}{625} + \tfrac{256}{625} + \tfrac{96}{625} + \tfrac{16}{625} + \tfrac{1}{625} = \tfrac{625}{625} = 1$$

Example 2

If 6 pennies are tossed together, what is the probability of 6 tails occurring?

Solution

$p = \tfrac{1}{2} = $ heads

$q = \tfrac{1}{2} = $ tails

With 6 pennies, the expansion is:

$$(p + q)^6 = 1$$

From Pascal's triangle, the relevant coefficients are 1, 6, 15, 20, 15, 6, 1.

Thus,
$$(p + q)^6 = p^6 + 6p^5q + 15p^4q^2$$
$$+ 20p^3q^3 + 15p^2q^4 + 6pq^5 + q^6$$

q^6 represents 6 tails.

Probability of 6 tails $= q^6 = (\tfrac{1}{2})^6$
$$= \tfrac{1}{2} \times \tfrac{1}{2} \times \tfrac{1}{2} \times \tfrac{1}{2} \times \tfrac{1}{2} \times \tfrac{1}{2}$$
$$= \tfrac{1}{64}$$

Example 3

In a certain community $\tfrac{2}{3}$ of the residents are regular TV viewers. Fifty investigators are sent out to interview 5 people each.
a) Calculate the probability that 4 or more people out of the 5, are regular viewers.
b) How many investigators would you expect to report that 4 or more people viewed TV only occasionally?

Solution

$p = \tfrac{2}{3} = $ regular TV viewers

$q = \tfrac{1}{3} = $ non-viewers or occasional viewers

With 5 people, the expansion is $(p + q)^5 = 1$.

From Pascal's triangle, the coefficients are 1, 5, 10, 10, 5, 1.

Thus the expansion is:

$$(p + q)^5 = p^5 + 5p^4q + 10p^3q^2 + 10p^2q^3$$
$$+ 5pq^4 + q^5$$

a) $p(4 \text{ viewers}) = 5p^4q$
$$= \tfrac{5}{1} \times \tfrac{2}{3} \times \tfrac{2}{3} \times \tfrac{2}{3} \times \tfrac{2}{3} \times \tfrac{1}{3} = \tfrac{80}{243}$$
$p(5 \text{ viewers}) = p^5 = \tfrac{2}{3} \times \tfrac{2}{3} \times \tfrac{2}{3} \times \tfrac{2}{3} \times \tfrac{2}{3} = \tfrac{32}{243}$
$p(4 \text{ or more viewers}) \quad = \tfrac{80}{243} + \tfrac{32}{244} = \tfrac{112}{243}$

b) $p(4 \text{ non-viewers}) = 5pq^4$
$$= \tfrac{5}{1} \times \tfrac{2}{3} \times \tfrac{1}{3} \times \tfrac{1}{3} \times \tfrac{1}{3} \times \tfrac{1}{3} = \tfrac{10}{243}$$
$p(5 \text{ non-viewers}) = q^5$
$$= \tfrac{1}{3} \times \tfrac{1}{3} \times \tfrac{1}{3} \times \tfrac{1}{3} \times \tfrac{1}{3} = \tfrac{1}{243}$$
$p(4 \text{ or more non-viewers}) = \tfrac{10}{243} + \tfrac{1}{243} = \tfrac{11}{243}$
Expected number of investigators
$$= \tfrac{11}{243} \times \tfrac{50}{1}$$
$$= \tfrac{550}{243} = 2.3 = \text{approximately } 2$$

PRACTICAL WORK

EXPERIMENT 1
The frequency of heads when six coins are tossed together
For the experiment divide yourselves into groups of 6 pupils, each pupil having a coin to toss.

Copy this table into your jotter.

Number of trials = 64

No. of heads	Tally	Total
0		
1		
2		
3		
4		
5		
6		

All 6 members of the group should toss their coins at the same time and count up the number of heads showing, recording this in the table. Repeat this process until 64 trials in all have been completed.

Let us compare these experimental frequencies with the expected frequencies. Calculate the expected frequencies of 0, 1, 2, 3, 4, 5 and 6 heads, when 6 coins are tossed simultaneously 64 times, by using the binomial expansion of $(p + q)^6$.

Complete this table.

Number of heads	0 1 2 3 4 5 6
Experimental frequency	
Theoretical frequency	

Using this frequency table draw frequency polygons on the same graph for the experimental and theoretical frequencies of the number of heads showing when 6 coins are tossed together.

Compare your graph with the graphs of the other groups.

Make up another frequency table for experimental and theoretical results by totalling up the results of all the groups, and draw a graph as before. Compare this graph with your first one.

What conclusions do you reach about the distributions and in particular about the symmetry of them?

EXPERIMENT 2 —————————

The frequency of sixes when four dice are rolled together
This experiment may be done either by individuals or by groups of two or three pupils.

Copy this table into your book.

Number of trials = 72

Number of sixes	Tally	Total
0		
1		
2		
3		
4		

Roll 4 dice together, 72 times in all, tallying the number of sixes obtained each time and record the results in the table.

Now, calculate the expected frequencies of 0, 1, 2, 3, and 4 sixes when 4 dice are rolled together, 72 times, using the binomial expansion of $(p + q)^4$.

Fill in the results in the following table.

Number of sixes	0 1 2 3 4
Experimental frequency	
Theoretical frequency	

Draw, on the same graph, frequency polygons for these experimental and theoretical frequencies of 0, 1, 2, 3, and 4 sixes showing when 4 dice are rolled together. (For this graph consider your vertical scale carefully.)

Compare your graph with the graphs of the other members of the class.

As in Experiment 1, form another frequency table by adding up all the results for the class. Draw a graph for these frequencies. Compare this graph with your previous one.

What do you notice about the symmetry of this distribution? Consider the second graph of Experiment 1. What reasons can you give for points of similarity or difference?

FURTHER EXPERIMENTS —————————

Various other experiments may be devised and carried out along the same lines as the above experiments.

133

Several pairs of dice may be rolled at the same time.

Several sets of dice may be rolled and a coin may be tossed simultaneously.

A tetrahedron with its faces numbered may be rolled in the same way as a die.

Several pairs of tetrahedrons may be thrown at the same time.

1 On the average, a marksman firing at a target hits the bull's-eye once in three shots. If he fires 6 times, what are the chances that he will hit the bull's-eye:
   a) twice? **b)** 4 times? **c)** not at all?

2 Another marksman, on average, hits the target 2 out of 3 times. In 4 shots what are his chances of hitting it 0, 1, 2, 3, or 4 times?

3 What is the probability of getting 4 heads in 8 tosses of a coin?

4 A shipment of oranges contains 10% bad ones. A random sample of 4 oranges is drawn from the shipment. Calculate the probability that the sample contains 0, 1, 2, 3 and 4 bad oranges.

5 In 10 throws of a coin what is the probability of obtaining 8 or more heads or tails?

6 In a certain large collection of plants, $\frac{2}{3}$ are single-flowered varieties and the rest are double-flowered. Calculate the probability of obtaining 0, 1, 2, 3, and 4 double-flowered plants in a row of 4 plants.

7 Fatima's chance of winning a set at tennis against David is $\frac{3}{4}$. Find her chance of winning at least 3 sets in a 5 set match assuming that all 5 sets are to be played.

8 An opinion poll finds that 3 out of 5 people are in favour of a certain proposal. What is the probability, that, if 3 people are taken at random, there will be a majority against the proposal?

9 In a certain town, the proportion of rainy to fine days in the month of June is 1 to 3. Assuming that each day is independent of the others, what is the chance that a week in June, in that town, will have:
   a) no wet days? **b)** 3 wet days?

10 From a box containing 6 white balls and 4 black balls, 3 balls are drawn at random. Find the probability that 2 are white and 1 is black.

11 In a certain industry the employees have a 20% chance of contracting an occupational disease. What is the probability that out of 6 employees, 4 or more will contract the disease?

12 What is the probability of throwing at least 3 sevens in 5 throws of a pair of dice?

13 A coin is tossed 6 times. What is the probability of getting:
   a) exactly 3 heads? **b)** at least 3 heads?

14 Seven dice are rolled. Calling a 5 or 6 a success, find the probability of having:
   a) exactly 4 successes.
   b) at most 4 successes.

15 Assuming that the chance of a child being a boy or a girl is $\frac{1}{2}$, what is the probability that in a family of 6 there will be no fewer than 2, or more than 5 boys? What is the chance there will be 3 boys?

16 In a very large batch of nails, 5% are defective. What is the probability of finding at least 1 defective in samples of 5, 10, 15 and 20 respectively?

17 A manufacturer knows that on average 1 out of 10 of his products is defective. What is the probability that a random sample of 4 articles will contain:
   a) no defectives?
   b) exactly 1 defective?
   c) at least 2 defectives?
   d) no more than 3 defectives?

18 In a packet of flower seeds 40% are known to be pink flowering and the remainder white flowering. Calculate the probabilities of 0, 1, 2, 3, 4 or 5 pink flowers in a row of 5 plants. If 500 rows each of 5 plants are planted, approximately how many rows will contain:

a) all pink flowers?
b) all white flowers?

19 In a certain community, 2 out of every 3 houses have a telephone. If 50 investigators each question 4 households selected at random, how many may be expected to report that:
a) only 1 household out of the four does not have a telephone?
b) at least 2 out of the four households have a telephone?

20 One hundred interviewers are told to select 5 people at random and to question them concerning their drinking habits. Assuming that 3 out of 4 people drink alcohol at least occasionally, how many interviewers may be expected to find that:
a) at least 2 people are total abstainers?
b) at least 3 people drink alcohol sometimes?

USING STATISTICAL TABLES

To obtain the required probability in some questions of Exercise A you will have added the probabilities of individual events occurring. Statistical tables exist which will give you cumulative binomial probabilities.

Let us consider 3 examples to illustrate the use of these tables, an example of which is shown below.

Note: The table shown gives the probability of obtaining $n - r$ or more successes in n independent trials, that is,

$$p^n + {}^nC_1 p^{n-1}q + {}^nC_2 p^{n-2}q^2 + \ldots + {}^nC_r p^{n-r}q^r.$$

Example 1

Calling a 7 or 8 a success, find the probability of getting at least 4 successes when an octagonal spinner with sides numbered 1–8 is spun 5 times.

	$p=$	0.05	0.10	0.15	0.20	0.25	0.30	0.35	0.40	0.45	0.50
$n=2$	$n-r=0$	1.0000	1.0000	1.0000	1.0000	1.0000	1.0000	1.0000	1.0000	1.0000	1.0000
	1	0.0975	0.1900	0.2775	0.3600	0.4375	0.5100	0.5775	0.6400	0.6975	0.7500
	2	0.0025	0.0100	0.0225	0.0400	0.0625	0.0900	0.1225	0.1600	0.2025	0.2500
$n=5$	$n-r=0$	1.0000	1.0000	1.0000	1.0000	1.0000	1.0000	1.0000	1.0000	1.0000	1.0000
	1	0.2262	0.4095	0.5563	0.6723	0.7627	0.8319	0.8840	0.9222	0.9497	0.9688
	2	0.0226	0.0815	0.1648	0.2627	0.3672	0.4718	0.5716	0.6630	0.7438	0.8125
	3	0.0012	0.0086	0.0266	0.0579	0.1035	0.1631	0.2352	0.3174	0.4069	0.5000
	4		0.0005	0.0022	0.0067	0.0156	0.0308	0.0540	0.0870	0.1312	0.1875
	5			0.0001	0.0003	0.0010	0.0024	0.0053	0.0102	0.0185	0.0313
$n=10$	$n-r=0$	1.0000	1.0000	1.0000	1.0000	1.0000	1.0000	1.0000	1.0000	1.0000	1.0000
	1	0.4013	0.6513	0.8031	0.8926	0.9437	0.9718	0.9865	0.9940	0.9975	0.9990
	2	0.0861	0.2639	0.4557	0.6242	0.7560	0.8507	0.9140	0.9536	0.9767	0.9893
	3	0.0115	0.0702	0.1798	0.3222	0.4744	0.6172	0.7384	0.8327	0.9004	0.9453
	4	0.0010	0.0128	0.0500	0.1209	0.2241	0.3504	0.4862	0.6177	0.7430	0.8281
	5		0.0016	0.0099	0.0328	0.0781	0.1503	0.2485	0.3669	0.4956	0.6230
	6		0.0001	0.0014	0.0064	0.0197	0.0473	0.0949	0.1662	0.2616	0.3770
	7			0.0001	0.0009	0.0035	0.0106	0.0260	0.0548	0.1020	0.1719
	8				0.0001	0.0004	0.0016	0.0048	0.0123	0.0274	0.0547
	9						0.0001	0.0005	0.0017	0.0045	0.0107
	10								0.0001	0.0003	0.0010

Solution

$p = \frac{2}{8} = 0.25 =$ getting a 7 or an 8.
Spinning 5 times the expansion is:

$$(p + q)^5 = 1$$

Probability of at least 4 successes is given by

$$^5C_0 p^5 + {}^5C_1 p^4 q$$

Previously you would have calculated and then added these two individual probabilities. To use the table we recognise that $n = 5$ and $p = 0.25$ and as the table gives the probability of $n - r$ or more successes then $n - r = 4$. The section of the table we should look at is shown below.

$p =$	0.25
$n = 5$ $n - r = 0$	1.0000
1	0.7627
2	0.3672
3	0.1035
4	0.0156
5	0.0010

The required probability can be simply read off, the answer being 0.0156.

Example 2

In a packet of 10 flower seeds there is a 90% chance of each individual seed germinating. Calculate the probability of at least 8 of the 10 seeds germinating.

Solution

$p = 0.90$ (each individual seed germinating)

The expansion is $(p + q)^{10} = 1$ and the probability of at least 8 seeds germinating is given by:

$$^{10}C_0 p^{10} + {}^{10}C_1 p^9 q + {}^{10}C_2 p^8 q^2$$

Looking at the table on page 135 you will notice that p only ranges from 0.05 to 0.50.

As $^{10}C_0 p^{10} + {}^{10}C_1 p^9 q + {}^{10}C_2 p^8 q^2$

$$= 1 - \left[\begin{array}{l} {}^{10}C_3 p^7 q^3 + {}^{10}C_4 p^6 q^4 + {}^{10}C_5 p^5 q^5 \\ + {}^{10}C_6 p^4 q^6 + {}^{10}C_7 p^3 q^7 + {}^{10}C_8 p^2 q^8 \\ + {}^{10}C_9 pq^9 + {}^{10}C_{10} q^{10} \end{array} \right]$$

$$= 1 - [{}^{10}C_{10} q^{10} + {}^{10}C_9 q^9 p + \ldots + {}^{10}C_3 q^3 p^7]$$

$$= 1 - [{}^{10}C_0 q^{10} + {}^{10}C_1 q^9 p + \ldots + {}^{10}C_7 q^3 p^7]$$

(using $^n C_r = {}^n C_{n-r}$)

We can still use the table on page 135, but this time using it to find the probability of at least 3 failures where the probability of each individual failure is 0.1.

Using $n = 10$ and $n - r = 3$ we should view the table as shown below:

$q =$	0.10
$n = 10$ $n - r = 0$	1.0000
1	0.6513
2	0.2639
3	0.0702
4	0.0128
5	0.0016
6	0.0001

So the probability of at least 8 of the 10 seeds germinating

$= 1 - p(3$ or more not germinating)

$= 1 - 0.0702$ (from table)

$= 0.9298$

Example 3

One in ten pupils at a school prefers cross-country running to swimming. What is the probability that a random sample of 5 pupils will contain exactly 2 pupils who prefer cross-country running to swimming?

Solution

$p = 0.10$ (selecting a pupil who prefers cross-country running to swimming)

The expansion is $(p + q)^5 = 1$ and the probability of exactly 2 pupils preferring cross-country running to swimming is given by

$$^5C_3p^2q^3$$

To use the table to evaluate this probability we must realise that:

$$^5C_3p^2q^3 = [^5C_0p^5 + {}^5C_1p^4q + {}^5C_2p^3q^2 + {}^5C_3p^2q^3]$$
$$- [^5C_0p^5 + {}^5C_1p^4q + {}^5C_2p^3q^2]$$
$$= [0.0815] - [0.0086] \text{ (from table)}$$
$$= 0.0729$$

EXERCISE B ───────────────

Use the table shown on page 135 to answer the following questions.

1 20% of the pupils in a second-year class are members of the school's film club. What is the probability that at least 4 of a sample of 10 pupils questioned are members of the school's film club?

2 A coin is tossed 5 times. What is the probability of getting at least 3 heads?

3 A pentagonal spinner with sides numbered 1–5 is spun 10 times. Calling a 4 or 5 a success, find the probability of having 6 or more successes.

4 In a very large batch of washers 80% are perfect. What is the probability of finding at least 7 perfect washers in a sample of 10?

5 An octagonal spinner with sides numbered 1–8 is spun 5 times. What is the probability that on at least 4 occasions a number greater than 2 is spun?

6 A biased coin is tossed 10 times. The probability of throwing a head each time the coin is tossed is 0.6. What is the probability of throwing at least 7 heads?

7 At a certain school 7 out of every 20 pupils usually travel to school by bus. What is the probability that a random sample of 10 pupils will contain exactly 6 pupils who usually travel to school by bus?

8 In a certain housing estate 4 out of every 10 houses has more than 1 television. What is the probability of exactly 3 houses in a sample of 5 having more than one television?

9 80% of the lecturers at a college prefer the students to write in pen rather than in pencil. A random sample of 10 lecturers was questioned. What is the probability that:
a) at least 5 lecturers preferred the students to write in pen rather than in pencil?
b) exactly 7 lecturers preferred the students to write in pen rather than in pencil?

10 10 000 electric light bulbs are delivered to a supermarket in boxes of 5. If 1 light bulb in 20 is defective, estimate how many boxes will contain at least 2 defectives?

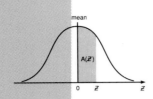

11 THE NORMAL DISTRIBUTION

FREQUENCY DISTRIBUTIONS

Let us consider the following frequency distributions where the total frequency is fairly high.

Example 1

This distribution shows the number of children per family in the families of all first-year pupils in a Secondary School in a country area. (This cannot be said to be quite typical of the families in the area as a whole since families with no children are not considered.)

Figure 11.1 shows the histogram for this distribution.

Number in family	Frequency
1	10
2	27
3	37
4	36
5	22
6	18
7	14
8	9
9	4
10	3
11	0
12	2
13	1

As you can see from the histogram, this is a rather 'lopsided' distribution. This distribution is said to be **positively skewed** (see Chapter 5).

Example 2

The results recorded in a cycling proficiency test given by the police to school children in Wigtownshire are shown below. This was not a compulsory test, pupils could enter or not as they wished. Most of the children were aged about 10–12 years.

Marks	Frequency
35–39	1
40–44	0
45–49	0
50–54	1
55–59	4
60–64	3
65–69	6
70–74	16
75–79	22
80–84	75
85–89	113
90–94	68
95–99	5

Figure 11.2 shows the histogram for the distribution.

This distribution is negatively skewed. Can you suggest any reason for this? What shape do you think the distribution might have had if every child in the area aged 10–12 had entered the test?

Fig. 11.1
Number of children per family

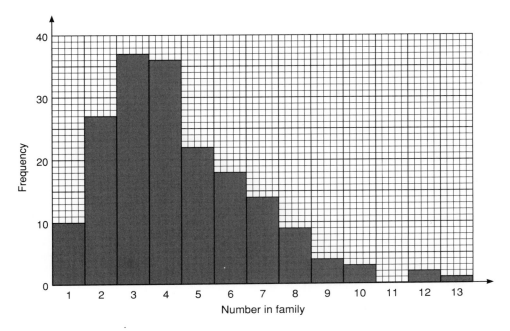

Fig. 11.2
Cycling proficiency test results

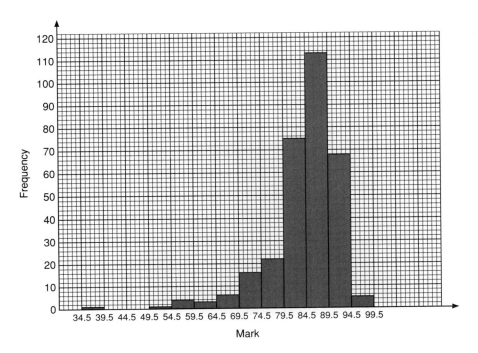

139

Example 3

These deaths (from all causes) were recorded one year in Scotland.

Age (years)	Frequency
0–4	1619
5–9	117
10–14	91
15–19	177
20–24	177
25–29	175
30–34	208
35–39	392
40–44	682
45–49	960
50–54	1846
55–59	2951
60–64	4165
65–69	4181
70–74	4343
75–79	4082
80–84	3182
85–89	1814
90–94	523
95–99	73
100+	5

Without any further grouping, draw a histogram for this distribution and discuss the shape of it.

This shape of distribution is the usual one for deaths and it is an example of what is called a U-shaped distribution.

Example 4

A ten sum test for speed and accuracy was given to all first-year pupils in a country area and the results were as follows.

Number of sums correct	Frequency
0	5
1	11
2	21
3	35
4	49
5	52
6	51
7	28
8	20
9	13
10	3

Figure 11.3 shows the histogram for this. This histogram is fairly symmetrical, as you might expect since it represents the complete range of abilities in this area. The mean, median and mode are all 5.

Fig. 11.3
Sum test results

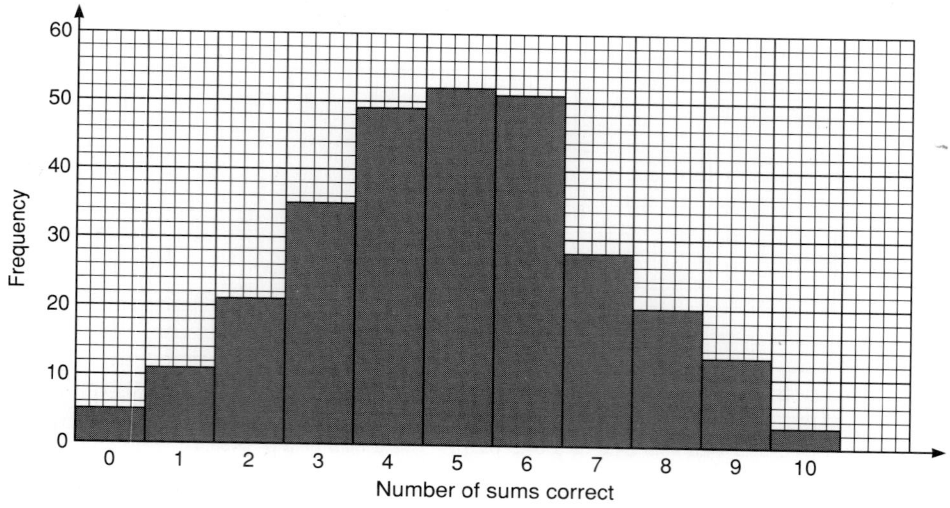

140

In this chapter we are principally interested in distributions of this type, that is, symmetrical about the mode and shaped like a bell. The standard distribution of this type is called a **Gaussian** or **normal distribution**.

PRACTICAL WORK

Collect some data of your own by undertaking some surveys. There are two principal types of surveys that may be conducted; those dealing with data about objects and those dealing with information about people.

Here are a few suggestions to follow up. A little thought and some help with apparatus from perhaps the science department, should enable them to be carried out fairly easily.

In each case a reasonably large number of observations should be taken and a frequency table constructed. Then the mean and standard deviation could be calculated and the results shown graphically as a histogram or frequency polygon.

Suggestions

1 An investigation could be conducted into the length of life of torch batteries. Here you would need to borrow some electrical equipment from the science department to set up electrical circuits.

2 The height of bounce of a large number of tennis (or golf) balls could be measured. In this experiment, the balls must be dropped from a fixed height and the heights of the resulting bounces judged against a background board marked off in suitable measuring units. Obviously this work requires a team of pupils working together.

3 An investigation into the weight range of 'standard' eggs could be very interesting. You should be able to 'borrow' a large number of 'standard' eggs from the school kitchen or the cookery teacher and weigh them accurately with a science balance. To obtain enough weighings, the experiment could be spread over several weeks. Once you have formed a frequency distribution you will know the range of weights which covers the category of 'standard' eggs. Then you can contact an egg-packing station and find out what the official range of weights is, and compare this with your own results.

4 A similar type of experiment may be done by very accurate weighing of packets, such as salt, custard powder, sugar, which have a stated weight on the packet.

5 A survey of the heights of a certain year group or age group in the school may be conducted quite readily (with some cooperation from the staff). All that is required is some kind of measuring instrument – at its simplest a metre stick tacked onto a wall. Here of course, boys and girls should be considered separately.

6 The same type of survey may be done by taking some other measurement of a group in the school, for example, weights.

These last two surveys can be broadened in scope by contacting another school or several schools in various parts of the country and 'swopping' information with them. This would give several distributions for purposes of comparison. It would also be interesting to keep a record of things like heights and weights in a school over a number of years.

7 Many other surveys may be conducted in a school, such as shoe sizes, the number of children per family, speed and accuracy sum tests, and so on.

SHAPES OF FREQUENCY DISTRIBUTIONS

The distributions we have considered so far have revealed a variety of frequency curves. Some of the most commonly occurring curves are shown in Figure 11.4.

Fig. 11.4a
Normal distribution

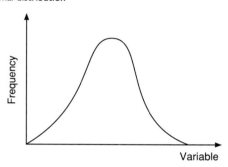

Fig. 11.4b
Positively skewed distribution

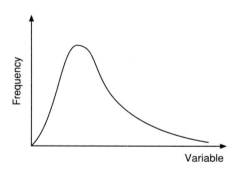

Fig. 11.4c
Negatively skewed distribution

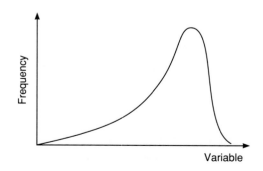

Fig. 11.4d
J-shaped distribution

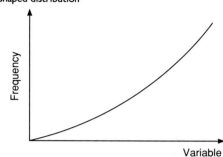

Fig. 11.4e
Reverse J-shaped distribution

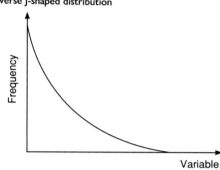

Fig. 11.4f
Bimodal distribution

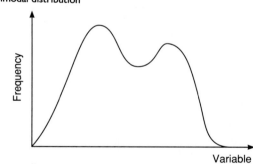

Fig. 11.4g
U-shaped distribution

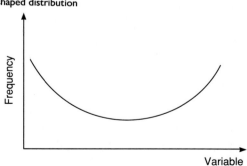

Fig. 11.5
Sum test results

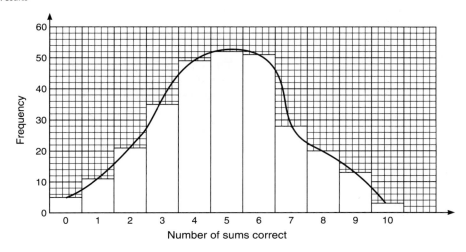

THE NORMAL DISTRIBUTION

In Example 4, at the beginning of the chapter, we saw a distribution symmetrical about the mode (and the mean and median) which approximated to a **normal distribution**. Figure 11.5 shows again the histogram of this distribution. This time a curve has been drawn through the tops of the columns. This is roughly the typical bell shaped curve of a normal distribution and is called the **normal curve**.

THE NORMAL CURVE

The algebraic study of this curve took place in the middle of the eighteenth century and is mainly attributed to De Moivre and Gauss. Their aim was to obtain the equation of a curve which corresponded to the symmetrical bell shape.

Although the mean, median and mode always coincide in this distribution the relative width of the 'bell' will depend on the spread of the distribution (Figure 11.6).

The details of this study are beyond the scope of this book but it is worth noting that

the equation that is used in relation to the normal distribution curve is:

$$y = \frac{N}{\sigma\sqrt{2\pi}}\, e^{-(x-\mu)^2/2\sigma^2}$$

where x is the continuous variable,
N is the total number of observations
μ is the mean of the distribution, and
σ is the standard deviation of the distribution.

Fig. 11.6
The normal distribution

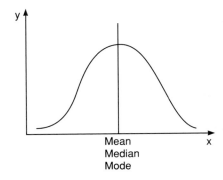

The size and shape of the 'bell' depend on the scales used (Figure 11.7). In Figure 11.7b

143

Fig. 11.7a

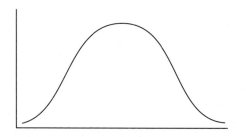

Fig. 11.7b

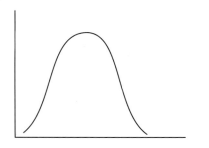

Fig. 11.7c

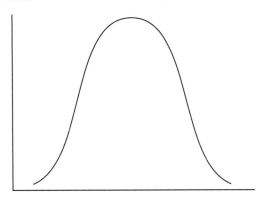

the horizontal scale has been shortened and in Figure 11.7c the vertical scale has been lengthened.

A distribution which is shaped like the normal curve is called a *normal distribution*. A great many distributions which occur naturally are normal distributions, such as, the weights of a certain age group of men, the number of tomatoes per plant, the number of peas in a pod. Your practical work should have produced normal distributions also.

THE MEAN AND STANDARD DEVIATION OF THE NORMAL CURVE

The mean of a normal distribution lies in the middle, the curve being symmetrical (Figure 11.8). The standard deviation gives us the measure of the spread or dispersion of the observations.

Fig. 11.8

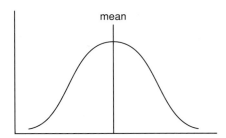

Figure 11.9 shows 3 normal distributions with the same mean but differing standard deviations.

It is clear that when examining any normal distribution we must take into account both the mean and the standard deviation.

In this way, we are able to compare normal distributions with one another, though in practice we compare all normal distributions with the special distribution which we have already called the normal curve.

Fig. 11.9

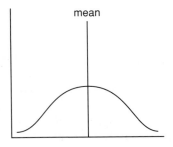

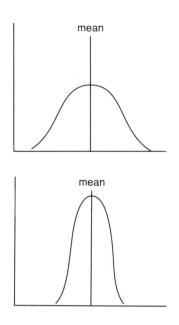

mean (μ) = 0, N = 1, and the standard deviation (σ) = 1. Further, the area between the curve and the x-axis is 1 unit and thus the area between the curve, the x-axis the ordinate x = a and the ordinate x = b is a measure of the probability that the variable x lies between x = a and x = b. These probabilities have all been accurately calculated and usually are tabulated in standard sets of tables. Some examples of these probabilities are illustrated in Figure 11.11.

Fig. 11.11

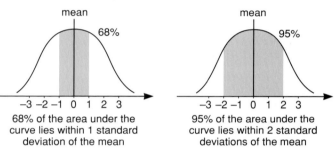

68% of the area under the curve lies within 1 standard deviation of the mean

95% of the area under the curve lies within 2 standard deviations of the mean

STANDARD NORMAL CURVE

Since the shape and position of each normal curve depend upon the mean and standard deviation of the distribution it will simplify our work if we standardise our data. Thus we obtain the **standard normal curve** which is a special version of the normal curve with the

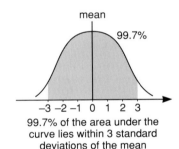

99.7% of the area under the curve lies within 3 standard deviations of the mean

STANDARDISING SCORES

A point x on a normal curve with mean = μ and standard deviation = σ corresponds to the point Z on the standard normal curve when:

Fig. 11.10
Standard normal curve

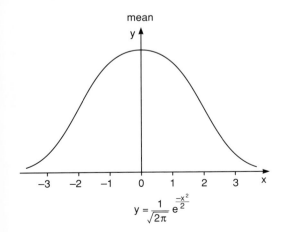

$$y = \frac{1}{\sqrt{2\pi}} e^{\frac{-x^2}{2}}$$

$$Z = \frac{x - \mu}{\sigma}$$

145

Thus we can calculate the corresponding standard score (Z) for any score (x) in a normal distribution by using the formula:

$$Z\text{(standard score)} = \frac{x - \mu}{\sigma}$$

(This process is called standardising the score.)

In this way, we can compare scores in different normal distributions by finding the standard score for each and seeing how they stand in relation to one another.

Fig. 11.12a
A normal curve

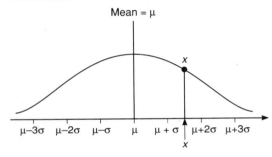

Fig. 11.12b
The standard normal curve

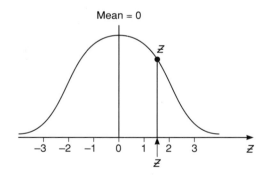

Example

In a French examination the mean mark was 78.0 and the standard deviation 8.0. In German, the mean was 73.0 and the standard deviation 7.6. A pupil scored 75 in French and 71 in German. In which examination was his relative standing higher?

Solution

French: $\mu = 78.0$ German: $\mu = 73.0$
$\qquad\quad \sigma = 8.0$ $\qquad\qquad\qquad \sigma = 7.6$
$\qquad\quad x = 75$ $\qquad\qquad\qquad\quad x = 71$

$$Z = \frac{x - \mu}{\sigma} \qquad\qquad Z = \frac{x - \mu}{\sigma}$$

$$= \frac{75 - 78}{8} \qquad\qquad = \frac{71 - 73}{7.6}$$

$$= \frac{-3}{8} \qquad\qquad\quad = \frac{-2}{7.6}$$

$$= -0.375 \qquad\qquad = -0.263$$

The standard score for French $= -0.375$ (0.375 below the mean)

The standard score for German $= -0.263$ (0.263 below the mean)

Relatively speaking, the pupil did better in German than in French.

Note It is of benefit in working this type of example to summarise the information given about each subject before going on to calculate the standard score.

EXERCISE A

1 Calculate the standard scores for **a, b, c, d**.

	a	b	c	d
x	72	45	63	71
μ	60	50	60	79
σ	9	5	11	5

2 A normal distribution has a mean $\mu = 120$ and a standard deviation $\sigma = 11$. What standard scores correspond to raw scores of: **a)** 115? **b)** 134? **c)** 93?

3 Shabana had a geography mark of 63 in one examination where the average mark

146

was 70 and the standard deviation 7. In the next examination, where the average was 71 she scored 65 (standard deviation being 5). Compare her standing in the two examinations.

4 John scored 75 in a mathematics test where the mean mark was 70 and the standard deviation 6. His sister Jane scored 70 in her mathematics test, the mean and standard deviation being 60 and 8 respectively. Which of two showed more ability in mathematics?

5 In an English examination the mean mark was 56 and the standard deviation was 8; in French the mean was 60 and standard deviation 14; in mathematics, the mean and standard deviation were 65 and 10 respectively. A pupil scored 60 in English, 67 in French and 70 in mathematics. Compare her standing in the three subjects.

6 Tom and Fiaz are friends who attend different schools. In the term examinations Tom had a mark of 70 in English and Fiaz had a mark of 80. The average mark in Tom's class was 65 with a standard deviation of 11. In Fiaz's class the average was 70 and the standard deviation was 10. Which of the boys had actually achieved the better result?

7 A pupil scored 50 in English and 62 in mathematics in the November examination, the average marks being 55 and 60 respectively. In May, he scored 55 in English and 60 in mathematics, the average mark being 58 for both subjects. The standard deviation for English was 7 in November and 5 in May; and for mathematics was 5 in November and 12 in May.
a) In which examination did he do better in English?
b) In which examination did he do better in mathematics?
c) In which of all 4 examinations had he the best results?
d) In which of all 4 examinations had he the poorest results?

8 In a normal distribution with mean 30 and standard deviation 3, what raw scores correspond to the following standard scores?
a) 1.4 b) 2.5 c) −1.5 d) −0.68

9 In a normal distribution with mean 55, the raw score 60 corresponds to a standard score of 1.3. What is the standard deviation of the distribution (correct to the second decimal place)?

10 A normal distribution has a mean of 72, and a raw score of 60 corresponds to a standard score of −1.2. What is the standard deviation?

11 What is the mean of a normal distribution which has a standard deviation of 5 and in which a raw score of 30 corresponds to a standard score of 1.7?

12 In a normal distribution, the standard deviation is 2.3, and a score of 62 corresponds to a standard score of −0.5. What is the mean of the distribution?

13 What are the mean and the standard deviation of a normal distribution when raw scores of 45 and 60 correspond to standard scores of −1 and 2 respectively?

14 In a normal distribution scores of 70 and 50 correspond to standard scores of 0.5 and −1.5 respectively. Calculate the mean and standard deviation of the distribution.

Area under the standard normal curve

Tables have been compiled whereby we can read off the size of part of the area under the standard normal curve provided we know the standard score. (See Table 1 of the appendix.)

Fig. 11.13a
The total area under the standard normal curve equals 1 (or 100%)

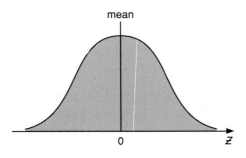

Fig. 11.13b
The area to the right of the mean (above the mean) equals 0.5 (or 50%). Similarly the area to the left of the mean (below the mean) equals 0.5 (or 50%)

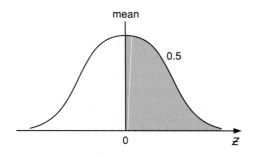

Fig. 11.13c
The shaded area under the curve A(Z) is the proportion of area between $Z = 0$ and any value Z

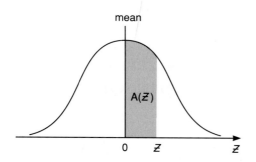

Example 1

Find the area under the normal curve between $Z = 0$ and $Z = 1.2$.

Solution

$$Z = 1.2$$
$$\therefore A(Z) = 0.385$$

Fig. 11.14a

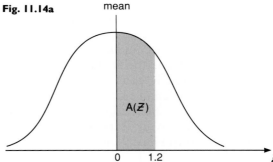

Example 2

Find the area under the normal curve to the right of $Z = 1.2$.

Solution

$$Z = 1.2$$
$$\therefore A(Z) = 0.385$$
$$\text{Required} = 0.5 - 0.385 = 0.115$$

Fig. 11.14b

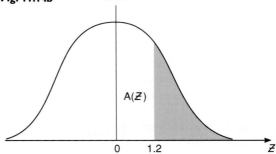

Note A (Z) is the area from the mean to Z. Since we require the area to the right of $Z = 1.2$, we must subtract A(Z) from the total area to the right of the mean which is 0.5.

Example 3

Find the area between $Z = 0$ and $Z = -1.2$.

Solution

$$Z = -1.2$$
$$\therefore A(Z) = 0.385$$

Fig. 11.15

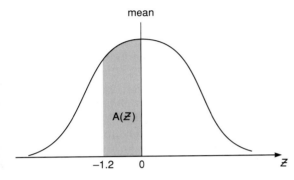

(In the tables, only positive values of Z are given. Since the curve is symmetrical, the area for $Z = -1.2$ is the same as the area for $Z = +1.2$.)

Example 4

What is the area between $Z = 0.81$ and $Z = 1.94$?

Solution

Fig. 11.16

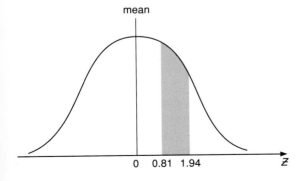

$$Z_1 = 1.94$$
$$\therefore A(Z_1) = 0.474$$
$$Z_2 = 0.81$$
$$\therefore A(Z_2) = 0.291$$
$$\text{Required area} = 0.474 - 0.291$$
$$= 0.183$$

Example 5

Calculate the area from $Z = -0.46$ to $Z = 1.21$

Solution

Fig. 11.17

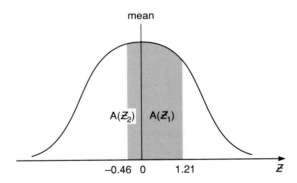

$$Z_1 = 1.21$$
$$\therefore A(Z_1) = 0.387$$
$$Z_2 = -0.46$$
$$\therefore A(Z_2) = 0.177$$
$$\text{Required area} = 0.387 + 0.177$$
$$= 0.564$$

Example 6

A normal distribution has mean $\mu = 10$ and standard deviation $\sigma = 2$. Find the area under the curve from $x = 8$ to $x = 13$.

149

Fig. 11.18

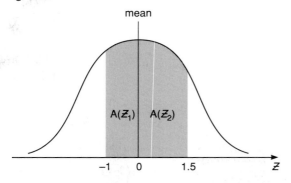

First of all, we must standardise the scores.

$x_1 = 8$

$$Z_1 = \frac{x_1 - \mu}{\sigma} = \frac{8 - 10}{2} = \frac{-2}{2} = -1$$

$x_2 = 13$

$$Z_2 = \frac{x_2 - \mu}{\sigma} = \frac{13 - 10}{2} = \frac{3}{2} = 1.5$$

$$Z_1 = -1$$

$$\therefore A(Z_1) = 0.341$$

$$Z_2 = 1.5$$

$$\therefore A(Z_2) = 0.433$$

$$\therefore \text{Required area} = 0.341 + 0.433$$

$$= 0.774$$

Note A diagram, such as Figures 11.18, for each example is of great benefit.

EXERCISE B

1 Find the area under the normal curve in each of the following cases.
   a) From $Z = 0$ to $Z = 1.3$
   b) From $Z = 0$ to $Z = 2.43$
   c) From $Z = 0$ to $Z = -0.6$
   d) From $Z = 0$ to $Z = -1.05$
   e) From $Z = -0.6$ to $Z = 1.23$
   f) From $Z = -1.78$ to $Z = 2.36$
   g) From $Z = 0.4$ to $Z = 1.7$
   h) From $Z = -0.62$ to $Z = -2.33$
   i) From $Z = 0.1$ to $Z = 0.33$
   j) From $Z = -1.6$ to $Z = -0.01$
   k) To the right of $Z = 1.2$
   l) To the right of $Z = 3.24$
   m) To the left of $Z = -0.62$
   n) To the left of $Z = -1.4$
   o) To the right of $Z = -2.11$
   p) To the right of $Z = -0.5$
   q) To the left of $Z = 1.32$
   r) To the left of $Z = 0.34$
   s) For values of Z greater than 0.78
   t) For values of Z greater than -0.78
   u) For values of Z less than 1.30
   v) For values of Z less than -0.88

2 A normal distribution has mean $\mu = 12$ and standard deviation $\sigma = 2$. Find the following areas under the normal curve.
   a) From $x = 10$ to $x = 13.5$
   b) From $x = 12.5$ to $x = 14$
   c) From $x = 8$ to $x = 9.6$
   d) For values of x exceeding 14
   e) For values of x less than 11

3 The following areas refer to areas under the standard normal curve. From the information given find the values of Z (use the tables of area).
   a) The area between 0 and Z is 0.379
   b) The area between 0 and Z is 0.486
   c) The area to the left of Z is 0.323
   d) The area to the right of Z is 0.192
   e) The area to the right of Z is 0.595
   f) The area to the left of Z is 0.9
   g) The area between 0 and Z is 0.493
   h) The area between 0 and Z is 0.497
   i) The area between 0 and Z is 0.490

PROBABILITY AND AREA

Probability and the areas of histograms or distribution graphs are very closely connected. Let us consider this frequency distribution of the number of children per family in 50 families.

Number of children	0	1	2	3	4	5	6	7
Frequency		3	6	12	15	8	3	2	1

The number of families out of the 50 with 3 children was 15. Thus the probability of choosing a family, at random, with 3 children in it is $\frac{15}{50}$.

Fig. 11.19

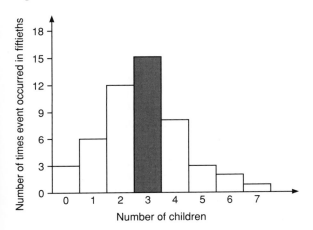

The scale of the histogram may be chosen so that the total area enclosed by the columns is 1. To do so in this case, the vertical scale is in fiftieths. Thus the area of the column representing the incidence of 3 children in a family is $\frac{15}{50}$.

So, the probability of picking out a family with 3 children is the same as the area of the column representing that incidence.

This principle applies when we consider normal distribution curves. The area under the standard normal curve is 1. This means that the total probability is 1, and an area of 0.3 is the same as a probability of 0.3.

Example

In a normal distribution with mean 10 and standard deviation 2, what is the probability that x is greater than 12?

Solution

Fig. 11.20

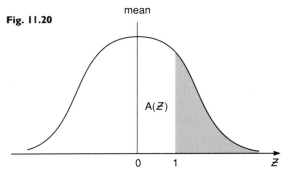

$$\mu = 10$$
$$\sigma = 2$$
$$x = 12$$

First we must standardise x.

$$Z = \frac{x - \mu}{\sigma}$$

$$= \frac{12 - 10}{2} = 1$$

$$A(Z) = 0.341$$
$$\text{Required area} = 0.5 - 0.341$$
$$= 0.159$$

The probability of x being greater than 12 is 0.159.

EXERCISE C

1 Given that x is normally distributed with mean 50 and standard deviation 5, use the tables to calculate the probability that:
a) $x > 60$ b) $x > 55$ c) $x < 43$
d) $x < 40$ e) $40 < x < 60$

2 Assuming that the stature (x) of female university students is normally distributed with mean 160 cm and standard deviation 5 cm, calculate the probability that:
a) $x > 152.5$ cm.
b) $150 < x < 165$ cm.

The normal curve as a limit of a frequency distribution of a continuous variable

The normal curve serves as a good approximation for the histograms obtained from many distributions of continuous variables.

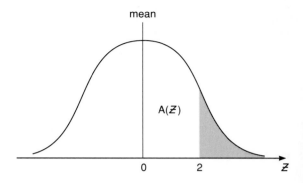

Fig. 11.21

Example 1

A brand of electric light bulbs has an average life of 1 year and a standard deviation of 3 months. What is the probability that a bulb chosen at random will have a life of at least 18 months?

Solution

$$\mu = 12 \text{ months}$$

$$\sigma = 3 \text{ months}$$

$$x = 18 \text{ months}$$

$$Z = \frac{x - \mu}{\sigma}$$

$$= \frac{18 - 12}{3}$$

$$= \frac{6}{3}$$

$$= 2$$

$$\therefore A(Z) = 0.477$$

$$\text{Required area} = 0.5 - 0.477$$

$$= 0.023$$

The probability of the bulb having a life of at least 18 months (18 months or more) is 0.023.

Example 2

Sacks of grain packed by an automatic machine loader have an average weight of 114 kg. It is found that 10% of the bags are over 116 kg. Find the standard deviation.

Solution

In this type of example we must start with the area under the curve and work back to Z.

We know 10% of the bags are over 116 kg. This means the area to the right of Z is 10% or 0.1.

$$A(Z) = 0.5 - 0.1$$

$$= 0.4$$

$$\therefore Z = 1.28$$

Fig. 11.22

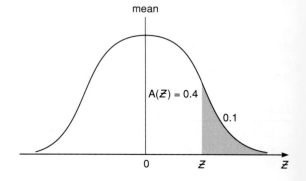

Now we know, $\mu = 114 \, \text{kg}$

$$\sigma = ?$$

$$x = 116 \, \text{kg}$$

$$Z = 1.28$$

$$Z = \frac{x - \mu}{\sigma}$$

$$\frac{1.28}{1} = \frac{116 - 114}{\sigma}$$

$$= \frac{2}{\sigma}$$

$$1.28\sigma = 2$$

$$\sigma = \frac{2}{1.28}$$

$$= 1.56 \text{ (correct to 2 d.p.)}$$

The standard deviation is 1.56.

Example 3

Given a normal distribution of a continuous variable (x) with 2000 variates, the mean and standard deviation being 20 and 5 respectively, find the number of variates between $x = 12$ and $x = 22$.

Solution

Fig. 11.23

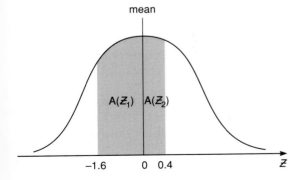

$$N = 2000$$

$$\mu = 20$$

$$\sigma = 5$$

$$x_1 = 12$$

$$x_2 = 22$$

$$Z_1 = \frac{x_1 - \mu}{\sigma}$$

$$= \frac{12 - 20}{5}$$

$$= -1.6$$

$$Z_2 = \frac{x_2 - \mu}{\sigma}$$

$$= \frac{22 - 20}{5}$$

$$= 0.4$$

$$\therefore A(Z_1) = 0.445$$

and $A(Z_2) = 0.155$

$$\therefore \text{Required area} = 0.445 + 0.155$$

$$= 0.600$$

The probability of x lying between 12 and 22 is 0.6.

$\therefore$ The expected number of variates between 12 and 22 $= 2000 \times 0.6$

$$= 1200$$

EXERCISE D

1 A hundred standard squash balls are tested by dropping them from a height of 250 cm and measuring the height of bounce. A ball is 'fast' if it rises above 80 cm. The average height of bounce was 75 cm and the standard deviation was 1.9 cm. What is the chance of getting a 'fast' standard ball?

2 Sacks of grain packed by an automatic loader have an average weight of 61 kg. It is found that 10% of the bags are below 59 kg. Find the standard deviation.

3 In the previous example, the machine is adjusted and the average weight per bag is now 60 kg. Assuming the standard deviation is unaltered calculate the probability that a bag is now below 59 kg.

4 Suppose your score in an examination in standard units is 1.2 and the scores are assumed to be normally distributed, what percentage of the students would be expected to score higher than you?

5 Two brands of torch batteries have the same average life of 55 hours but different standard deviations of $1\frac{1}{4}$ hours and $1\frac{3}{4}$ hours. In each case, what is the chance that a battery will burn for at least 58 hours?

6 A physical education teacher gives grades to all his classes for athletic events. If experience has shown that the average height is 178 cm and the standard deviation is 10 cm in the high jump, and the teacher gives 20% As, how high would a pupil need to jump to expect an A?

7 If a normal distribution of a continuous variable has mean 21.2 and standard deviation 3.10, find the probability that a variate selected at random will be larger than 30 or less than 15.

8 The weight of grapefruit from a large shipment averages 420 g with a standard deviation of 42 g. If these weights are normally distributed, what percentage of all these grapefruit would be expected to weigh between 420 and 476 g?

9 If the average life of a certain make of storage battery is 30 months with a standard deviation of 5 months, what percentage of these batteries can be expected to last 24 to 36 months?

10 Records indicate that the average life of TV tubes is 3 years 6 months and the standard deviation is 18 months. Tubes lasting less than a year are replaced free.

For every 200 sets (one tube per set) sold, how many tubes can be expected to have to be replaced free?

11 The average yearly rainfall in a certain town is 75 cm with a standard deviation of 25 cm. Assuming this yearly rainfall follows a normal distribution, in how many years out of a period of 100 years could the residents of the town expect less than 37.5 cm of rain?

12 The heights of 1000 male college students closely follow a normal distribution with a mean of 172.5 cm and a standard deviation of 6.25 cm.
a) How many of these students would you expect to be at least 180 cm tall?
b) What range of heights would include the middle 50% of the men in this group?

13 In grading a certain type of plum, 20% are called small, 55% medium, 15% large and 10% very large. If the weights follow a normal distribution, and the average weight is 138 g with a standard deviation of 33.5 g, what are the lower and upper bounds for the weight of medium plums?

14 In a normal distribution with a standard deviation of 2, the probability that a variate selected at random exceeds 26 is 0.05. Find the mean of the distribution and the variate above which lie 80% of all variates of the distribution.

15 In an examination, the average mark was 60 and the standard deviation 10. The teacher gave 30 students with marks between 51 and 69 a grade of C. If the marks are assumed to follow a normal distribution, how many students sat the examination?

16 A normal distribution has a mean of 30 and a standard deviation of 7. If it is known that 346 variates exceed 32.5, what is the total number of variates in the distribution?

17 A teacher who gives 10% As, 20% Bs, 40% Cs, 20% Ds and 10% Es, sets an examination in which the average mark is 54. If the borderline between the Cs and the Ds is 44, what is the standard deviation in that examination?

18 In a normal distribution with mean 100 and standard deviation 44, there are 150 variates greater than 180. How many variates should we expect between 120 and 180?

19 In a population of adult men 20% are 175 cm or over in height and 10% are less than 155 cm. Find the mean and standard deviation of the population.

20 In an examination 10% of the class receive a grade of A, 20% B, 55% C and 15% D. The C grade ranges from 55 to 70. Assuming a normal distribution, what are the mean and standard deviation of the marks?

THE NORMAL DISTRIBUTION AS AN APPROXIMATION TO THE BINOMIAL DISTRIBUTION

If a frequency distribution is obtained by using the terms of the binomial expansion, it is called a binomial distribution, for example, the expected frequencies of the occurrence of heads in tossing N coins follow a binomial distribution.

The histograms representing the expected frequencies of heads in 64 tosses of 1, 2, 3, 4, 5 and 6 coins are shown in Figure 11.24.

If the number of the sample, N, is large the calculation of frequencies and probabilities by means of the binomial theorem becomes tedious. Since many practical problems involve samples of a large size, it is important to find a more rapid method of calculating probabilities. Such a method is furnished by the normal distribution which is the most important continuous probability distribution.

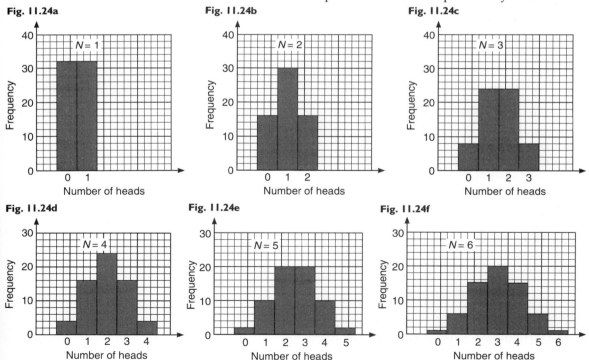

Fig. 11.24a $N = 1$

Fig. 11.24b $N = 2$

Fig. 11.24c $N = 3$

Fig. 11.24d $N = 4$

Fig. 11.24e $N = 5$

Fig. 11.24f $N = 6$

From Figure 11.24 it is apparent as N increases the tops of the rectangles of the histograms approach a bell-shaped curve. This limiting frequency curve obtained as N becomes larger and larger is called the normal frequency curve (or normal probability curve). The curve approaches the horizontal axis but never touches it.

The total area under the normal probability curve representing the probability that x will fall anywhere is equal to 1.

Hence, by using the tables for finding the areas under the standard normal curve, we can find the probability of a certain event occurring.

Fig. 11.25

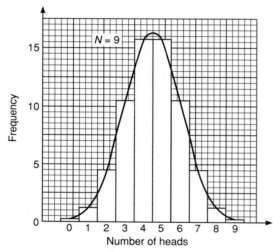

Number of heads

To calculate the standard score (or Z score), we must know the mean and standard deviation of the distribution. The proof of the values of these measures is beyond our scope and here we shall only quote the results. If p is the probability of the success of an event in a *single trial* and q is the probability of its failure, then the binomial distribution giving the expected frequencies for $0, 1, 2, \ldots, N$ successes in N trials has

$$\text{mean } \mu = Np$$

and standard deviation $\sigma = \sqrt{Npq}$

Note The binomial distribution deals with *discrete* variables only. For example, the number of times a head is obtained when tossing a coin, the number of times a 6 is obtained with a die, the number of defective TV tubes or light bulbs, and so on. This means that in working examples, if we wish to include a certain score we have to adjust the x value used.

Let us look at Figure 11.24c of the expected number of heads obtained in 64 tosses of 3 coins. If we wish to know how many times we obtained 2 heads or more, then to include 2 heads we must use the lower boundary of the '2' column which is 1.5. If we want to know how many times we obtained 1 or less heads we must use the upper boundary of the '1' column which is 1.5 (Figure 11.26).

Fig. 11.26

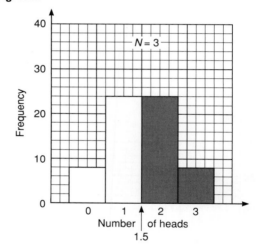

Number of heads
1.5

Example 1

Using the normal curve approximation, find the probability that 3–6 heads are obtained in a toss of 9 coins (that is, the probability that x lies between and *includes* 3 and 6).

Solution

$$p = \tfrac{1}{2} = \text{heads}$$
$$q = \tfrac{1}{2} = \text{tails}$$
$$N = 9$$

$$\mu = Np$$
$$= 9 \times \tfrac{1}{2}$$
$$= 4.5$$
$$\sigma = \sqrt{Npq}$$
$$= \sqrt{9 \times \tfrac{1}{2} \times \tfrac{1}{2}}$$
$$= 1.5$$
$$x_1 = 2.5 \text{ (to include 3 heads)}$$
$$x_2 = 6.5 \text{ (to include 6 heads)}$$

$$Z_1 = \frac{x_1 - \mu}{\sigma}$$

$$= \frac{2.5 - 4.5}{1.5}$$

$$= \frac{-2}{1.5}$$

$$= -1.33$$

$$A(Z_1) = 0.408$$

$$Z_2 = \frac{x_2 - \mu}{\sigma}$$

$$= \frac{6.5 - 4.5}{1.5}$$

$$= \frac{2}{1.5}$$

$$= 1.33$$

Fig. 11.27

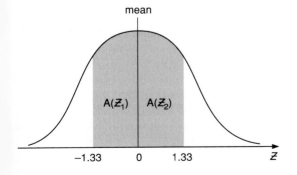

$$A(Z_2) = 0.408$$
$$\text{Required area} = 0.408 + 0.408$$
$$= 0.816$$

The probability of obtaining 3–6 heads is 0.816.

Example 2

If 12 dice are thrown, what is the probability, using the normal curve approximation, that 6 or more dice will show a 5?

Solution

Fig. 11.28

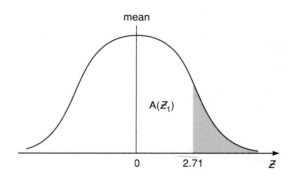

$$p = \tfrac{1}{6} = \text{a 5}$$

$$q = \tfrac{5}{6} = \text{any other number}$$

$$N = 12$$

$$\mu = Np$$

$$= 12 \times \tfrac{1}{6}$$

$$= 2$$

$$\sigma = \sqrt{Npq}$$

$$= \sqrt{12 \times \tfrac{1}{6} \times \tfrac{5}{6}}$$

$$= 1.29$$

$$x = 5.5 \text{ (to include 6 fives)}$$

$$Z_1 = \frac{x - \mu}{\sigma}$$

$$= \frac{5.5 - 2}{1.29}$$

$$= \frac{3.5}{1.29}$$

$$= 2.71$$

$$A(Z_1) = 0.497$$

Required area $= 0.5 - 0.497$

$$= 0.003$$

The probability of obtaining 6 or more fives is 0.003.

Example 3

A manufacturer producing tea cups finds that 10% of them are defective. What is the probability that in a sample of 50 cups, no more than 4 are defective?

Solution

Fig. 11.29

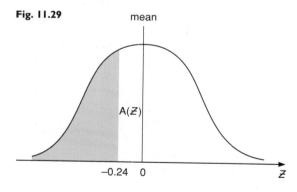

$$p = \tfrac{1}{10} = \text{defective}$$

$$q = \tfrac{9}{10} = \text{not defective}$$

$$N = 50$$

$$\mu = Np$$

$$= 50 \times \tfrac{1}{10}$$

$$= 5$$

$$\sigma = \sqrt{Npq}$$

$$= \sqrt{50 \times \tfrac{1}{10} \times \tfrac{9}{10}}$$

$$= 2.12$$

$x = 4.5$ (to include 4)

$$Z = \frac{x - \mu}{\sigma}$$

$$= \frac{4.5 - 5}{2.12}$$

$$= \frac{-0.5}{2.12}$$

$$= -0.24$$

$$A(Z) = 0.095$$

Required area $= 0.5 - 0.095$

$$= 0.405$$

The probability of obtaining no more than 4 (4 or less) defectives is 0.405.

EXERCISE E

1 A coin is tossed 100 times. Use the normal curve approximation to find the probability of obtaining:
   a) 60 or more heads.
   b) exactly 50 heads.
2 Use the normal curve approximation to find the probability of obtaining exactly 16 sixes in 96 tosses of a die.
3 For a binomial frequency for which $p = \tfrac{1}{4}$ find the probability of obtaining 25 or more successes in 80 trials.
4 If 40% of students have defective eyesight, what is the probability that at least half of the members of a class of 50 students will have defective eyesight? Use the normal curve approximation.
5 If 10% of TV tubes burn out before their guarantee has expired:
   a) what is the probability that a shopkeeper who has sold 200 such tubes will have to replace at least 30 of them?
   b) what is the probability that she will

replace at least 10 and not more than 30 tubes?
Use the normal curve approximation.

6 If 25% of the drivers in a certain town have at least one accident in a year's driving, what is the probability that 30% or more of 500 customers of an insurance company will have an accident during the next year? Use the normal curve approximation.

7 Assume that half of the people in a certain community are regular viewers of TV. Of 100 investigators, each interviewing 10 individuals regarding their viewing habits, how many would you expect to report that 3 people or fewer were regular TV viewers? (Use the normal distribution.)

8 A manufacturer of light bulbs finds that on average 5% are defective. What is the probability that out of 1000 such bulbs selected at random 30 or more are defective?

9 A pair of dice is rolled 25 times. What is the probability that a 7 will show 10 or more times?

10 Within a certain age group of children it is known that 20% require dental attention. A sample of 80 such children are to be studied.
a) Calculate the mean and standard deviation of the number of children in such a sample who require dental attention.
b) Assuming that the distribution is approximately normal calculate the probability that
   i) 20 or more children require dental attention,
   ii) 15 to 20 inclusive of the children require dental attention.

11 An examination consists of 40 multiple-choice questions, each with 4 possible responses, of which 1 is correct. If a candidate is completely unprepared for the examination and decides to choose his answers at random, find the mean and standard deviation of the number of questions answered correctly.
   Using the normal distribution as an approximation to the distribution, calculate the probability that he answers correctly 6 or fewer questions. In the examination, 18 or more questions answered correctly gained a pass. On this basis find how many, out of a group of 500 students who chose to select their answers at random, would be expected to gain a pass.

12 A factory making ballpoint pens is experimenting with a new method of production. 5% of the pens are rejected as below standard. A sample of 50 pens is examined.
   a) Calculate the mean and standard deviation of the number of pens rejected in such a sample.
   b) Given that the distribution of the number of rejected pens is approximately normal, calculate the probability that
   i) 3 or fewer pens are rejected,
   ii) from 2 to 5 pens are rejected.

13 According to a certain insurance company, the probability of a man aged 45 dying within a year is 0.05. If the company has 20 000 policies in force on men of this age estimate the probability that the company will have to pay out more than 900 death claims on this group of men within a year.

14 A manufacturer of radio valves knows that on average 2% of his products are defective. Using the normal curve approximation, what is the probability that a sample of 100 valves will contain exactly 5 defective valves?

15 How many times would 2 dice have to be rolled so that there is a 50% chance of getting at least 3 fives?

$$p(k \text{ occurrences}) = e^{-\lambda}\frac{\lambda^k}{k!}$$

12 THE POISSON DISTRIBUTION

CALCULATING PROBABILITIES

As we saw in Chapter 10, when we are dealing with discrete variables, we can calculate the probability of an event happening using the binomial distribution if there is a fixed number of trials and a definite number of successes. However, we sometimes encounter cases where the number of trials is not known and then we have to find another method of calculating the probability of a specified number of events occurring. In this situation, provided we are dealing with events that occur randomly, we can use the Poisson distribution to find the probability of a specified number of events occurring when we know only the mean number of times the events occur in a given time.

If a certain event occurs on average λ times within a specified time or region, then the probability of k occurrences of that event within the same specified time or region is given by the expression:

$$p(k \text{ occurrences}) = e^{-\lambda}\frac{\lambda^k}{k!}$$

where e is a constant called the **exponential number**.

Note Working with the constant e, which has approximate value 2.718, is not a problem as most calculators store e to an even greater

accuracy. $k!$ is the notation used to represent the product of the first k natural numbers. For example $3! = 3 \times 2 \times 1 = 6$. Note that $0! = 1$.

Example 1

A new ski resort has, on average, 5 serious accidents per day. Calculate the probability that there will be 8 serious accidents on a given day.

Solution

$$\lambda = 5$$
$$k = 8$$
$$p(k) = e^{-\lambda}\frac{\lambda^k}{k!}$$
$$p(8 \text{ serious accidents}) = \frac{e^{-5}\,(5)^8}{8!}$$
$$= 0.0653 \text{ (4 d.p.)}$$

Example 2

On average 4 pupils per day, in a first-year mathematics class, require tracing paper. Calculate the probability that less than three pupils will require tracing paper on a given day.

Solution

$$\lambda = 4$$
$$p(k) = e^{-\lambda}\frac{\lambda^k}{k!}$$

p(less than 3 pupils require tracing paper)

$= p$(0 pupils require tracing paper)

$+ p$(1 pupil requires tracing paper)

$+ p$(2 pupils require tracing paper)

$$= e^{-4}\frac{(4)^0}{0!} + e^{-4}\frac{(4)^1}{1!} + e^{-4}\frac{(4)^2}{2!}$$

$$= 0.0183 + 0.0733 + 0.1465$$

$$= 0.2381 \text{ (4 d.p.)}$$

Example 3

On average 6 motorists are caught speeding each week on a particular section of road.
Calculate:
a) the average number of motorists caught speeding per day on that particular section of road.
b) the probability of exactly three motorists being caught speeding, on that particular section of road, on a given day.

Solution

a) Average number of motorists caught speeding per day $= \frac{6}{7}$

b) $\lambda = \frac{6}{7}$

$k = 3$

$$p(k) = e^{-\lambda}\frac{\lambda^k}{k!}$$

So p(exactly 3 motorists caught speeding on a given day)

$$= e^{-(6/7)}\frac{\left(\frac{6}{7}\right)^3}{3!}$$

$$= 0.0445 \text{ (4 d.p.)}$$

EXERCISE A

1 On average a local fire station receives 4 emergency calls per day. Calculate the probability that there will be only 2 emergency calls tomorrow.

2 The number of textbooks handed into a school's lost property office is, on average, 3 per day. Calculate the probability that there will be exactly 1 book handed in tomorrow.

3 On average a typist makes 1 mistake per page. Calculate the probability of 3 mistakes on a given page.

4 An emergency plumber is called out, on average, 12 times a week. What is the probability that she will be called out less than three times next week?

5 A taxi company finds that, on average, 3 telephone calls per day are hoaxes. Calculate the probability that there will be less than five hoax calls next Tuesday.

6 The demand for a certain model of car from a hire company is, on average, 2 per day. The hire company own 4 such models.
Calculate:
a) the probability that there is no demand for that particular model tomorrow.
b) the probability that there is a hiring request tomorrow, made for that particular model, which cannot be fulfilled (that is, a request for more than four cars of this model).

7 A fifty-page school magazine contained 4 spelling mistakes.
Calculate:
a) the average number of spelling mistakes per page.
b) the probability of 2 spelling mistakes on a given page.

8 A police station receives, on average, 4 complaints of excessive noise per week.
Calculate:
a) the average number of complaints per day.
b) the probability of 2 complaints on a given day.

Using statistical tables

Statistical tables exist which give, using the Poisson distribution, the probability of a specified number of events occurring (k) where the mean number of events occurring is known (λ). Before looking at two examples illustrating the use of these tables, it is worth noting that the mean and standard deviation of the Poisson distribution are λ and $\sqrt{\lambda}$ respectively.

Example 1

The demand per day for a particular computer package from store follows a Poisson distribution of mean 1.5. Two such computer packages are kept in stock. On how many of 190 school days is there no demand for the computer package?

Solution

$$\lambda = 1.5$$

$$k = 0$$

$$p(k \text{ occurrences}) = e^{-\lambda}\frac{\lambda^k}{k!}$$

$$p(0 \text{ demand}) = e^{-1.5}\frac{(1.5)^0}{0!}$$

The section of the table we should look at is shown below.

$\lambda =$	1.5
$k = 0$	0.2231
1	0.3347
2	0.2510
3	0.1255
4	0.0471

From the table the required probability is 0.2231 and the number of days when there is no demand

$$= 0.2231 \times 190$$

$$= 42.389$$

$$= 42 \text{ (approximately)}$$

$\lambda =$	0.5	1.0	1.5	2.0	2.5	3.0	3.5	4.0	4.5	5.0
$k = 0$	0.6065	0.3679	0.2231	0.1353	0.0821	0.0498	0.0302	0.0183	0.0111	0.0067
1	0.3032	0.3679	0.3347	0.2707	0.2052	0.1494	0.1057	0.0733	0.0500	0.0337
2	0.0758	0.1839	0.2510	0.2707	0.2565	0.2240	0.1850	0.1465	0.1125	0.0842
3	0.0126	0.0613	0.1255	0.1804	0.2138	0.2240	0.2158	0.1954	0.1687	0.1404
4	0.0016	0.0153	0.0471	0.0902	0.1336	0.1680	0.1888	0.1954	0.1898	0.1755
5	0.0002	0.0031	0.0141	0.0361	0.0668	0.1008	0.1322	0.1563	0.1708	0.1755
6		0.0005	0.0035	0.0120	0.0278	0.0504	0.0771	0.1042	0.1281	0.1462
7		0.0001	0.0008	0.0034	0.0099	0.0216	0.0385	0.0595	0.0824	0.1044
8			0.0001	0.0009	0.0031	0.0081	0.0169	0.0298	0.0463	0.0653
9				0.0002	0.0009	0.0027	0.0066	0.0132	0.0232	0.0363
10					0.0002	0.0008	0.0023	0.0053	0.0104	0.0181
11						0.0002	0.0007	0.0019	0.0043	0.0082
12						0.0001	0.0002	0.0006	0.0016	0.0034
13								0.0002	0.0006	0.0013
14								0.0001	0.0002	0.0005
15										0.0002

This table gives the probability of k occurrences where the mean number of occurrences is λ.

$$p\left(k \text{ occurrences} = e^{-\lambda}\frac{\lambda^k}{k!}\right)$$

Example 2

The demand per day for a certain model of car from a hire company follows a Poisson distribution of mean 1.0. How many cars of this particular model should the hire company own so that there is a less than 10% chance of a request for that particular model which cannot be fulfilled?

Solution

We shall start by looking at the column where $\lambda = 1.0$ and adding the probabilities associated with the demand per day for that particular model of car being 6 and 7.

$\lambda =$	1.0
$k = 0$	0.3679
1	0.3679
2	0.1839
3	0.0613
4	0.0153
5	0.0031
6	0.0005
7	0.0001

p(demand for 6 or 7 cars) $= 0.0005 + 0.0001$

$$= 0.0006$$

$$= 0.06\%$$

This means that if the hire company owned 5 cars of that particular model, the probability of a request for that model which cannot be fulfilled is only 0.06%. So the hire company can own less than 5 cars of that particular model and we proceed by calculating the cumulative total of probabilities up the column, but the total must not reach 10%.

The last cumulative total less than 10% is 8.03% as shown below.

p(demand for 3, 4, 5, 6 or 7 cars)

$$= 0.0613 + 0.0153 + 0.0031 + 0.0005 + 0.0001$$

$$= 0.0803$$

$$= 8.03\%$$

$\lambda =$	1.0
$k = 0$	0.3679
1	0.3679
2	0.1839
3	0.0613
4	0.0153
5	0.0031
6	0.0005
7	0.0001

So the hire company must own at least 2 cars of that particular model so that there is a less than 10% chance of a request for that particular model of car which cannot be fulfilled.

EXERCISE B

Use the table on page 162 to answer the following questions.

1 From experience a shopkeeper reckons that on average each delivery of electric light bulbs contains three defectives. What is the probability that the next delivery will contain 5 defectives?

2 The number of pairs of spectacles left in a cinema is, on average, 5 per week. What is the probability that only 3 pairs of spectacles will be left in the cinema next week?

3 A confectionery firm reckons that, on average, 4 chocolate eggs are broken when each batch is removed from its moulding. What is the probability that a given batch will contain 6 broken eggs?

4 The demand per day for a certain video from a hire company follows a Poisson distribution of mean 2.0. How many copies of the video should be kept in stock so that there is a less than 15% chance of a request for that particular video which cannot be fulfilled?

5 The number of defectives per batch from a manufacturing process follows a Poisson distribution of mean 3.5. The manufacturer wishes to state that there is a less than $x\%$ chance of a batch

containing more than 6 defectives. What is the value of x?

POISSON APPROXIMATION TO THE BINOMIAL DISTRIBUTION

In Chapter 11 we saw that the normal distribution could be used as an approximation to the binomial distribution. When p is small this approximation is not very accurate and provided certain conditions are satisfied the Poisson distribution will give a better approximation. p must be small (0.1 or less), the sample size large (50 or more) and np a reasonable size and constant for each trial.

Example 1

A machine in a factory produces metal washers, 0.5% of which are defective.
    Calculate the probability that a sample of 100 will contain:
a) 0
b) 1
c) 2 or more defective washers.

Solution

$N = 100$

$p = 0.005$

$\mu = \lambda = Np = 100(0.005) = 0.5$

a) $p(0 \text{ defectives}) = e^{-0.5} \dfrac{(0.5)^0}{0!}$

$= 0.6065 \text{ (4 d.p.)}$

b) $p(1 \text{ defective}) = \dfrac{e^{-0.5} (0.5)^1}{1!}$

$= 0.3033 \text{ (4 d.p.)}$

c) $p(2 \text{ or more defectives})$

$= 1 - [\text{probability of 0 or 1 defective washers}]$

$= 1 - 0.6065 - 0.3033$

$= 0.0902$

EXERCISE C

Use the Poisson approximation to the binomial distribution in each of the following examples.
1 A manufacturer knows that 2% of metal screws produced by a machine are faulty. Calculate the probability that a sample of 100 screws will contain 5 which are faulty.
2 Calculate the probability that in a school of 780 pupils, 2 pupils will have birthdays on the 31st May.
3 A process for making glass bottles produces on average 1 defective bottle per 150. Calculate the probability that a sample of 200 will contain:
a) 0
b) 1 defective bottle.
4 A box contains rubber plugs which are known to be 4% defective. Calculate the probability that a sample of 200 plugs taken from the box will contain fewer than 3 defectives.
5 A certain manufacturing process produces articles, 6% of which are faulty. Calculate the probability that a batch of 150 articles will contain fewer than 4 faulty ones.

EXERCISE D

By selecting the most appropriate distribution to use, calculate the answers to the following questions.
1 A new drug cures 7 out of 8 people suffering from a certain disease. Calculate the probability that when the drug is given to 6 patients suffering from the disease at least 5 will be cured.
2 A manufacturer knows that $1\frac{1}{2}$% of glass

sheets produced are flawed. If 500 sheets are delivered to a glazier, calculate the probability that more than 3 sheets are flawed.

3 On average 1 golfer in 6 will drive out of bounds at the ninth hole on a particular golf course. If a group of 3 golfers is selected at random, calculate the probability that 2 of the 3 will drive out of bounds at the ninth.

4 Assuming that a child is as likely to be a boy as a girl, calculate the probability that a family with 5 children will contain at least 4 boys.

5 In a town 72% of households have a colour television. If 4 households are selected at random, calculate the probability that at least $\frac{1}{2}$ of them will have a colour television.

6 750 dozen eggs are delivered to a supermarket in trays of 60. If one egg in 20 is cracked estimate how many trays will contain more than 4 cracked eggs.

7 30% of the pupils attending a school live within a $\frac{1}{2}$ mile radius of the school. What is the probability that of a group of 10 pupils questioned, exactly 4 will live within $\frac{1}{2}$ mile of the school?

8 The demand per lesson for the use of a mathematics department calculator by a class of 30 pupils follows a Poisson distribution of mean 3.0. How many calculators should a teacher keep in stock so that there is a less than 10% chance of a request for a calculator which cannot be fulfilled?

9 If 4 out of every 5 workers at a factory are under 25 years of age, calculate the probability that out of 8 workers questioned, only 3 will be under 25 years of age.

10 In a five-day working week, on average, 8 employees who have bought a dinner ticket do not turn up for their meal. Calculate the probability that on the next working day 3 employees who have bought dinner tickets do not turn up for their meal.

11 A casting process is 5% defective. Find the largest batch which can be made so that the probability of more than 5 defectives is no greater than $8\frac{1}{2}$%.

165

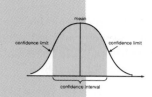

13 SAMPLE MEASURES

In Chapter 3 we looked at the problem of obtaining a satisfactory sample. We now consider some measures pertaining to samples and their relationship with the measures of the parent population from which the sample was taken.

NOTATION USED FOR SAMPLES AND POPULATIONS

Population is the general term given to the aggregate of whatever we are considering. It only means a human population when people are being considered. A **sample** is a part of the population.

The following notation is used:

	Sample	Population
Number of variates	N	n
Mean	$\bar{X}$	μ
Standard deviation	s	σ

A numerical characteristic of a population, such as its mean or standard deviation, is called a **parameter**.

A quantity calculated from a sample, such as its mean and standard deviation, is called a **statistic**.

Since parameters of a given population are based upon *all* its variates, they are fixed for that population. On the other hand, since statistics are based upon only a *part* of the population, they usually vary from sample to sample.

SAMPLING DISTRIBUTIONS

The results of an arithmetic test for speed and accuracy given to all first-year pupils (179) in a secondary school are shown below. Mean number of sums correct = 4.14.

Number of sums correct	Frequency
0	4
1	10
2	20
3	33
4	39
5	29
6	25
7	13
8	4
9	2
10	0

We wished to use this distribution for sampling purposes. Using random numbers the scores for 40 of the pupils were selected and the mean was calculated as shown below. This sample was then returned to the distribution and the procedure repeated until 50 samples in all had been taken (all samples of size 40). In each case the mean of the sample was calculated.

Sample 1		
Number of sums correct (X)	Frequency (f)	fX
0	0	0
1	2	2
2	6	12
3	8	24
4	6	24
5	7	35
6	7	42
7	1	7
8	2	16
9	1	9
10	0	0
	$\Sigma f = 40$	$\Sigma fX = 171$

The means of the samples (or sample means) were formed into a frequency distribution (**sampling distribution**) as shown in the table below.

Sampling distribution	
Sample means	Frequency
3.50–3.59	1
3.60–3.69	1
3.70–3.79	3
3.80–3.89	3
3.90–3.99	5
4.00–4.09	10
4.10–4.19	12
4.20–4.29	5
4.30–4.39	4
4.40–4.49	3
4.50–4.59	2
4.60–4.69	1

$$\bar{X} = \frac{\Sigma fX}{f}$$

$$= \frac{171}{40}$$

$$= 4.275$$

$$\text{approximately} = 4.28$$

$$\text{Mean of } sample\ 1 = 4.28$$

The mean of this sampling distribution was calculated and found to be 4.11, that is the mean of the sample means was 4.11.

This histogram below shows that the sampling distribution is reasonably near to a normal distribution considering that the number of samples is only 50.

The mean of the sampling distribution (or mean of the sample means) is 4.11, very close to the mean of the population 4.14.

Try an experiment like this yourselves with some data of your own. You should use a distribution which is approximately normal with a fairly large total frequency.

Fig. 13.1
Sampling distribution

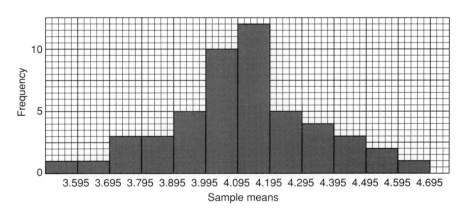

DISTRIBUTION OF THE SAMPLE MEANS

A variable X has a normal distribution with mean μ and standard deviation σ.

If observations are collected, not individually but as random samples of size N, then the means of the samples can be formed into a frequency distribution which will be approximately normal. This distribution is called a sampling distribution, the variable this time being $\bar{X}$.

The mean of the sampling distribution is called $\mu_{\bar{x}}$ to distinguish it from the population mean μ. Similarly the standard deviation of the sampling distribution is called $\sigma_{\bar{x}}$.

There is a definite correlation between the mean and standard deviation of the sampling distribution, and the mean and standard deviation of the population.

For practical purposes we can assume that the mean of the sampling distribution (that is, the mean of the sample means) $\mu_{\bar{x}}$ is approximately the same as the population mean.

$$\mu_{\bar{x}} = \mu$$

Also, $\sigma_{\bar{x}}$ the standard deviation of the sampling distribution is equal to the population standard deviation, σ, divided by the square root of N, the number in the samples.

Fig. 13.2

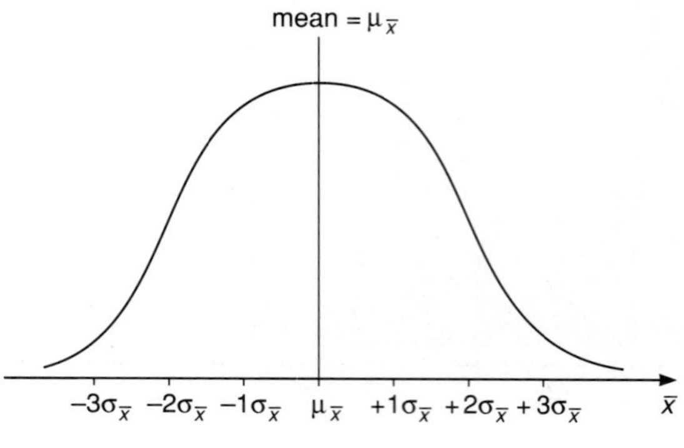

mean $= \mu_{\bar{x}}$

$-3\sigma_{\bar{x}}$ $-2\sigma_{\bar{x}}$ $-1\sigma_{\bar{x}}$ $\mu_{\bar{x}}$ $+1\sigma_{\bar{x}}$ $+2\sigma_{\bar{x}}$ $+3\sigma_{\bar{x}}$ $\bar{x}$

$$\sigma_{\bar{x}} = \frac{\sigma}{\sqrt{N}}$$

This standard deviation, $\sigma_{\bar{x}}$, of the sample mean $\bar{X}$ from the population mean μ is known as the **standard error** of the sample mean from the population mean.

$$\text{Standard error} = \frac{\sigma}{\sqrt{N}}$$

Obviously as N, the size of the sample, increases, the standard error of the sample mean from the population mean, that is, the difference between the sample mean and the population mean, becomes smaller and the standard deviation, s, of a simple *large* sample approximates to σ, the standard deviation of the population, that is, $s = \sigma$.

We standardise a score X of a normal distribution with mean μ and standard deviation σ by using this formula.

$$\text{Standard score, } Z = \frac{X - \mu}{\sigma}$$

In the same way we may standardise a score $\bar{X}$ of the sampling distribution with mean $\mu_{\bar{x}}$ and standard deviation $\sigma_{\bar{x}}$ by using the same formula.

$$\text{Standard score, } Z = \frac{X - \mu_{\bar{x}}}{\sigma_{\bar{x}}}$$

Example 1

The mean height of 1000 university students is 171.25 cm and the standard deviation is 6.25 cm. Find the probability that in a sample of 100 students, the mean will be greater than 172.50 cm.

Solution

$$\text{Population: } \mu = 171.25 \text{ cm}$$

$$\sigma = 6.25 \text{ cm}$$

Sampling: $\mu_{\bar{x}} = \mu = 171.25$ cm

$$\sigma_{\bar{x}} = \frac{\sigma}{\sqrt{N}}$$

$$= \frac{6.25}{\sqrt{100}}$$

$$= \frac{6.25}{10}$$

$$= 0.625 \text{ cm}$$

We must find the area under the normal curve to the right of $\bar{X} = 172.50$ (the mean of the sample of 100 students).

$$Z = \frac{\bar{X} - \mu_{\bar{x}}}{\sigma_{\bar{x}}}$$

(We are standardising the sample mean $\bar{X} = 172.50$ in the sampling distribution.)

$$= \frac{172.50 - 171.25}{0.625}$$

$$= \frac{1.25}{0.625}$$

$$= 2$$

$$\therefore A(Z) = 0.477$$

$$\therefore \text{Required area} = 0.5 - 0.477$$

$$= 0.023$$

The probability of the sample mean being greater than 172.50 cm $= 0.023$

Example 2

Assume that the heights of 3000 men are normally distributed with mean 172.5 cm and standard deviation 7.5 cm. If 50 samples of 25 men each (assuming replacement) are obtained, what would be the expected mean and standard deviation of the resulting sampling distribution? In how many samples would you expect to find the mean between 168.75 and 173.75 cm?

Solution

Population: $\mu = 172.5$ cm

$$\sigma = 7.5 \text{ cm}$$

Sampling: $\mu_{\bar{x}} = \mu = 172.5$ cm

$$\sigma_{\bar{x}} = \frac{\sigma}{\sqrt{N}}$$

$$= \frac{7.5}{\sqrt{25}}$$

$$= \frac{7.5}{5}$$

$$= 1.5 \text{ cm}$$

Fig. 13.3

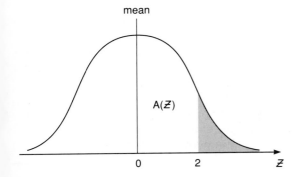

Fig. 13.4

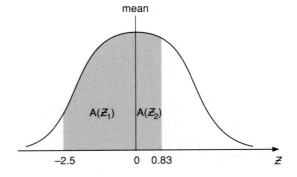

169

We must find the area under the normal curve from:

$$\bar{X}_1 = 168.75 \text{ to } \bar{X}_2 = 173.75$$

$$Z_1 = \frac{\bar{X}_1 - \mu_{\bar{x}}}{\sigma_{\bar{x}}}$$

$$= \frac{168.75 - 172.50}{1.5}$$

$$= \frac{-3.75}{1.5}$$

$$= -2.5$$

$$Z_2 = \frac{\bar{X}_2 - \mu_{\bar{x}}}{\sigma_{\bar{x}}}$$

$$= \frac{173.75 - 172.50}{1.5}$$

$$= \frac{1.25}{1.5}$$

$$= 0.83$$

$$A(Z_1) = 0.494$$

$$A(Z_2) = 0.297$$

$$\text{Required area} = 0.494 + 0.297$$

$$= 0.791$$

Therefore the probability of the sample mean being between 168.75 and 173.75 cm = 0.791

Expected number of samples

$$= \text{probability} \times \text{number of samples}$$

$$= 0.791 \times 50$$

$$= 39.55$$

$$= \text{approximately } 40$$

EXERCISE A

1 In a normal distribution with mean 73.5 and standard deviation 2.80, find the probability that in a sample of 100 variates, the mean will be:
   a) more than 74.
   b) less than 72.6.

2 In a normal distribution with mean 53.6 and standard deviation 3.50, find the probability that in a sample of 36 variates, the mean will be:
   a) less than 52.8.
   b) between 53.2 and 54.

3 In a building society, the average account is £1608.50 with a standard deviation of £180. What is the probability that a group of 81 accounts taken at random, will show an average deposit of £1650 or more?

4 The heights of a certain group of adults are normally distributed with a mean of 170.75 cm and a standard deviation of 6.25 cm. If 25 people are chosen at random from the group, what is the probability that their mean height will be 172.25 cm or more?

5 If all possible samples of size 36 are drawn from a normally distributed population with mean 30 and standard deviation 3, within what range will the middle 50% of the sample means lie?

6 The weekly wages of a certain industry are normally distributed with a mean of £200. If 10% of the mean wages of samples of 25 workers fall below £195, what is the standard deviation of weekly wages in this industry?

7 a) Assuming that the heights of men are normally distributed with a standard deviation of 5 cm, how large a sample should be taken to be fairly sure (with a probability of 0.95) that the sample mean does not differ from the population mean by more than 1.0, in absolute value?
   b) How large a sample would need to be taken to be 99% sure?

8 A normal population has a standard deviation of 3. How large a sample should be taken in order to be 99% sure that the sample mean differs from the true mean by less than 0.5?

Confidence limits

Suppose we have a sample of N variates with mean $\bar{x}$ and standard deviation s selected from a normal population. Let us consider the problem of estimating the mean of the population from this single sample. It is obviously impossible to determine the population mean precisely, since this sample could have been taken from any population with roughly the same size of mean. What we can do, is establish **limits** within which the mean of the population will fall with a specified probability or **confidence**.

To illustrate this, suppose a random sample of 100 variates is taken from a normal population. The mean of the sample is found to be 30 and the standard deviation is 5. From this one sample we will try to estimate the mean of the population with a probability of 95% (or 95% confidence).

With a probability of 0.95 the population mean will fall in the shaded area of the diagram.

Fig. 13.5

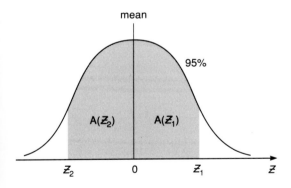

That is, $A(Z_1) = 0.475$

$$A(Z_2) = 0.475$$

$$\mu_{\bar{x}} = \mu$$

$$\sigma_{\bar{x}} = \frac{\sigma}{\sqrt{N}}$$

We do not know either $\sigma_{\bar{x}}$ or σ. However, the standard error, $\sigma/\sqrt{N}$, of the sample mean from the population mean i.e. the difference between the sample mean and the population mean becomes smaller as N becomes larger, so that for a **large sample**, we may assume that the standard deviation of the sample, s, approximates to σ.

Thus $\qquad \sigma_{\bar{x}} = \dfrac{\sigma}{\sqrt{N}}$

$$= \frac{s}{\sqrt{N}} = \frac{5}{\sqrt{100}} = \frac{5}{10} = 0.5$$

From the tables we find that

$$Z = +1.96$$
$$Z = -1.96$$

that is, we must say

$$Z = \pm 1.96$$

$$Z = \frac{\bar{X} - \mu_{\bar{x}}}{\sigma_{\bar{x}}}$$

$$\pm 1.96 = \frac{30 - \mu}{0.5}$$

$$\therefore \pm 1.96 \times 0.5 = 30 - \mu$$

$$\therefore \mu = 30 - (\pm 1.96 \times 0.5)$$

$$= 30 \pm 1.96 \times 0.5$$

$$= 30 \pm 0.980$$

With 95% confidence we can say that the population mean lies within the limits 30 ± 0.980. (The answer is very often left in this form.)

We could also have given the answer like this: the 95% confidence limits for the population mean are 30 ± 0.980. (These limits define the interval which would contain the population mean with a probability of 95%.)

The interval between the confidence limits is called the **confidence interval**.

Fig. 13.6

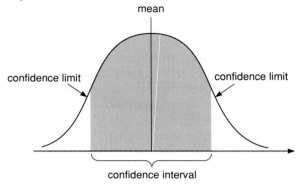

mean

confidence limit ← → confidence limit

confidence interval

With 95% confidence limits, we find Z_1 and Z_2 by using the tables to find the Z score corresponding to these areas

$A(Z_1) = \frac{1}{2}$ of $0.95 = 0.475$

$A(Z_2) = \frac{1}{2}$ of $0.95 = 0.475$

Fig. 13.7a
95% confidence limits

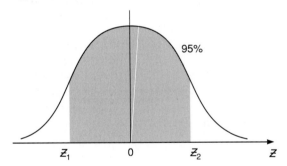

95%

Z_1 0 Z_2 Z

With 99% confidence limits, we find Z_1 and Z_2 by using these areas.

$A(Z_1) = \frac{1}{2}$ of $0.99 = 0.495$

$A(Z_2) = \frac{1}{2}$ of $0.99 = 0.495$

Similarly we can find Z for any specified confidence.

Note We can only use the above method for estimating a population mean when the sample is large, where it is permissible to assume that the standard deviation of the sample can be taken as an approximation of the standard deviation of the population.

Fig. 13.7b
99% confidence limits

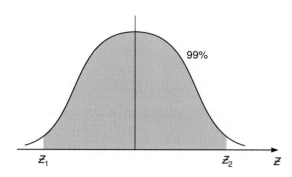

99%

Z_1 Z_2 Z

Example

A sample of 80 variates has a mean of 60 with a standard deviation of 5.5. Find the 98% confidence limits for the mean of the population.

Solution

Here $\bar{X} = 60$

$s = 5.5$

$N = 80$

And, $\mu_{\bar{x}} = \mu$

$\sigma_{\bar{x}} = \dfrac{\sigma}{\sqrt{N}}$

$= \dfrac{s}{\sqrt{N}}$ (Since the sample is large σ can be taken as s.)

$= \dfrac{5.5}{\sqrt{80}} = \dfrac{5.5}{8.94} = 0.62$

172

Fig. 13.8

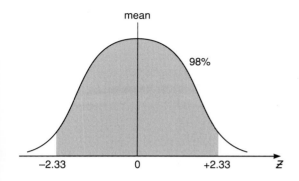

mean

98%

−2.33   0   +2.33 z

With a probability of 0.98

$$A(Z_1) = \tfrac{1}{2} \text{ of } 0.98 = 0.49$$

and

$$A(Z_2) = 0.49$$

$$\therefore \; Z_1 = +2.33$$

$$\therefore \; Z_2 = -2.33$$

that is

$$Z = \pm 2.33$$

$$Z = \frac{\overline{X} - \mu_{\overline{x}}}{\sigma_{\overline{x}}}$$

$$\therefore \; \pm 2.33 = \frac{60 - \mu}{0.62}$$

$$\therefore \; \pm 2.33 \times 0.62 = 60 - \mu$$

$$\therefore \; \mu = 60 \pm 2.33 \times 0.62$$

$$= 60 \pm 1.4446$$

$$= 60 \pm 1.44$$

The 98% confidence limits for the population mean are:

$$60 \pm 1.44$$

EXERCISE B

1 In a sample of 60 variates, the mean is 30 and the standard deviation 3.8. Find the limits within which the population mean is expected to lie, with a probability of 95%.

2 A sample of 100 variates has a mean of 65 and a standard deviation of 2.5. Find the 99% confidence limits for the mean of the population.

3 Find the 98% confidence limits for the mean of a population, if a sample of 90 variates taken from the population has a mean of 12.6 and a standard deviation of 3.

4 Suppose the standard deviation of heights in males is 6.25 cm. Two hundred male students in a large university are measured and their average height is found to be 171.05 cm. Within what range of heights would you expect to find the mean height of the men in this university with a confidence of 95%?

5 In the same university, the heights of 100 women students were measured and the mean height was found to be 161.25 cm with a standard deviation of 5.5 cm. With 95% confidence, find the limits within which the mean height of the women in that university lie.

6 A sample of 50 light bulbs was taken from a very large batch produced in a factory. The mean life of the bulbs was found to be 2.5 years with a standard deviation of 6 months. Estimate the mean life of the batch of bulbs with a probability of 99%.

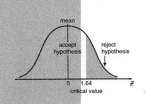

14 SIGNIFICANCE TESTS

In statistics, we often wish to find out if something that occurs is within the normal range of events or whether it is so far out with the normal range that something is wrong somewhere.

For instance, we find that in tossing a coin 100 times, we obtain 60 heads. Is this a 'reasonable' number of heads to get or is there something wrong with the coin? Is it biased in some way? (We assume the coin is being tossed properly.)

This is the kind of thing we are concerned with in significance testing. What we have to do is to formulate a **statistical hypothesis** and then test this hypothesis.

Suppose we wish to test the honesty of the coin mentioned above. We first make the assumption that the coin is honest, that is, that it is equally likely to show a head or a tail. This is our statistical hypothesis (**null hypothesis**). Then working on this basis, we calculate the probability of obtaining 60 or more heads out of 100 tosses. (We do not use exactly 60 heads since the probability of obtaining exactly 60 heads is extremely small.)

Method

$$\text{Hypothesis: } p = \tfrac{1}{2} \text{ (head)}$$

$$q = \tfrac{1}{2}$$

$$N = 100$$

$$\mu = Np$$

$$= 100 \times \tfrac{1}{2}$$

$$= 50$$

$$\sigma = \sqrt{Npq}$$

$$= \sqrt{\tfrac{100}{1} \times \tfrac{1}{2} \times \tfrac{1}{2}}$$

$$= 5$$

We have now calculated the mean and standard deviation of the binomial distribution given by $(p + q)^{100}$.

The score we are interested in is 60 heads. To include 60 heads we take X as 59.5; and calculate the standard score.

$$Z = \frac{X - \mu}{\sigma}$$

$$= \frac{59.5 - 50}{5}$$

$$= \frac{9.5}{5}$$

$$= 1.9$$

$$A(Z) = 0.471$$

$$\therefore \text{ Required area} = 0.5 - 0.471$$

$$= 0.029$$

The probability of obtaining

60 or more heads $= 0.029$

We have calculated that if an honest coin is tossed 100 times, the probability of obtaining 60 or more heads is 0.029; certainly not a high probability.

Fig. 14.1

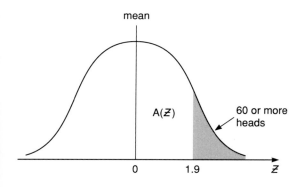

From this result we are justified in drawing one of two conclusions.

1 *The hypothesis is correct but a rare event has occurred.*

2 *The hypothesis is not correct.*

In statistics, we decide that if the probability is less than a given value α, called the **significance level**, then the hypothesis is not correct; if the probability is greater than α, then the hypothesis is correct. We leave ourselves open to two types of error here.

A type I error is when a correct hypothesis is rejected.

A type II error is when an incorrect hypothesis is accepted.

If the calculated probability is less than α, indicating the hypothesis is false, the result is said to be **significant**.

The value give to α may be different in different situations. So we must always state that our conclusions are based on a certain level of significance. We customarily take α to have the value 0.05 (the 5% level of significance).

Looking back at our example about the coin.

The probability of 60 or more heads = 0.029

Significance level, $\alpha = 0.05$

The probability is less than α.

This is a *significant result*.

Thus, at the 5% level of significance the

hypothesis is rejected so the coin is not honest.

If we were testing a new and potentially dangerous drug, a much smaller level of significance would be chosen, perhaps $\alpha = 0.01$.

ONE- AND TWO-TAILED TESTS

In the significance test on the coin in the last section, we used only one end or 'tail' of the normal curve. This was a **one-tailed test**. If both 'tails' are used, we refer to this as a **two-tailed test**.

The decision to use a one- or two-tailed test must be reached by careful consideration of the question to be answered. If the interest in the problem is restricted to the fact that a very low or very high result is obtained (but not both) a one-tailed test is called for, otherwise a two-tailed test should be applied. In case of doubt, a two-tailed test is recommended.

When $\alpha = 0.05$, a result in a two-tailed test is significant if Z falls in the shaded part of Figure 14.2a, that is, if Z is greater than $+1.96$ or less than -1.96, where 1.96 is the value of Z obtained from the tables for each of the shaded areas, equal to 0.025 (half of 0.05).

Similarly in a one-tailed test, the result is significant if Z falls in the shaded area of

Fig. 14.2a
Two-tailed test for $\alpha = 0.05$

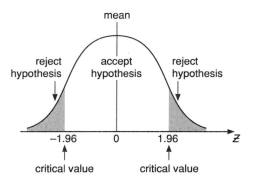

Fig. 14.2b
One-tailed test for $\alpha = 0.05$

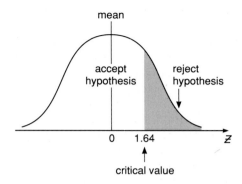

Figure 14.2b, that is, if Z is greater than 1.64, where 1.64 is the Z value for the shaded area of 0.05.

These values of Z (± 1.96 and 1.64) are called **critical values**.

Example

According to genetic theory, we know that certain crosses of peas should give tall plants and short plants in a ratio of 4:1. In a particular experiment, 170 tall plants and 30 short plants were obtained. Is this a significant deviation from the theory on the basis of the 5% level of significance?

Solution

Here we are testing the hypothesis that the probability of obtaining tall plants is $\frac{4}{5}$.

Fig. 14.3

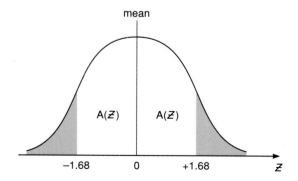

Since this question concerns a deviation from theory, and this deviation may occur on either side of the expected result, a two-tailed test is applicable.

Hypothesis: $p = \frac{4}{5}$ (tall plants)

$$q = \frac{1}{5}$$

$$N = 200$$

$$\mu = Np$$

$$= 200 \times \frac{4}{5}$$

$$= 160$$

$$\sigma = \sqrt{Npq}$$

$$= \sqrt{\frac{200}{1} \times \frac{4}{5} \times \frac{1}{5}}$$

$$= \sqrt{32}$$

$$= 5.66$$

The score we are interested in is 170 tall plants.

So, we take x as 169.5 to include 170

$$Z = \frac{x - \mu}{\sigma}$$

$$= \frac{169.5 - 160}{5.66}$$

$$= \frac{9.5}{5.66}$$

$$= 1.68$$

$$A(Z) = 0.454$$

Since a two-tailed test is used:

required area for $Z \quad > 1.68 = 0.5 - 0.454$

$$= 0.046$$

required area for $Z \quad < -1.68 = 0.046$

total area $= 0.092$

probability $= 0.092$

$$\alpha = 0.05$$

The probability is greater than α.

On the 5% level of significance, this result is not significant, so there is no significant deviation from the genetic theory.

EXERCISE A

Unless told otherwise, use the 5% level of significance. Answer each question exactly in the form in which it is asked.

1 A die is rolled 120 times. If a 6 is obtained 26 times, have we cause to doubt the honesty of the die?

2 A coin is tossed 400 times. Heads turn up 250 times. Is this an honest coin?

3 A pair of dice are rolled 360 times. Two sixes show 15 times. Have we any reason to think the dice are 'loaded'?

4 From experience it is known that 30% of a certain kind of seed germinate. If in an experiment only 70 out of 300 seeds germinate, is this a significantly poor germination at the 1% level of significance?

5 In a factory manufacturing a certain product it is known from long experience that 7% of the articles do not come up to standard and have to be discarded. A new worker who has been taken on has made 400 articles of which 36 are defective. Is there any reason to doubt the person's ability to do the job?

6 According to genetic theory, the offspring of a certain cross between rabbits should be white to not white in a ratio of 3:7. In one experiment the number of rabbits not white was 71, and the number of white rabbits was 19. Was this result consistent with the genetic theory?

7 A sample of 100 has a mean of 55 and a standard deviation of 9.
a) Does the mean of this sample differ significantly at the 5% level of significance from a population mean of 56?
b) Is the sample mean significantly better at the 5% level than a population mean of 53 (using a one-tailed test)?
c) Calculate from the sample the 95% confidence limits for the population mean.

8 The heights of adult men in a certain town have a mean of 171.55 cm with a standard deviation of 6.0 cm. A sample of 144 men living in a poor area is found to have a mean height of 170.00 cm. Does this indicate that the residents of this area are significantly checked in growth on the basis of the 1% level of significance?

9 A manufacturer of springs has established from several years' experience that the springs he makes have a mean stretching point of 14.6 kg (the springs do not go back into shape after this point) with a standard deviation of 2.2 kg. After a change in the manufacturing process, a sample of 50 springs is taken and the mean stretching point is found to be 13 kg with a standard deviation of 2 kg. Has the new process had a significantly damaging effect on the strength of the springs?

10 A car manufacturer claims that his cars use an average of 2.80 gallons of petrol for each 100 miles. A car salesman tests 40 cars made by this company, for petrol mileage, and he finds the average petrol consumption to be 2.88 gallons for each 100 miles with a standard deviation of 0.2 gallons. Do these results cast doubts on the manufacturer's claim (1% level)?

15 DEMOGRAPHIC STATISTICS

The statistical study of human populations is called **demography**. Demographic studies provide the facts and figures that are essential for the efficient magagement of a country by its government. In this country, population statistics are collected in two main ways. Firstly, **vital statistics** (statistics pertaining to 'life') are obtained on a continuous basis because, by law, all births, deaths and marriages must be registered. Secondly, every tenth year, a **national census** is conducted.

The first complete census of Britain was taken in 1801 and censuses have been taken at ten-yearly intervals since then, with the exception of 1941 when the Second World War was in progress. Traditionally, the census day is a Sunday in late March or early April, chosen so that it does not coincide with the Easter weekend. The questions on the census forms cover, for individuals, such things as name, date of birth, sex, marital status, usual address, country of birth, job description, employment status, higher educational qualifications after the age of 18 and so on. For the household, there may be questions about the nature of the building, the number of rooms, type of housing tenure, provision of bathrooms, and so on. The questions vary from one census to another and are compiled to provide the government with whatever information it would like to have with regard to the population. Before the census forms are finalised, the proposed questions must be acceptable to Members of Parliament.

Conducting a national census is a mammoth task and costs millions of pounds. The planning of a census begins five years before it is due to take place. The country is divided up into enumeration districts corresponding to local administration areas and enumerators are recruited to deal with distributing the census forms in person and then collecting in the completed forms. A form is delivered to every household, hotel, hospital, boarding school, and so on, in the district. The head of a household is responsible for filling in the form with respect to every individual in the house on census night. In establishments such as hotels, individuals fill in separate forms (to protect their confidentiality) which are handed over to the person in charge of the establishment. It is against the law not to fill in a census form and any person refusing to complete one is taken to court and fined. The enumerators collect the forms after census night and must check that all questions have been answered. They may also help anyone who has difficulty filling in the form, for example, someone who is blind or illiterate, or they can arrange for the services of an interpreter if there is a language problem.

The names and addresses of individuals are used only as a check that all households and persons have been enumerated. After the forms have been processed by computer, they are stored away for 100 years before they become available to the Public Records Office.

So, no information about particular persons is accessible to anyone outside the census organisation for 100 years.

In the past, it used to take several years to collate all the data collected in a census as compiling the information by hand was a long, laborious process. Nowadays, with the help of computers, some of the data is available almost immediately, for example, the total population figure. The detailed processing, county by county, may take nearly a year before the statistics are published.

By using both the vital statistics and the census returns, demographers can classify the population with respect to such variables as age, sex, marital condition and geographical distribution and calculate secondary statistics such as birth rates, death rates and fertility rates. Also, depending on the questions on the census forms, information can be gained about things like the housing conditions of the population. For example, how many people own their homes, or how many households have no proper bathroom facilities.

POPULATION PYRAMIDS

A special type of horizontal histogram called a **population pyramid** is often used to illustrate population statistics. The graph is shaped like a pyramid, wide at the base and narrowing towards the top. It is composed of two charts, one for males and one for females, arranged 'back to back', with the vertical scale giving the age range in years, from zero at the bottom to 100 at the top. The horizontal axis gives the numbers or percentages of each age group in the total population, reading from the centre to the right for females and from the centre to the left for males.

Population pyramids are a useful way of comparing two populations particularly when the horizontal scale is given in percentages. Demographers may wish to study the age distribution of the present population of a

Population of England and Wales (1981 Census)		
Age (years)	Number of males (thousands)	Number of females (thousands)
0–4	1493	1418
5–9	1647	1560
10–14	1972	1875
15–19	2054	1966
20–24	1805	1760
25–29	1648	1627
30–34	1835	1882
35–39	1554	1538
40–44	1405	1387
45–49	1351	1338
50–54	1381	1404
55–59	1403	1474
60–64	1196	1337
65–69	1100	1326
70–74	871	1191
75–79	544	914
80–84	248	573
85 and over	119	388

Fig. 15.1
Population of England and Wales (1981 Census)

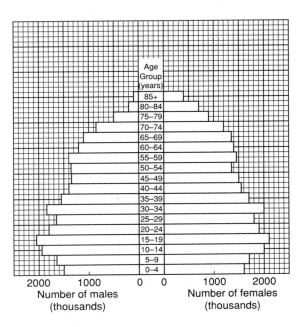

2000   1000   0   0   1000   2000
Number of males (thousands)   Number of females (thousands)

Fig. 15.2
Population of a developing country

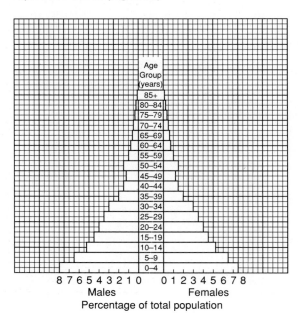

Age Group (years)

85+
80–84
75–79
70–74
65–69
60–64
55–59
50–54
45–49
40–44
35–39
30–34
25–29
20–24
15–19
10–14
5–9
0–4

8 7 6 5 4 3 2 1 0   0 1 2 3 4 5 6 7 8
Males   Females
Percentage of total population

Although in most countries there are fewer female than male births, females tend to live longer than males so the female side of the pyramid is broader at the top.

DEMOGRAPHIC RATES

The information obtained from the population census and from the registration of vital statistics can be used to calculate many demographic rates. In this study, we are mainly interested in birth and death rates.

Birth rate

The simplest measure of the birth rate is the **crude birth rate** which is the number of live births in one year per 1000 of the population.

Crude birth rate

$$= \frac{\text{total number of live births in 1 year}}{\text{total population at middle of year}} \times 1000$$

The crude birth rate depends on the age and sex distribution within the population and is not as useful as the **fertility rate** which is the number of live births in one year per 1000 women of child-bearing age, that is, aged between 15 and 44 years.

Death rate

The simplest measure of mortality is the **crude death rate** which is the number of deaths per 1000 of the population.

Crude death rate

$$= \frac{\text{number of deaths in 1 year}}{\text{total population at middle of year}} \times 1000$$

Again, this is not particularly useful as its value depends on the age distribution of the population in question. For instance, a district with a large number of elderly residents would have a higher crude death rate than would be the case for a district, such as a new

country compared to what it was in previous years or they may wish to compare the populations of different countries for the same year.

A marked difference can be seen in diagrams comparing the age distribution of developed countries with that of developing countries. In developing countries, the pyramid narrows quite quickly (Figure 15.2), whereas in developed countries the pyramid tapers much more slowly (for example, Figure 15.1) because of the lower mortality rate in all age groups. A very noticeable difference is seen at the base of the pyramids. In developing countries, the pyramid has a broad base which thereafter narrows rapidly, indicating a high birth rate with a subsequently high mortality rate in infants and young children. In developed countries, there has been a general fall in the birth rate and so the pyramid does not have its widest part at the base.

Age group	Population at mid-year (thousands)	Deaths	*Age-specific death rate per 1000	Standard population as percentage	Expected number of deaths per 1000 in standard population
0–4	25	200	$\dfrac{200}{25\,000} \times 1000 = 8$	6.0	$8 \times 6\% = 0.48$
5–9	23	46	$\dfrac{46}{23\,000} \times 1000 = 2$	6.6	$2 \times 6.6\% = 0.132$
10–14	26	26	$\dfrac{26}{26\,000} \times 1000 = 1$	7.9	$1 \times 7.9\% = 0.079$
15–24	60	120	$\dfrac{120}{60\,000} \times 1000 = 2$	15.6	$2 \times 15.6\% = 0.312$
25–44	120	360	$\dfrac{360}{120\,000} \times 1000 = 3$	26.4	$3 \times 26.4\% = 0.792$
45–64	85	1275	$\dfrac{1275}{85\,000} \times 1000 = 15$	22.5	$15 \times 22.5\% = 3.375$
65+	35	2800	$\dfrac{2800}{35\,000} \times 1000 = 80$	15.0	$80 \times 15\% = 12.0$
Total	374	4827		100	17.17

town, with a much more youthful population. It is therefore more useful to calculate the **standardised death rate** for an area. To calculate the standardised death rate we consider a **standard population** and calculate what the death rates in the area would have been if the area had had this standard age distribution. The standard population used, is chosen by the demographers, and for an area in England it might be the age distribution for the total population of England and Wales.

The table above shows how the standardised death rate can be calculated for a district with a population of 374 000 and a total of 4827 deaths.

*Age-specific death rate per 1000

$$= \frac{\text{number of deaths}}{\text{population at mid-year}} \times 1000$$

Crude death rate per 1000

$$= \frac{\text{number of deaths}}{\text{population at mid-year}} \times 1000$$

$$= \frac{4827}{374\,000} \times 1000$$

$$= 12.91 \ (2 \text{ d.p.})$$

Standardised death rate per 1000

$$= 17.17 \ (\text{from table})$$

As we can see from the calculations, the crude death rate is considerably lower than the standardised death rate. This is due to the fact that there is a relatively small number of elderly people in this particular population.

EXERCISE A _____

1 The population pyramid (Figure 15.3) shows the age distribution of a small town with 5000 inhabitants.
a) What percentage of the population is under 20 years of age?
b) Which age group shows the same number of males and females?
c) Which age group has twice as many women as men?

181

Fig. 15.3
Population of a small town

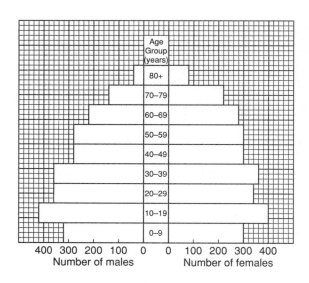

400 300 200 100 0   0 100 200 300 400
Number of males   Number of females

Age (years)	Number of males (1000s)	Number of females (1000s)
0–4	158.2	150.1
5–9	176.3	168.1
10–14	218.2	207.0
15–19	227.8	218.8
20–24	199.8	194.6
25–29	172.8	170.0
30–34	180.5	178.3
35–39	149.5	150.8
40–44	141.3	146.9
45–49	139.5	146.2
50–54	139.6	150.1
55–59	138.4	151.3
60–64	114.4	136.8
65–69	105.7	135.1
70–74	83.2	120.3
75–79	50.9	91.6
80–84	22.5	55.8
85 and over	10.5	35.1

d) How many males are there aged 60 and over?

e) How many females are there aged 60 and over?

f) Suggest a reason for your answers to (d) and (e).

g) What percentage of the population is aged 60 and over?

h) What percentage of the population is under 60 years but at least 20 years old?

2 The age distribution of the population of Scotland (1981 Census) is shown in the table at the top of the next column. Draw a population pyramid similar to Figure 15.1 to illustrate these figures.

3 The second table in the next column gives the age distribution of the population of England and Wales obtained from the censuses conducted in the years shown.

a) The 1981 Census figures show a decrease in the total population compared to the 1971 figures. Give an explanation for this fact.

Population of England and Wales (1000s)

Age (years)	1951	1961	1971	1981
0–4	3718	3597	3905	2910
5–14	5974	6897	7671	7053
15–29	8912	8925	10 236	10 859
30–44	9767	9263	8595	9541
45–64	10 563	11 836	11 849	10 884
65–74	3257	3520	4178	4488
75+	1568	1976	2318	2786
Total	43 758	46 105	48 750	48 522

b) What trend is noticeable from 1951 to 1981 for the age group 65 years and over?

c) Calculate, for each year, the percentage of people aged 65 years and over in the population. Give a reason for the answers you obtained.

d) Calculate, for each year, the percentage of children under 5 years old in the population. Comment on your answers.

182

Table 1

Age (years)	Town A		Town B		Town C	
	Male	Female	Male	Female	Male	Female
0–14	1297	1167	940	847	1623	1444
15–44	2624	2524	2141	2049	3568	3550
45–64	1291	1401	1450	1555	564	601
65+	720	1080	1035	2010	204	306

4 Table 1 shows the age distribution one year of the populations of three small towns of the same approximate size.

Table 2

	Town A	Town B	Town C
Deaths	155	232	95
Births	157	129	213

Table 2 shows the number of births and deaths for the same year.

Use these tables to calculate, for each town:

a) the crude death rate.

b) the crude birth rate.

c) the fertility rate.

Comment on the differences or similarities in these rates and try to explain them.

5 Calculate the crude and standardised death rates for Town X and Town Y using the data given in the table below.

Note When using a calculator to get the standardised death rate, do *NOT* round off the intermediate answers.

Age (years)	Town X		Town Y		Standard population as a percentage
	Population	Number of deaths	Population	Number of deaths	
0–4	1200	19	900	15	6.0
5–9	1300	6	975	5	6.6
10–14	1580	5	1170	5	7.9
15–24	3180	24	2115	18	15.6
25–44	5400	30	3390	25	26.4
45–64	4140	76	3450	70	22.5
65+	3200	150	3000	140	15.0
Totals	20 000	310	15 000	278	100

ANSWERS

CHAPTER 1

EXERCISE A   Page 7 ——————————

  1 Fatima, Pauline
  2 Frank, Gino, Henry, Fatima, Shaheen
  3 Denzil, Tom, Pauline, Shaheen
  4 Susan
  5 1
  6 Norma, Susan
  7 Fatima
  8 3
  9 Henry
 10 Henry, Shaheen

EXERCISE B   Page 9 ——————————

  1 a) To show that the 'suns' are all the
    same size
    b) 10 hours
    c) 25, 35, 40, 40 hours
    d) 5 hours
    e) $2\frac{1}{2}$ hours

EXERCISE C   Page 11 ——————————

  1 a) Service bus or school bus
    b) Private car
    c) Walk
    d) Service bus or school bus
    e) 15
    f) 16
    g) 178
  2 a) Asia
    b) Australia
    c) 6200 m

    d) Aconcagua
    e) Africa
    f) Markham
  3 a) £42 000
    b) Perth
    c) Edinburgh and Inverness
    d) £8000
  4 b) 6600 km
    c) Irtysh
    d) Amazon
    e) Mississippi Missouri and Amazon or
    Yangtze and Irtysh
  7 a) Class B
    b) 5
    c) 4
    d) 13
    e) i) 1st Wednesday–1st Thursday
      ii) 1st Monday–1st Tuesday
    f) 1st Tuesday, 1st Thursday, 1st Friday

EXERCISE D   Page 14 ——————————

  1 a) 5800
    b) 3000
    c) 48%
    d) $\frac{20}{23}$
    e) $\frac{3}{35}$

EXERCISE E   Page 15 ——————————

  1 a) More or less apart from the drop in
    July and August
    b) July and August
    c) April to May
    d) June–July and September–October

EXERCISE F   Page 21 ——————

1 Full employment   47
  Full-time education   45
  YTS   49
  Unemployment   30
  Unknown   9

EXERCISE G   Page 23 ——————

6 a) Henry
  b) Fiona
  c) Morag, Henry
9 The temperature scale does not start at zero and any changes appear exaggerated. The time scale is not regular
10 The diameters of the suns are in proportion to the hours of sunshine, but the areas shown by the circles are not to the same ratio
11 The time-scale is not regular. The points are not plotted to scale with regard to the profit figures

CHAPTER 2

EXERCISE A   Page 26 ——————

1 a) 5.63   **d)** 0.0068
  b) 10.1   **e)** 6
  c) 10   **f)** 120
2 a) 11.7   **e)** 7.0
  b) 9.8   **f)** 15.8
  c) 69.0   **g)** 15.8 or 15.9
  d) 0.1   **h)** 15.9
3 a) 600 000
  b) 580 000
  c) 583 000
  d) 582 700
  e) 582 730

EXERCISE B   Page 27 ——————

1 a) i) 1 cm   ii) 1 m   iii) 1 h   iv) 0.1 kg
  v) 0.1 g   vi) 0.001 litres   vii) 0.01 mile
  viii) 0.1 s
  b) i) 0.5 cm   ii) 0.5 m   iii) 0.5 h
  iv) 0.05 kg   v) 0.05 g   vi) 0.0005 l
  vii) 0.005 mile   viii) 0.05 s

c) i) 7.5 cm, 6.5 cm   ii) 186.5 m, 185.5 m
  iii) 17.5 h, 16.5 h   iv) 9.25 kg, 9.15 kg
  v) 12.85 g, 12.75 g   vi) 2.6835 l, 2.6825 l
  vii) 1.215 mile, 1.205 mile
  viii) 16.55 s, 16.45 s

EXERCISE C   Page 28 ——————

1 a) i) 0.5 m   ii) 0.5 kg   iii) 0.05 l
  iv) 0.05 s   v) $\frac{1}{14}$ vi) $\frac{1}{70}$ vii) $\frac{1}{34}$ viii) $\frac{1}{500}$
  ix) $\frac{1}{2500}$ x) $\frac{1}{30000}$
  b) i) $\frac{1}{300}$ ii) $\frac{1}{70}$ iii) $\frac{1}{30}$ iv) $\frac{1}{46}$ v) 7.1%
  vi) 1.4%   vii) 2.9%   viii) 0.20%
  ix) 0.040%   x) 0.0033%

EXERCISE D   Page 29 ——————

1 a) 14.80 cm, 14.60 cm
  b) 33.0 g, 31.0 g
  c) 41.0 m, 39.0 m
  d) 40.0 litres, 38.0 litres
2 a) 1.0 m
  b) 1.0 kg
  c) 0.10 g
  d) 0.010 cm
3 a) 15.0 cm, 13.0 cm
  b) 6.0 kg, 4.0 kg
  c) 7.40 m, 7.20 m
  d) 3.70 litres, 3.50 litres
4 a) 1.0 m
  b) 1.0 ml
  c) 0.55 cm
  d) 0.55 g

EXERCISE E   Page 30 ——————

1 a) 503.75   **d)** 165.1425
  b) 19.65   **e)** 10.47
  c) 34.77   **f)** 9.30
2 a) 14.75
  b) 0.43
  c) 0.65
  d) 8.11

EXERCISE F   Page 30 ——————

1 a) 0.5 kg
  b) $\frac{1}{102}$
  c) 0.98%
2 a) 0.05 seconds

b) $\frac{1}{1270}$
c) 0.079%
3 183 cm, 181 cm
4 19 035 ml, 18 965 ml
5 a) 302 m and 298 m
   b) 5075.25 m^2 and 4925.25 m^2
6 13.5375 m^2 and 13.4625 m^2

CHAPTER 3

EXERCISE A   Page 34 ─────────

1 b)

Year	1	2	3	4	5	6
Number of pupils	24	24	26	14	8	4

2

Age (years)	0–4	5–15	16–45	46–65	65+
Number of people	3	9	10	15	3

3

Class	1	2	3	4	5	6	7
Number of pupils	6	6	7	7	7	9	8

4 Numbers for sample: 295, 297, 281, 264, 167, 276, 272, 35, 132, 107
5 Numbers for sample: 29, 52, 79, 70, 2
6 a) Every twentieth employee
   b) Numbers for sample: 356, 360, 87, 2, 153, 89, 112, 56, 23, 167, 295, 297, 254, 314, 379, 276, 252, 90, 430, 271, 332, 159, 65, 192, 412
7 a) Every eighth employee
   b) Numbers for sample: 35, 63, 60, 8, 70, 2, 59, 11, 53, 56

CHAPTER 4

EXERCISE A   Page 36 ─────────

1 Quantitative − continuous
2 Quantitative − discrete
3 Qualitative

4 Quantitative − continuous
5 Qualitative
6 Quantitative − discrete
7 Quantitative − continuous
8 Quantitative − continuous
9 Quantitative − discrete
10 Quantitative − discrete
11 Quantitative − continuous
12 Qualitative
13 Quantitative − continuous

EXERCISE B   Page 38 ─────────

1

Stem	Leaf
9	9
10	7 8 8 8 9 9 9
11	0 0 1 1 2 2 3 3 4 4 5
12	1

2

Stem	Leaf
5	1 2 2
6	0 1 2 6 8 8 9
7	1 4 7 8 9
8	0 1 4
9	1 2

3

Class A		Class B
	0	8 8 9
9	1	3 5 7 7 8 9
5 5 4 3	2	0 1 1 2 7 7 8 8 9
9 7 6 6 5 5 4 4 3 1 1 0	3	0 1 2 2 3
8 7 3 2 1 0 0	4	3 4
0	5	

4

School A		School B
7 2 2 1	0	1 2
9 9 8 8 7 3 3 1 0	1	3 4 4 6
9 6 4 4 3 2	2	1 1 3 4 4 5 8
3 1 0	3	1 3 4 4 5 6 7
1 1	4	0 2 5 7

1

Heights	Frequency
142	1
144	1
146	0
148	3
150	5
152	8
154	10
156	4
158	6
160	1
162	0
164	1

a) Continuous
b) 22 cm
c) 154 cm
d) 0.25 or 25%
e) 5
f) 5%
g) 67.5%

3

Number of children	Frequency
1	2
2	4
3	5
4	2
5	4
6	7
7	1
8	1
9	1
10	2

a) Discrete
b) 6 children
c) Families with no children
d) 5
e) 37.9%

5 a)

Goals	0	1	2	3	4
Frequency	3	14	4	6	1

b) Discrete
c) 4 goals

d) 1 goal
e) 0.5 or 50%
f) 39.3%

1 a) 22   d) 0.18
  b) 13   e) 6
  c) 16   f) 6

2 a) The half sizes do not have as large frequencies as might be expected. We discovered that this trend was markedly obvious all through the school for all age groups of boys and girls. To try to explain this, some pupils visited shoe shops in the area and interviewed the managers. The two main explanations for this trend were that mothers were inclined to buy the next whole size of shoe to allow for growth, rather than take the half size; and that the cheaper makes of shoes are often only made in whole sizes
  b) 68
  c) 5
  d) 0.29 or 29%
  e) 0.103 or 10.3%

3

Number of words	Frequency
1	1
2	0
3	2
4	0
5	2
6	4
7	3
8	11
9	7
10	3
11	3
12	1
13	1

a) 38   e) 8
b) 8   f) 3
c) 12   g) 18
d) 0.18

5 b) 32
   c) 4
   d) 8
   e) 21.9

EXERCISE E   Page 44 ────────────

1 a) 30
   b) 8
   c) 76
4 a) 3.6
5

Goals	Frequency	Relative frequency (%)
0	6	13.6
1	17	38.6
2	10	22.7
3	6	13.6
4	4	9.1
5	1	2.3

EXERCISE F   Page 47 ────────────

1

Mark	Frequency
1–5	2
6–10	6
11–15	8
16–20	10
21–25	6
26–30	3
31–35	2
36–40	1
41–45	1
46–50	1

a) 23   **e)** 0.2
b) 25.5   **f)** 20%
c) 5.5   **g)** 60%
d) Fourth class

2

Score	Frequency
25–29	1
30–34	4
35–39	9
40–44	17
45–49	6
50–54	3

4

Number of rainy days	Frequency
140–149	1
150–159	4
160–169	4
170–179	7
180–189	11
190–199	10
200–209	9
210–219	2
220–229	5
230–239	4
240–249	3
250–259	2
260–269	3

a) 174.5   **d)** Fifth class
b) 189.5   **e)** 37
c) 239.5   **f)** 56.9%

EXERCISE G   Page 48 ────────────

1 a) 65   **e)** Second class
   b) 50.5   **f)** 0.4
   c) 125.5   **g)** 20%
   d) 88   **h)** 7.7%
2 a) 80   **e)** 55–59 kg
   b) 49.5   **f)** 52
   c) 44.5   **g)** Fourth class
   d) 45–49 kg   **h)** 0.325

EXERCISE I   Page 53 ────────────

1 a) 10

EXERCISE J   Page 55 ────────────

1

Heights (cm)	Cumulative frequency
146	1
146–148	1
146–150	2
146–152	5
146–154	8
146–156	12
146–158	15
146–160	20
146–162	26
146–164	27
146–166	29
146–168	30

a) 1
b) 60%
c) 3

2 a)

Time	Cumulative frequency
0–20	0
0–40	2
0–60	6
0–80	13
0–100	24
0–120	52
0–140	72
0–160	88
0–180	98
0–200	104
0–220	107

b) 6
c) 51.4%

3 Frequency table is shown below
   a) 29
   b) 6
   c) 7

Weight (kg)	Cumulative frequency
35–39	1
35–44	3
35–49	6
35–54	14
35–59	22
35–64	26
35–69	27
35–74	27
35–79	28
35–84	29

4 a)

Score	Frequency
65	1
66	2
67	2
68	8
69	7
70	7
71	5
72	2
73	2
74	2
75	2

b)

Score	Cumulative frequency
65	1
65–66	3
65–67	5
65–68	13
65–69	20
65–70	27
65–71	32
65–72	34
65–73	36
65–74	38
65–75	40

c) 20
d) 8

EXERCISE L   Page 57 ───────────

1 a) Qualitative
   b) Quantitative — discrete
   c) Qualitative
   d) Quantitative — continuous

2 a)

Length (cm)	Cumulative frequency
0–19	0
0–20	1
0–21	4
0–22	6
0–23	10
0–24	19
0–25	27
0–26	33
0–27	38
0–28	39
0–29	39
0–30	40

b)

Length (cm)	Cumulative frequency
20	1
21	3
22	2
23	4
24	9
25	8
26	6
27	5
28	1
29	0
30	1

c) 19
d) 7
e) 24 cm
f) 23.5 cm

3 b)

Interval (min)	Frequency
3	2
4	1
5	3
6	1
7	2
8	2
9	2
10	4
11	2
12	2
13	1

d) 10 minutes
e) 13

4 a)

Weight (kg)	Frequency
35–39	0
40–44	1
45–49	2
50–54	6
55–59	4
60–64	3
65–69	3
70–74	1

b) 50–54 kg
c) 45–49 kg
d) 44.5–49.5 kg

5

Year	Number of pupils
1	150
2	162
3	156
4	138
5	114

6 a) 1600–1799 h
c)

Lifetime (h)	Cumulative frequency
0–999	0
0–1199	8
0–1399	24
0–1599	52
0–1799	84
0–1999	96
0–2199	100
0–2399	100

d) 52

CHAPTER 5

EXERCISE A   Page 61

1

	Mean	Median	Mode
a)	approx. 9.2	10	11
b)	23	22.5	21
c)	3	3	3

2 The mode, because it is the lowest
3 a) 162 cm
  b) 158 cm or 162 cm
  c) 162.1 cm
6 The mode would be the easiest to find and the mean the hardest
7 Mean = £6.80 Median = £6.20

EXERCISE B   Page 62

1 Approximately 1.25 goals
3 Approximately 3.9 children
5 Approximately 9.3 words per line

EXERCISE C   Page 64

1 Approximately 56.4 marks
2 Approximately 39.4 years
3 Approximately 39.7 years
4 Approximately 77.4 hours
5 23.8
6 479.8 g
7 £84.38

EXERCISE D Page 66 ────────

1 a) 29.5
  b) 23.5
2 a) 23.8
  b) 55%
  c) 45%
3 a) 158.1 cm
  b) 122.5 seconds
  c) 55 kg
  d) 69.7 strokes
4 a) 572 deaths

EXERCISE E Page 69 ────────

1 i) 6 ii) 2.4 iii) 3.1 iv) 4.8 v) 4.4
  vi) 6.6 vii) 3.7 viii) 5.5 ix) 5.2 x) 3.5
2 122
3 134
4 £273.86

EXERCISE F Page 69 ────────

1 a) 5, 5, 5
  b) 79, 83, 90
  c) 42, $35\frac{1}{2}$, 24
2 a) 6
  b) 11.1
  c) 6.4
3 a) 5.1, 5, 4
  b) Mean
4 a) 2   **c)** 5.7%
  b) 2.5   **d)** 41.5%
5 b) 49.9 min
  c) 52 min
  d) 24%
6 a) 21.9 kg   **c)** 18.5 kg
  b) 21.7 kg   **d)** 77.5%
7 a) 3
  b) 4.2
  c) 4
8 a) 4.6
  b) 54.5
  c) 24.7 cm
9 8.1 mins
10 a) 48 kg
  b) 56.75 kg
11 a) 1571.5 hours
  b) 1590 hours (approximately)

12 a) Mode
  b) All equal
  c) Mean

CHAPTER 6

EXERCISE A Page 75 ────────

1
  a)

  b)

  c)

  d)

	Range	Semi-interquartile range
a)	6	1.5
b)	10	3
c)	10	3
d)	8	3

2 a) Median = 70.3 kg
  b) Interquartile range = 2.8 kg
  c) 6 kg
  d) 27 boys
  e) 22 boys

  f)

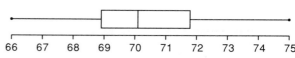

3 a) 46 marks; 64 marks
  b) 9.2 marks; 12.7 marks
  c) 76 pupils
  d) 45.7%
  e) 65 marks
4 a) Boys: 162.2 cm Girls: 161.5 cm
  b) Boys: 4 cm Girls: 2.5 cm
  c) 7 girls

d) 9 boys
e) 8 girls
f) 16 boys
g)

| 147 | 149 | 151 | 153 | 155 | 157 | 159 | 161 | 163 | 165 | 167 | 169 | 171 |

5

	Median	Quartiles	Semi-interquartile range
French	51	41, 59.5	9.25
English	52.5	48, 57.5	4.75

EXERCISE B   Page 77 _____

1 a) 2.86
b) 4
c) 5.5

EXERCISE C   Page 80 _____

1 a) Mean = 7, s^2 = 8.5, s = 2.92
b) Mean = 23.4, s^2 = 10.53, s = 3.24
c) Mean = 65, s^2 = 7.43, s = 2.73
d) Mean = 35.5, s^2 = 8.75, s = 2.96
e) Mean = 29.2, s^2 = 57.76, s = 7.60
2 Mean = 25°C, s^2 = 3, s = 1.73
3 Mean = −9.3°C, s^2 = 6.01, s = 2.45
4 North Scotland mean = 19.4, s = 4.37
East Scotland mean = 16.6, s = 3.82
West Scotland mean = 19.8, s = 4.14
5 Mean = 163.05 cm, s = 6.37 cm
6 Mean = 156.47 cm, s = 5.48
8 Mean = 24.5 marks, s = 8.15
9 Mean = 53.25 kg, s = 9.67 kg
11 1964 mean = 9.77, s = 1.71
1989 mean = 9.74, s = 1.75
12 Mean = 18 s, s = 4.8 s

EXERCISE D   Page 83 _____

1 a) 45, 6   **d)** 20, 2
b) 30, 4   **e)** 7.5, 1
c) 25, 2   **f)** 12, 2
2 a) 25, 2.25   **d)** 120, 9
b) 300, 27   **e)** 205, 18
c) 90, 9   **f)** 45, 4.5

3 a) 115, 12.5   **e)** 48, 5
b) 24, 2.5   **f)** 67, 7.5
c) 20, 2.5   **g)** 50, 5
d) 11.5, 1.25   **h)** 11, 1.25
4 a) 105, 15.6   **d)** 25, 3.9
b) 25, 3.9   **e)** 186, 23.4
c) 114, 15.6
5 a) 7
b) 2.67
c) 19, 5.34
6 a) 58.3   **c)** 34.15, 2.74
b) 5.48   **d)** 12.575, 1.37

EXERCISE E   Page 85 _____

1 May
2 a) Third exam
b) No, it was the same
3 a)

Pupil	Mark	Deviate from mean	Standard score
Alan	68	68 − 64 = + 4	$+\frac{1}{2}$
Betty	72	72 − 64 = + 8	+1
Eion	56	56 − 64 = − 8	−1
Mario	60	60 − 64 = − 4	$-\frac{1}{2}$
Evelyn	80	80 − 64 = +16	+2
Fay	76	76 − 64 = +12	$+1\frac{1}{2}$

b)

Pupil	Mark	Deviate from mean	Standard score
Alan	58	+9	$+1\frac{1}{2}$
Betty	52	+3	$+\frac{1}{2}$
Eion	43	−6	−1
Mario	49	0	0
Evelyn	64	+15	$+2\frac{1}{2}$
Fay	55	+6	+1

c) Alan
d) Betty and Fay
e) Eion
4 Mary
5 Lois, Rosa, Mary

EXERCISE F   Page 86 ———————

1 a) 13, 2
  b) i) 15, 2   ii) 26, 4   iii) 28, 4
  c) 32, 38, 44, 50, 56, 62, 68
2 a) 7   **f)** 3.14
  b) 7   **g)** 14.86
  c) 3.5   **h)** 3.85
  d) 12   **i)** 19, 7.70
  e) 7
3 a) 15   **e)** 4.89
  b) 18   **f)** 29.11
  c) 11.5   **g)** 5.40
  d) 17   **h)** 7.5, 2.71
4 a) 17   **d)** 13.5
  b) 13.5   **e)** 5.59
  c) 10   **f)** 57.5, 27.95
5 a) 3 or 4   **f)** 6
  b) 8   **g)** 2.44
  c) 5   **h)** 7.33
  d) 5   **i)** 2.71
  e) 2.5   **j)** 3.67, 0.90
6 a) 10
  b) 65
7 a) 2   **c)** 1.07
  b) 4   **d)** 7.16
8 a) 6   **c)** 1.66
  b) 24   **d)** 82
9 a) 24.3
  b) 6.0
  c) 24.0
10 a) 23 kg   **c)** 23.4 kg
  b) 7.5 kg   **d)** 5.73 kg
11 6.33, 1.84, 5
12 a) 38.5 y, 10.7 y
  b) 37 y, 9 y, 29.5 y
13 a) 3.5, 1.40
  b) 63.5, 1.40
14 82.4, 12.3
15 a) 64
  b) 12
16 Y, 64

Chapter 7

EXERCISE A   Page 93 ———————

1 a) i) 11   ii) 34
  b) i) 21   ii) 44

2 a) i) 16.5   ii) 30.5
  b) 19
3 a) i) 30.5   ii) 38
  b) 21
4 a) 5.3
  b) 5.5
5 a) i) 16.5   ii) 30
  b) i) 24   ii) 30; 46
6 a) i) 15   ii) 38
  b) i) 21   ii) 64
7 a) 49
  b) 88
  c) 75
8 a) i) 50.5   ii) 65   iii) 79.5
  b) i) 22   ii) 97.5
9 a) 17.5
  b) 30
  c) 40

EXERCISE B   Page 96 ———————

1 a) $y = 2x - 6$
  b) $y = 7 - x$
  c) $y = \frac{1}{2}x + 3\frac{1}{2}$
  d) $y = \frac{2}{3}x + 1\frac{2}{3}$
2 a) $y = \frac{3}{2}x - \frac{1}{2}$
  b) $y = 3\frac{1}{2} - \frac{1}{4}x$
3 $y = \frac{1}{2}x + 5$, 22
4 $y = -1.7x + 11.3$
  a) 6.2
  b) 2.8
5 $y = 0.4x + 7$
6 $y = 0.65x + 8$
7 $y = -6x + 648$
8 $y = 400 - 5t^2$
  a) 400 m
  b) 8.9 s
9 $y = \frac{6}{x} + 4$
  a) 4.6 p
  b) 1200 m

EXERCISE C   Page 100 ———————

1 0.94
2 1
3 −1
4 0.99
5 1

6 -0.875
7 0.46
8 -1
9 1
10 0.93
11 0.14
12 a) 0.33 **c)** 0.60
     b) 0.57 **d)** 0.40

CHAPTER 8

EXERCISE A   Page 105

1 $13\frac{1}{3}$, 10, 9, 10, $11\frac{2}{3}$, 16, $16\frac{2}{3}$, $16\frac{2}{3}$
2 12.4, 10.0, 10.0, 14.0, 14.0, 14.6
3 $41\frac{3}{4}$, $41\frac{1}{4}$, $40\frac{3}{4}$, $38\frac{1}{4}$, $35\frac{3}{4}$, 35, 35, 36, 38
4 7.50, 7.63, 7.78, 8.03, 8.15, 8.10, 8.05,
8.00, 7.88, 7.95, 8.03, 8.03, 8.28, 8.33,
8.48, 8.70
5 384, 333, 317, 300, 280, 125, 139, 129, 129,
116, 129, 90, 59
6 £670, £677, £687, £675, £697, £712, £732,
£742, £757, £750, £778, £852, £923, £922,
£933, £958, £978, £1002, £1068, £1068,
£1062, £1043, £1015, £963, £880
7 4425, 4500, 4550, 4625, 4700, 4675, 4650,
4600, 4700, 4675, 4675, 4825, 4900
8 31.4, 31.8, 32.3, 34.0, 35.3, 36.7, 37.8,
38.4, 39.6, 40.5, 42.0, 43.9, 44.3, 44.7,
45.1, 45.4

EXERCISE B   Page 108

1 a) 18
     b) 2.5, 2.9, 2.3, 2.7; 21.5
2 2350, 2375, 2400, 2450, 2525, 2575, 2575,
2550, 2600, 2575, 2575, 2675, 2625; 2200;
1090
3 9.2 thousand
4 3600, 2500, 2650
5 52.5, 46.8
6 433, 537

EXERCISE C   Page 110

1 8
2 17
3 50%

4 7.5 g per cm^3
5 35.5
6 63.6

EXERCISE D   Page 111

1 A 105, B 120, C 80, D 154, E 184
2 A £10.50, B £9.36, C £1.05, D £335, E £355
3 A 120, B 120, C 90, D 80, E 109
4 147
5 99

EXERCISE E   Page 113

1 156
2 119, 19%
3 111
4 114
5 110

CHAPTER 9

EXERCISE A   Page 119

1 $\frac{5}{6}$
2 a) $\frac{3}{13}$
     b) $\frac{2}{13}$
3 a) $\frac{1}{6}$ **c)** 0
     b) $\frac{1}{3}$ **d)** $\frac{1}{2}$
4 a) $\frac{1}{13}$ **d)** $\frac{3}{13}$
     b) $\frac{1}{52}$ **e)** 0
     c) $\frac{1}{4}$
5 a) $\frac{25}{51}$
     b) $\frac{2}{51}$
     c) Either $\frac{4}{51}$ or $\frac{3}{51}$ depending on whether
the black card removed was a king
6 $\frac{1}{3}$
7 $\frac{3}{4}$
8 a) $\frac{1}{20}$
     b) $\frac{85}{99}$
9 a) $\frac{2}{5}$ **c)** 0
     b) $\frac{3}{5}$ **d)** 1
10 a) $\frac{1}{9}$ **d)** 0
     b) 0 **e)** 1
     c) $\frac{1}{12}$
11 $\frac{1}{4}$
12 a) $\frac{1}{8}$
     b) $\frac{1}{2}$
     c) $\frac{1}{8}$

13 a) $\frac{1}{12}$
   b) $\frac{1}{12}$
   c) 0
14 a) $\frac{1}{4}$
   b) $\frac{1}{2}$
15 a) $\frac{1}{2}$
   b) $\frac{9}{16}$
16 a) $\frac{1}{4}$
   b) $\frac{1}{4}$
17 a) $\frac{1}{8}$ **c)** $\frac{1}{12}$
   b) $\frac{1}{6}$ **d)** $\frac{1}{4}$
18 a) $\frac{1}{12}$
   b) $\frac{1}{24}$
   c) $\frac{1}{2}$
19 $\frac{1}{16}$
20 $\frac{1}{32}$

EXERCISE B   Page 121 ———————

1 £27.50
2 £87.50
3 £5 loss
4 a) Both won, £24 gain
   b) Both lost, £15 loss
   c) Thunder won and Lightning lost, £10 gain
   d) Thunder lost and Lightning won, £1 loss
5 a) £40 gain
   b) £50 loss

EXERCISE C   Page 124 ———————

1 a) $\frac{1}{4}$
   b) $\frac{1}{6}$
   c) $\frac{1}{6}$
2 a) $\frac{1}{9}$ **c)** $\frac{1}{27}$
   b) $\frac{4}{9}$ **d)** $\frac{8}{27}$
3 a) $\frac{1}{15}$ **c)** $\frac{2}{15}$
   b) $\frac{1}{15}$ **d)** $\frac{2}{5}$
4 a) $\frac{5}{12}$
   b) $\frac{3}{4}$
5 a) $\frac{3}{10}$ **c)** $\frac{5}{12}$
   b) $\frac{8}{15}$ **d)** $\frac{17}{30}$
6 a) $\frac{1}{42}$ **d)** $\frac{5}{6}$
   b) $\frac{9}{14}$ **e)** $\frac{11}{21}$
   c) $\frac{9}{14}$

7 a) $\frac{1}{2}$
   b) $\frac{1}{5}$
   c) $\frac{3}{5}$
8 $\frac{1}{64}$
9 $\frac{15}{77}$
10 $\frac{1}{36}$
11 a) $\frac{1}{60}$ **d)** $\frac{1}{15}$
   b) $\frac{1}{30}$ **e)** $\frac{1}{15}$
   c) $\frac{1}{60}$

EXERCISE D   Page 126 ———————

1 a) $\frac{5}{33}$
   b) $\frac{7}{22}$
   c) $\frac{35}{66}$
2 a) $\frac{7}{15}$
   b) $\frac{1}{15}$
3 $\frac{2}{5}$
4 a) $\frac{1}{30}$
   b) $\frac{1}{6}$
   c) $\frac{7}{10}$

EXERCISE E   Page 126 ———————

1 50
2 a) 30
   b) 60
   c) 40
3 a) 20
   b) 40
4 80
5 20
6 a) 46
   b) 75
7 200
8 367
9 80
10 9
11 120

EXERCISE F   Page 127 ———————

1 a) 500
   b) i) $\frac{43}{500}$ ii) 0 iii) $\frac{13}{125}$
2 a) 0.4
   b) 0.36
   c) 0.84
   d) 36
3 $P(\text{P}) + P(\text{Q}) + P(\text{R})$ cannot exceed 1

4 a) i) $\frac{7}{69}$ ii) $\frac{62}{69}$ iii) $\frac{70}{253}$
  b) $\frac{1}{4}$
5 a) i) $\frac{343}{1000}$ ii) $\frac{657}{1000}$
  b) 3
6 a) i) $\frac{1}{36}$ ii) $\frac{1}{18}$ iii) $\frac{1}{12}$ iv) $\frac{1}{9}$ v) $\frac{5}{36}$
  b) i) 3 ii) 6 iii) 8 iv) 11 v) 14 vi) 17
  vii) 14 viii) 11 ix) 8 x) 6 xi) 3

CHAPTER 10

EXERCISE A Page 134 ─────────────

1 a) $\frac{80}{243}$
  b) $\frac{20}{243}$
  c) $\frac{64}{729}$
2 $\frac{1}{81}, \frac{8}{81}, \frac{24}{81}, \frac{32}{81}, \frac{16}{81}$
3 $\frac{35}{128}$
4 0.6561, 0.2916, 0.0486, 0.0036, 0.0001
5 $\frac{7}{64}$
6 $\frac{16}{81}, \frac{32}{81}, \frac{24}{81}, \frac{8}{81}, \frac{1}{81}$
7 $\frac{459}{512}$
8 $\frac{44}{125}$
9 a) $\frac{2187}{16384}$
  b) $\frac{2835}{16384}$
10 0.432
11 $\frac{53}{3125}$
12 $\frac{23}{648}$
13 a) $\frac{5}{16}$
  b) $\frac{21}{32}$
14 a) $\frac{280}{2187}$
  b) $\frac{696}{729}$
15 $\frac{7}{8}, \frac{5}{16}$
16 0.22, 0.40, 0.53, 0.64
17 a) 0.6561 **c)** 0.0523
  b) 0.2916 **d)** 0.9999
18 $\frac{243}{3125}, \frac{810}{3125}, \frac{1080}{3125}, \frac{720}{3125}, \frac{240}{3125}, \frac{32}{3125}$
  a) 5
  b) 39
19 a) 20
  b) 44
20 a) 37
  b) 90

EXERCISE B Page 137 ─────────────

1 0.1209
2 0.5000
3 0.1662

4 0.8791
5 0.6328
6 0.3823
7 0.0689
8 0.2304
9 a) 0.9936
  b) 0.2013
10 45.2

CHAPTER 11

EXERCISE A Page 146 ─────────────

1 a) 1.33 **c)** 0.273
  b) -1 **d)** -1.6
2 a) -0.455
  b) 1.273
  c) -2.455
3 She did better in the first exam
4 Jane
5 She did equally well in all three subjects
6 Fiaz
7 a) May
  b) November
  c) November maths
  d) November English
8 a) 34.2 **c)** 25.5
  b) 37.5 **d)** 27.96
9 3.85
10 10
11 21.5
12 63.15
13 $\mu = 50, \sigma = 5$
14 $\mu = 65, \sigma = 10$

EXERCISE B Page 150 ─────────────

1 a) 0.403 **l)** 0.001
  b) 0.492 **m)** 0.268
  c) 0.226 **n)** 0.081
  d) 0.353 **o)** 0.983
  e) 0.617 **p)** 0.691
  f) 0.953 **q)** 0.907
  g) 0.300 **r)** 0.633
  h) 0.258 **s)** 0.218
  i) 0.089 **t)** 0.782
  j) 0.441 **u)** 0.903
  k) 0.115 **v)** 0.189

2 a) 0.614
  b) 0.242
  c) 0.092

d) 0.159
e) 0.309

3 a) ±1.17
  b) ±2.20
  c) −0.46
  d) 0.87
  e) −0.24

f) 1.28
g) ±2.46
h) ±2.75
i) ±2.32 or 2.33

EXERCISE C   Page 151 ——————

1 a) 0.023
  b) 0.159
  c) 0.081
2 a) 0.933
  b) 0.818

d) 0.023
e) 0.954

EXERCISE D   Page 153 ——————

1 0.004
2 1.56
3 0.261
4 11.5%
5 0.008, 0.044
6 186.4 cm
7 0.025
8 40.8%
9 77%
10 9
11 7 years
12 a) 115
   b) 168.3 cm and 176.7 cm
13 109.860 g and 160.445 g
14 $\mu = 22.72, 21.04$
15 47
16 964
17 19.05
18 1288
19 $\mu = 167.1$ cm, $\sigma = 9.43$ cm
20 $\mu = 64.9, \sigma = 9.55$

EXERCISE E   Page 158 ——————

1 a) 0.029
  b) 0.08
2 0.112
3 0.123
4 0.097
5 a) 0.013
  b) 0.986

6 0.006
7 17
8 0.999
9 0.002
10 a) 16, 3.58
   b) i) 0.164 ii) 0.559
11 10, 2.74, 0.100, 1 or 2
12 a) 2.5, 1.54
   b) i) 0.742 ii) 0.716
13 0.999
14 0.031
15 23

CHAPTER 12

EXERCISE A   Page 161 ——————

1 0.1465
2 0.1494
3 0.0613
4 0.0005
5 0.8153
6 a) 0.1353
  b) 0.0527
7 a) $\frac{2}{25}$
  b) 0.0030
8 a) $\frac{4}{7}$
  b) 0.0922

EXERCISE B   Page 163 ——————

1 0.1008
2 0.1404
3 0.1042
4 3
5 $x > 6.52$

EXERCISE C   Page 164 ——————

1 0.0361
2 0.2695
3 a) 0.2636
  b) 0.3515
4 0.0138
5 0.0212

1 Binomial $\dfrac{218\,491}{262\,144}$

2 Poisson 0.9409

3 Binomial $\dfrac{5}{72}$

4 Binomial $\dfrac{3}{16}$

5 Binomial $\dfrac{363\,528}{390\,625}$

6 Poisson 27.7

7 Binomial $\dfrac{3^5 \times 7^7}{10^9} = 0.2001$

8 Poisson 5

9 Binomial $\dfrac{3584}{390\,625}$

10 Poisson 0.1378

11 Poisson 60

CHAPTER 13

1 a) 0.037
  b) 0.001
2 a) 0.084
  b) 0.510
3 0.019
4 0.115
5 From 29.665 to 30.335
6 £19.53
7 a) 96
  b) 166
8 240

1 30 ± 0.96
2 65 ± 0.65
3 12.6 ± 0.74
4 171.05 ± 0.865 cm
5 161.25 ± 1.08 cm
6 2.5 ± 0.18

CHAPTER 14

1 No, as probability = 0.18 for a two-tailed test
2 No, as the Z score is 4.95, much higher than the critical value of $Z = 1.96$ in a two-tailed test.
3 No, as probability = 0.075 for a one-tailed test
4 Yes, as probability = 0.007 for a one-tailed test
5 No, as probability = 0.071 for a one-tailed test
6 Yes, as probability = 0.086 for a two-tailed test
7 a) No, as probability = 0.133 for a one-tailed test
  b) Yes, as probability = 0.013
  c) 55 ± 1.76
8 Yes, as probability = 0.001 for a one-tailed test
9 Yes, as Z is much less than the critical value of -1.64 in a one-tailed test
10 Yes, as probability = 0.006 for a one-tailed test

CHAPTER 15

1 a) 28.8%
  b) 30–39 years
  c) 80 years and over
  d) 400
  e) 580
  f) Women tend to live longer

g) 19.6%

h) 51.6%

3 a) Although there is an increase in the number of older people in the population in 1981, this is less than the decrease in the number of children

b) There is a steady increase in the number of people aged 65 years and over

c) 1951 11.0%; 1961 11.9%; 1971 13.3%; 1981 15.0%

People are living longer due to healthier life styles and better medical care

d) 1951 8.5%; 1961 7.8%; 1971 8.0%; 1981 6.0%

There is a downward trend in the number of young children due to the fall in the birth rate

4

		Town A	Town B	Town C
a)	Crude death rate	12.8	19.3	8.0
b)	Crude birth rate	13.0	10.7	18.0
c)	Fertility rate	62.2	63.0	60.0

The age distribution is quite different in the three towns. Town A has a fairly normal type of distribution, so the birth and death rates are similar to what they are in the whole country. Town B has a relatively small number of young people and a large number of elderly people, so the birth rate is low and the death rate is high. Town C – possibly a New Town – has a high proportion of people under the age of 45 years, so the birth rate is high and the death rate is low. The fertility rates are approximately the same for each town, so the differences in the number of births are due simply to the difference in the age distribution.

5

	Town X	Town Y
Crude death rate	15.5	18.53
Standardised death rate	15.31	16.52

APPENDIX

TABLE 1 AREA UNDER THE NORMAL DISTRIBUTION CURVE

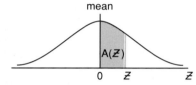

The function tabulated is

$$A(Z) = \frac{1}{\sqrt{2\pi}} \int_0^Z e^{-1/2 t^2} dt$$

$A(Z)$ is the proportion of area under the normal curve between the mean ordinate at 0 and the ordinate at any value Z.

Z	A(Z)	Z	A(Z)
0.00	0.000	0.15	0.060
0.01	0.004	0.16	0.064
0.02	0.008	0.17	0.067
0.03	0.012	0.18	0.071
0.04	0.016	0.19	0.075
0.05	0.020	0.20	0.079
0.06	0.024	0.21	0.083
0.07	0.028	0.22	0.087
0.08	0.032	0.23	0.091
0.09	0.036	0.24	0.095
0.10	0.040	0.25	0.099
0.11	0.044	0.26	0.103
0.12	0.048	0.27	0.106
0.13	0.052	0.28	0.110
0.14	0.056	0.29	0.114

Z	A(Z)	Z	A(Z)
0.30	0.118	0.70	0.258
0.31	0.122	0.71	0.261
0.32	0.126	0.72	0.264
0.33	0.129	0.73	0.267
0.34	0.133	0.74	0.270
0.35	0.137	0.75	0.273
0.36	0.141	0.76	0.276
0.37	0.144	0.77	0.279
0.38	0.148	0.78	0.282
0.39	0.152	0.79	0.285
0.40	0.155	0.80	0.288
0.41	0.159	0.81	0.291
0.42	0.163	0.82	0.294
0.43	0.166	0.83	0.297
0.44	0.170	0.84	0.300
0.45	0.174	0.85	0.302
0.46	0.177	0.86	0.305
0.47	0.181	0.87	0.308
0.48	0.184	0.88	0.311
0.49	0.188	0.89	0.313
0.50	0.191	0.90	0.316
0.51	0.195	0.91	0.319
0.52	0.198	0.92	0.321
0.53	0.202	0.93	0.324
0.54	0.205	0.94	0.326
0.55	0.209	0.95	0.329
0.56	0.212	0.96	0.331
0.57	0.216	0.97	0.334
0.58	0.219	0.98	0.336
0.59	0.222	0.99	0.339
0.60	0.226	1.00	0.341
0.61	0.229	1.01	0.344
0.62	0.232	1.02	0.346
0.63	0.236	1.03	0.348
0.64	0.239	1.04	0.351
0.65	0.242	1.05	0.353
0.66	0.245	1.06	0.355
0.67	0.249	1.07	0.358
0.68	0.252	1.08	0.360
0.69	0.255	1.09	0.362

Z	A(Z)	Z	A(Z)	Z	A(Z)	Z	A(Z)
1.10	0.364	1.65	0.451	2.20	0.486	2.75	0.497
1.11	0.367	1.66	0.452	2.21	0.486	2.76	0.497
1.12	0.369	1.67	0.453	2.22	0.487	2.77	0.497
1.13	0.371	1.68	0.454	2.23	0.487	2.78	0.497
1.14	0.373	1.69	0.454	2.24	0.487	2.79	0.497
1.15	0.375	1.70	0.455	2.25	0.488	2.80	0.497
1.16	0.377	1.71	0.456	2.26	0.488	2.81	0.498
1.17	0.379	1.72	0.457	2.27	0.488	2.82	0.498
1.18	0.381	1.73	0.458	2.28	0.489	2.83	0.498
1.19	0.383	1.74	0.459	2.29	0.489	2.84	0.498
1.20	0.385	1.75	0.460	2.30	0.489	2.85	0.498
1.21	0.387	1.76	0.461	2.31	0.490	2.86	0.498
1.22	0.389	1.77	0.462	2.32	0.490	2.87	0.498
1.23	0.391	1.78	0.462	2.33	0.490	2.88	0.498
1.24	0.393	1.79	0.463	2.34	0.490	2.89	0.498
1.25	0.394	1.80	0.464	2.35	0.491	2.90	0.498
1.26	0.396	1.81	0.465	2.36	0.491	2.91	0.498
1.27	0.398	1.82	0.466	2.37	0.491	2.92	0.498
1.28	0.400	1.83	0.466	2.38	0.491	2.93	0.498
1.29	0.401	1.84	0.467	2.39	0.492	2.94	0.498
1.30	0.403	1.85	0.468	2.40	0.492	2.95	0.498
1.31	0.405	1.86	0.469	2.41	0.492	2.96	0.498
1.32	0.407	1.87	0.469	2.42	0.492	2.97	0.499
1.33	0.408	1.88	0.470	2.43	0.492	2.98	0.499
1.34	0.410	1.89	0.471	2.44	0.493	2.99	0.499
1.35	0.411	1.90	0.471	2.45	0.493	3.00	0.499
1.36	0.413	1.91	0.472	2.46	0.493	3.01	0.499
1.37	0.415	1.92	0.473	2.47	0.493	3.02	0.499
1.38	0.416	1.93	0.473	2.48	0.493	3.03	0.499
1.39	0.418	1.94	0.474	2.49	0.494	3.04	0.499
1.40	0.419	1.95	0.474	2.50	0.494	3.05	0.499
1.41	0.421	1.96	0.475	2.51	0.494	3.06	0.499
1.42	0.422	1.97	0.476	2.52	0.494	3.07	0.499
1.43	0.424	1.98	0.476	2.53	0.494	3.08	0.499
1.44	0.425	1.99	0.477	2.54	0.494	3.09	0.499
1.45	0.426	2.00	0.477	2.55	0.495	3.10	0.499
1.46	0.428	2.01	0.478	2.56	0.495	3.11	0.499
1.47	0.429	2.02	0.478	2.57	0.495	3.12	0.499
1.48	0.431	2.03	0.479	2.58	0.495	3.13	0.499
1.49	0.432	2.04	0.479	2.59	0.495	3.14	0.499
1.50	0.433	2.05	0.480	2.60	0.495	3.15	0.499
1.51	0.434	2.06	0.480	2.61	0.495	3.16	0.499
1.52	0.436	2.07	0.481	2.62	0.496	3.17	0.499
1.53	0.437	2.08	0.481	2.63	0.496	3.18	0.499
1.54	0.438	2.09	0.482	2.64	0.496	3.19	0.499
1.55	0.439	2.10	0.482	2.65	0.496	3.20	0.499
1.56	0.441	2.11	0.483	2.66	0.496	3.21	0.499
1.57	0.442	2.12	0.483	2.67	0.496	3.22	0.499
1.58	0.443	2.13	0.483	2.68	0.496	3.23	0.499
1.59	0.444	2.14	0.484	2.69	0.496	3.24	0.499
1.60	0.445	2.15	0.484	2.70	0.497	3.25	0.499
1.61	0.446	2.16	0.485	2.71	0.497	3.26	0.499
1.62	0.447	2.17	0.485	2.72	0.497	3.27	0.499
1.63	0.448	2.18	0.485	2.73	0.497	3.28	0.499
1.64	0.449	2.19	0.486	2.74	0.497		